FAST TRACK

FAST TRACK

**Everything the high-flying executive
ought to know about Information Technology**

Dennis Jarrett

Published in association with Philips Business Systems

McGRAW-HILL BOOK COMPANY

London · New York · St Louis · San Francisco · Auckland · Bogotá · Guatemala
Hamburg · Lisbon · Madrid · Mexico · Montreal · New Delhi · Panama · Paris
San Juan · São Paulo · Singapore · Sydney · Tokyo · Toronto

Published by

McGRAW-HILL Book Company (UK) Limited

MAIDENHEAD · BERKSHIRE · ENGLAND

British Library Cataloguing in Publication Data

Jarrett, Dennis

  Fast Track.
  1. Management.   Information Systems
  I. Title II. Philips Business Systems
  658.4′038

ISBN 0-07-707074-7

Library of Congress Cataloging-in-Publication Data

Jarrett, Dennis.

  Fast Track .

  "Published in association with Phillips Business Systems."
  Bibliography: p.
  Includes index.
  1. Business — Data processing.   2. Business — Communication systems.   3. Information technology.
  I. Title.
  HF5548.2.J287 1988   004′.024658   88-785
ISBN 0-07-707074-7

123 CUP 898

Designed and typeset by TP Group, London
Printed and bound in Great Britain at the University Press, Cambridge

This is the fourth in a series of handbooks which Philips Business Systems has sponsored. Our aim is to help bridge the gap which inevitably exists between fast-moving technology and people's understanding of what it can do for them today.

Why 'fast track' executives? Our research showed that a whole generation of managers missed out on the computer familiarization which their younger colleagues — the graduates of the eighties — receive at school and university as a matter of course. These managers need to know how business technology can help them to progress more rapidly in their careers. This book sets out to tell them.

Dennis Jarrett is a highly respected computer journalist and author with a reputation for being bluntly realistic about his subject. There is no better guide to the nuts and bolts of electronic information systems, and we are proud to be associated with such a clear-signted observer of our industry.

I hope this book helps every reader spot at least one way in which he or she can use the computers in their office to do better, quicker or more productive work.

John Bunce
Divisional Director
Philips Business Systems

CONTENTS

This book was written between June and November 1987, using a desktop publishing package (NEWSWRITER by Cognita Software) running on AT-compatibles. Design and production were done by my own company, TP Group, with output of printer's masters from an ageing Canon LBP-1 laser printer — all text was produced in this way, the photographs and other artwork being added before printing.

Writing a book like this is something of a team effort — the author is to some extent a conduit for other people's ideas and opinions. This is particularly true in the case of Adrian Wheeler of Sterling Public Relations, who identified the need for this kind of book in the first place.

Production of this book was in effect underwritten by Philips Business Systems. Sponsored books are often thinly-veiled PR exercises designed to impose one company's views; in this case I was under no pressure to favour the views or products of Philips, and apart from some constructive comments on work-in-progress there was actually very little contact with the sponsor. I'd like to thank Mike Couzens, marketing director of Philips Business Systems, for his enlightened attitude; I also appreciate the generally constructive comments and factual input from those PBS managers who were able to take the time to read relevant sections of the manuscript.

The book wouldn't actually have been written without the support and sympathy of my colleagues at TP Group — of whom Roger Gann and Terry Duggan deserve more reward than they'll ever get in the way of rounds at the *Waterside*. In an ideal world, more rewards would go to Bob Webb, who loaned me a fast hard-disk Victor V286 computer at very short notice when I discovered the LCD screen on my portable was driving me nuts on a book-sized piece of text.

Nancy Sutcliffe of Façade Studios was responsible for line illustration. Picture research was done by Michelle Bayliss of Sterling Public Relations; I would like to thank all companies who allowed me to use their photographs.

The other key parties were the manufacturer of Blend 37, without whom I'd still be asleep; an understanding and helpful publisher at McGraw-Hill, Roger Horton; and for hand-holding and brow-mopping services well beyond the call of duty, Nancy Sutcliffe.

Accordingly, this book is for Nancy.

DENNIS JARRETT
ISLINGTON, DECEMBER 1987

There is a revolution going on in the organization. It involves new technology, new services, new ways of handling and using information.

And like any new discipline, it requires something extra from the managers who will have to use it. It demands new skills, a new approach — and that will often mean a fundamental reorientation of attitude.

The use of information systems is an entrepreneurial activity: information is a corporate resource, resources should be managed, and information systems greatly increase the opportunities that are available. To capitalize on those opportunities requires energy, direction and flair.

Opportunities

These are the key advantages that should be sought from any new-technology information system:

- *Quicker decisions* because information can be supplied faster
- *Better decisions* because the information is complete, succinct and up-to-date
- *Improved control* because information is available for all levels of team or project activity
- *Better use of management time* because much of the bureaucracy is automated or eliminated
- *More acute decisions* because the information overload problem is reduced — usable information is timely and relevant
- *Better management* because the systems can more closely fit the goals of the organization, the department ... and the individual

Information systems are a tool, not an end in themselves. They require application and control. The systems might be technologically wonderful, but they will not produce the desired results if misused. Crucially, they will not produce the results unless the user has the right attitude to the potential of such systems.

Winning the information systems game

To survive in today's organizations, management needs to be aware of that potential. This book details the possibilities in terms of the products, services and techniques currently available.

More important, perhaps, it will indicate other opportunities — other ways in which information systems can be *used*.

The information system is designed to help individuals do their job. The key to successful use of information systems is to go one stage further — to utilize the system in an innovative and imaginative manner, to seize the opportunities it makes available.

- *The system is a tool for getting the job done.*
- *Individual managers will have their own ideas for how the job can be done better.*
- *The system also provides the tools for putting those ideas into practice.*

With the right approach, managers will be able to do their current job better and advance personal ambitions:

- *Make better use of the financial and other resources available to their part of the organization.*
- *Make better use of their own time.*
- *Deliver a service to high-level management that is not currently provided.*

Reading the book

This book is by no means the last word on the management side of information systems or on the technology involved.

Instead, it is a primer on the content and possibilities in information systems; read it all the way through in one sitting, or use its index and contents list for instant reference.

The book covers:

- *The technical background*
- *The terminology*
- *The social and organizational issues*
- *The practicalities — with drawbacks as well as possible benefits*
- *The procedures*

It is structured into six parts:

1. *The digital world:* an overview summarizing the broad reasons for the changes happening in offices and the technical background.

2. *The Workstation* considers the two principal structures for information systems — the 'information centre' and the 'management workstation'.

3. *Computers in detail* looks at the components of the workstation, which will usually be a desktop computer of some kind. This section includes a substantial chapter on *local area networks*, the 'glue' that will bind most integrated information systems; and another on *IBM-compatibility*, a prime consideration for most users since in large part it will determine what is available and what is possible.

4. *Packages for computers* considers the tools available at the workstation to aid management productivity. Realistically, this is one of the two most important sections of the book.

5. *Comms* is the other key aspect of the information system — using communications to increase and improve the availability and flow of information. Here are detailed the practical considerations and the scale of services available.

6. *Being a user* suggests how the concerned end-user can contribute to the design and implementation of information systems with a pragmatic approach to problems and procedures.

There are major changes afoot in the organization and administration of offices, with consequent implications for the nature and style of management. The reasons include a new emphasis on productivity from white-collar workers, fuelled by the availability of new technology at reasonable cost which can serve that goal. In practical terms, the two most visible signs of the development of integrated information systems are the 'management workstation' — the manager's access to the system — and the development of the corporate 'information centre', to provide overall support and control for such systems.

As an ever-increasing proportion of the world's population ends up in white-collar employment, there is a concomitant stress on improving the effectiveness and costs of the office. The organization's competitiveness and other corporate aims are highly susceptible to the quality of its administrative and planning procedures; the office cannot be allowed to get away with uncontrolled *ad hoc* systems.

Tasks for management

In general, the task of management is to achieve defined objectives by planning, organizing, directing and controlling a number of interrelated tasks and services:

- *Objectives*. The management process presupposes the existance of defined objectives, particularly in terms of the contribution of the manager (or department or team) to corporate goals. Setting those objectives is probably the key task for management, since it (a) defines a role within the corporate strategy and (b) implies the tasks and services in question.

- *Planning*. Essentially determines a strategy for the team (where is it going) and policies (how it should get there). It will involve an appraisal of internal and external constraints, requirements and demands on resources; it will produce forecasts, action plans, schedules and checkpoints.

- *Organization*. Deciding who does what and how — identify, define and allocate activities; establish responsibilities; assign resources; establish methods and procedures for communication, coordination and control.

- *Direction*. Ensuring that the team works as planned. Leadership and motivation will be required as well as the more pragmatic concern of making sure that everyone knows their responsibilities and the timescales.

- *Control*. Progress should be monitored and compared with plans; corrective action will be applied as required.

Obviously not all managers will operate this rigidly, but the broad framework applies.

Information

The essence of each element in the management process is common: *information*. This is the only significant commodity that is input to, processed by and output from the office. The purpose of the office is to process and communicate information efficiently and effectively; the job of management is to utilise that information in making decisions.

This puts a premium on the type of information:

- It must be *comprehensive* (*all* the relevant information is required).
- It must be *appropriate* (the emphasis should be on 'relevant' — too much information is worse than too little).
- It must be *accurate* (as well as complete).
- It must be *up-to-date*.
- It must be *accessible*.

In short, information must be *useful*, *usable* and *applicable*. If the present system does not allow management access to and use of such information, it is probably ripe for change.

The concerns of management may include:

- *Stabilization (and if possible reduction) of the overheads of doing business*. In particular, those costs directly attributable to the information-processing task.

- *Removal (or at worst alleviation) of bottlenecks* in the system that prevent information getting to the right place at the right time.

- *Better use of management time*. This is the manager's principal resource. Making more time may be important, but it should be more *usable* time — maybe not better decisions, but better decision-making.

☐ *Improved access to information* and *better* information: the right facts, all of them, delivered in concise form as quickly as possible.

☐ *A reduction in the volume of information.* Too much information clogs up and slows down the system, and the need to winnow information can impede effective and timely decision-making.

☐ *More and better communication* between individuals, teams and corporate resources like centralized files. This will improve the quality of information, the quality of decision-making and the distribution of information.

☐ *Standardization* to remove incompatibilities of procedure and information-handling between individuals, teams and corporate groups.

☐ *Integration* of disparate functions and facilities that can usefully contribute to the task of handling and processing information.

The tools are available to cover all of these concerns — and more.

The possibilities in new information technology derive from a convergence of existing technologies — primarily telecommunications, computing and image processing. The two key elements are *digitization* and the *microprocessor*.

Digitization

Binary digits are the standard method by which computers handle information, encoding it as a series of on/off pulses (or, more usually, high/low pulses). Computers can easily detect a difference in voltage levels along a wire, so this fits their operation rather well.

The two states — on/off, high/low — are conventionally called '1' and '0' to simplify things: hence the phrases *binary digit* (and its abbreviation 'bit', both meaning a digit which can be one of two numbers) and *digitization* (the process of encoding information from some other form into binary digits).

- Just about any form of information can be represented in this way. For *text*, different patterns of on/off pulses can be interpreted as different characters — just as Morse code uses only two types of signal (dot and dash) in different combinations to represent different letters of the alphabet.

  The two-state code also fits the operation of many *graphics* devices. The encoding is done by treating the original document as a matrix of tiny dots, each of which can be black or white. A black point gets an 'on' code, a white area gets an 'off'. A binary 'map' of the image is built up in this way, and it can be passed on to a device that *prints* a dot when it receives an 'on' signal.

- *Speech* can be digitized, too. Speech is a series of air pressure waves that vary in intensity and pitch; by sampling the wave frequently and at regular intervals, a binary equivalent of the waveform can be produced as a series of bits. (You might think this would result in a less accurate rendering of the voice, but in fact it produces a much better reproduction when transmitted, because the original 'analogue' signals of speech are much more prone to distortion and corruption from external electromagnetic influences.)

If all forms of information can be represented in this way, it should be possible to pass information in digitized form from one device to another — without the receiver knowing what the original form actually was. Indeed, that is possible ... up to a point.

Certainly the same transmission medium, the same cables or radio waves, can be used. But the receiver might have difficulty actually producing some intelligible output. A telephone can take the human voice and digitize it for onward despatch; a fax machine at the other end might have some difficulty in converting those signals into an image. Both ends have to be told about what kind of transmission is going on, and both ends have to be able to convert the incoming information into a form they can actually reproduce.

The ubiquitous microprocessor

Digitization is providing a common means of encoding information; the microprocessor is providing a common means of handling that data.

- Microprocessors and associated circuitry can be small enough (and cheap enough) to fit inside just about any equipment.
- Microprocessors are inherently very reliable — there are no moving parts to wear out — and servicing them is pretty simple (a straight replacement).
- Crucially, microprocessors are programmable. This means they can be given programs to automate much of the control and alternative operations of the host, enabling a very versatile device to be designed.

Some management tools from information systems

TELEPHONE
- ☐ Voice messaging
- ☐ Electronic mail

INFORMATION ACCESS
- ☐ On-line information services
- ☐ Corporate and departmental files
- ☐ Personal files
- ☐ Laser disk records
- ☐ Expert systems

WRITING
- ☐ Voice entry
- ☐ Word processing software
- ☐ Outliners
- ☐ Presentation options (desktop publishing, graphics)

PROOFREADING
- ☐ Automatic check on calculations
- ☐ Voice annotation for comments
- ☐ Automatic spelling check

TRAVEL
- ☐ Conferencing
- ☐ Telecommuting
- ☐ Laser disk records of meetings and seminars

SCHEDULED MEETINGS
- ☐ Conferencing
- ☐ Presentation options (35mm graphics, OHP foils, interactive laser disk)
- ☐ On-line records of meetings
- ☐ Laser disk records
- ☐ Appointments diaries with reminders

UNSCHEDULED MEETINGS
- ☐ Ad hoc contact via electronic mail or conferencing
- ☐ Team appointments diaries

READING
- ☐ Electronic mail
- ☐ Laser disk records
- ☐ On-line records
- ☐ Sort/select facilities

CALCULATING
- ☐ Spreadsheets and financial modelling
- ☐ Data from existing internal and external sources
- ☐ Presentation options (graphics, inclusion in word-processed and/or desktop-published reports)

INCOMING MAIL
- ☐ Electronic mail
- ☐ Voice messaging
- ☐ Conferencing
- ☐ Forward with comments appended

OUTGOING MAIL
- ☐ Electronic mail
- ☐ Voice messaging
- ☐ Conferencing
- ☐ Distribution lists and automatic routing

THINKING
- ☐ Outliners
- ☐ 'What if' calculations
- ☐ Expert systems

Coopers and Lybrand have defined the aim of 'office automation' in these terms:

> '... to boost white-collar productivity and effectiveness by systematically applying the appropriate technology to the office environment ...'.

This has a number of implications:

☐ *Productivity* and *effectiveness*. How are they to be assessed? Is there an appropriate measure for 'management effectiveness'? There seems little point in implementing any system if the true benefits cannot be established to measure against costs.

It seems that new methodologies are required, new approaches to assessing the performance of individual managers and information systems. In particular, objectives for both may have to be defined and related to the organization's goals.

☐ *Systematic* application. How should an 'office automation' system be specified, designed, implemented and monitored?

The emphasis is on the need for control at each stage of the information system project. Many desktop computers within organizations are currently being used with no effective restrictions on duplication of information, incompatibilities where communication is desirable and necessary, and a prevalent view of the computer as a mere status symbol or management toy.

☐ *Appropriate* technology. The range of possibilities is vast, but blind enthusiasm is as bad as kneejerk condemnations.

As the Coopers and Lybrand report continues: 'while the cost-performance ratio [for new technology] continues to improve, technological advances have all but outpaced the buyer's capacity to assimilate them'. The same is true for the end-users. The introduction of new-technology products and services should be designed to meet immediate and future needs, but those needs should be evaluated carefully — too many information systems are filled with under-utilized and redundant features, and the availability of too many options is demonstrably confusing or intimidating. The facilities available to the manager should be those that will be used in meeting the balance of requirements of the individual, the team and the organization.

Potential problems

The current thinking in organizational management favours a shift from bureaucratic, hierarchical structures towards decentralization, a more flexible 'matrix' style of management. This increases personal accountability and means more delegation; it is a less formal style, often featuring task-specific project and team concepts.

Such an approach fits well with the technological possibilities of integrated information systems. The drawback is that they are harder to administer efficiently.

The problems are compounded when decentralized management gets its own information system: in particular, there is likely to be:

☐ Initial *suspicion* of new systems from management used to existing procedures.

☐ *Duplication* of effort and resources.

☐ *Incompatibilities* between information produced by different individuals.

☐ *Overenthusiasm*, with a tendency to integrate systems and add enhancements for their own sake — to the detriment of the original intentions, planned benefits, and (crucially) corporate goals. This is particularly seen in the provision of too much information; it is only useful when it aids effective management, but access to information can be overdone. Information can become an end in itself.

☐ *Inefficiency*. One effect of the uncontrolled installation of desktop computers is that an individual often takes on the mantle of 'microcomputer guru' to support other members of the team. This diverts employees from doing their jobs and also leads to the enthusiastic but naive development of idiosyncratic systems that do not fit the organization's goals and can be used and amended only by the originator.

The difficulties are compounded by a hangover from the days of Management Information Systems in the late seventies:

☐ *Dependence*. Systems come to dominate rather than support the users. The system can become so elaborate that it hampers effective management and imposes rock-solid strictures. For example, some financial systems have integrated business planning, management accounting and business accounting to the extent where any change is difficult.

On the other hand, controlling the information system may be difficult:

☐ *Resentment*. Decentralization and increased personal responsibility often work as an effective motivator. The imposition of any job assessment or monitoring procedures is likely to be resented.

☐ *Evaluation* of system performance is difficult, given the intangible nature of many of the goals and expected benefits.

Opportunities for information systems

☐ Providing information of better quality — more selective, more accurate, more up-to-date
☐ Quicker access to information — which also encourages the use of more and better information for decision-taking
☐ Cost savings through elimination of paperwork and bureaucracy
☐ Coherence and standardization through use of a common system and shared access
☐ Information that is difficult to lose or damage
☐ A better fit with the organization's goals

The manager's principal mode of access to the corporate information system will normally be via a desktop computer. This section looks at the principal options for using computers as management workstations.

4. THE INFORMATION CENTRE

Not very long ago, being a microcomputer manager in a large organization was a heady experience. No formal training was available on acquisition, implementation, strategic planning, standardization, monitoring; it was widely felt that a new breed of technical manager was required to provide end-user microcomputing, while the traditional data processing department had no place in such systems.

To some extent that is true. But the days of the enthusiastic micro specialist are numbered; the DP department is becoming the data centre, or rather the corporate information centre. The structure, orientation and skills it includes can support an important functional separation in information technology, a distinction between what some term *core* systems and *peripheral* systems.

□ *Core systems* provide the organization with an IT infrastructure. These capture basic information and perform unchanging day-to-day functions at the corporate level. Examples are the traditional DP applications — payroll, order processing, accounting, inventory control, production management. The information centre necessarily retains responsibility for developing and running such systems, because they are central to the day-to-day operation of the organization. Because that is the case, the information centre manager should probably be a main board member — if that individual gets the basic information processing wrong, it jeopardizes corporate performance as a whole.

□ *Peripheral systems* are those that deliver real benefits, typically in supporting management decision-making. Here the users control the applications, and the responsibility for delivering benefits should come from them. The information centre does have a crucial support role, however — advising on technical aspects, monitoring operations and enforcing standards.

Such support is particularly important when voice, data and image systems are integrated; the information centre is the only element of the organization that is equipped to oversee the different technologies.

The support may include:

□ *Training*
□ *Analysis of end-user requirements*
□ *Hot-line technical support*
□ *Selection of hardware and software*
□ *Access to corporate data*
□ *Programming for specific applications*

More important, the information centre must devise and maintain overall standards if everything is to work properly.

□ Different applications software packages store their data in different formats — which usually means that one package cannot read data created by another.

□ Alternatively, resources may be duplicated — the same kind of file can be set up by two different people.

□ The enthusiastic but naive development of idiosyncratic systems may subsequently require time-consuming modifications.

□ Those applications can be so personal that no-one else can understand or alter them when the individual in question leaves the department.

□ Sloppy operating procedures and bad habits can become ingrained. It's only when an untrained user loses all his or her files that the importance of taking regular 'backup' copies is brought home.

□ Without some guidance, local systems can grow like Topsy under the influence of newly converted users who believe all they read in computer magazines.

□ There will always be minor technical problems that are amenable to a quick solution from a professional.

□ Unrestricted calls to outside service companies can be expensive — especially if there's a quick and simple fix available in-house, most especially if the user does not realize that the equipment is still under warranty.

Development of the information centre

The nature of the information centre is illustrated by an annual survey taken by the US consultancy CRWTH. The 1987 figures cover 450 information centres. Key points:

- Around 80 per cent of the sample have been established only since 1982.
- Nearly all support both mainframes and microcomputers, suggesting that their genesis lay in traditional DP departments and their role started to change with the US microcomputer boom of the mid eighties.
- Despite established mainframe usage, the bulk of the users supported have desktop computers.
- Even in the two years since CRWTH's last survey, some marked contrasts are evident in the kind of services provided by information centres. With the exception of end-user training (which remains a dominant application), all services show considerable growth — especially the provision of links to mainframes, analysis of end-user requirements (now the principal service, offered by over 90 per cent of respondents) and applications programming.

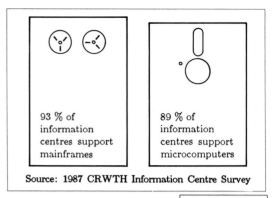

93 % of information centres support mainframes

89 % of information centres support microcomputers

Source: 1987 CRWTH Information Centre Survey

Types of system

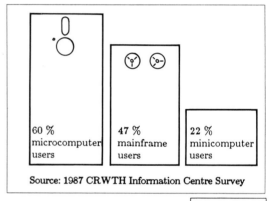

60 % microcomputer users

47 % mainframe users

22 % minicomputer users

Source: 1987 CRWTH Information Centre Survey

Types of user

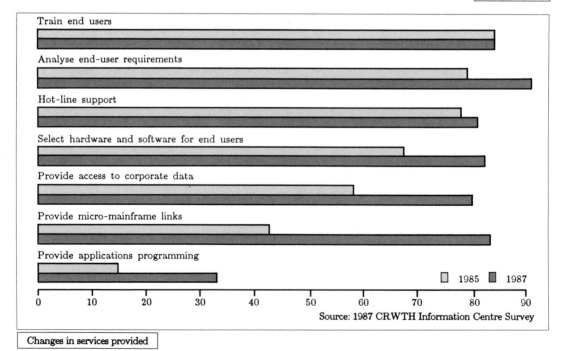

Train end users

Analyse end-user requirements

Hot-line support

Select hardware and software for end users

Provide access to corporate data

Provide micro-mainframe links

Provide applications programming

☐ 1985 ■ 1987

Source: 1987 CRWTH Information Centre Survey

Changes in services provided

The principal point of access to an information system is the user's workstation. In practice the workstation is a small computer with the ability to run programs and store information locally, with links to other such devices and to other office systems, and with a variety of different software facilities.

In those terms the device can be viewed as an extension of existing small computers, where programmability and ease of interfacing do at present provide for multiple functions.

The workstation has to emphasize general accessibility, however, by delivering sophisticated facilities while ensuring that they are always easy to use. Such facilities would include file management with automatic file searching (perhaps by referencing content) as well as automatic file indexing.

The workstation will provide:

□ *Access to information*
   — Personal files
   — Shared departmental or team files
   — Centrally held corporate files
   — External databases

□ *Information processing and presentation*
   — Spreadsheets and business modelling
   — Information-handling and manipulation
   — Presentation options (graphics, high-quality output, etc.)

□ *Document creation and despatch*
   — Word processing
   — Automatic spelling checks
   — Electronic mail and other messaging
   — Automated document distribution
   — Access to various types of printer

□ *Management support*
   — Decision support systems ('expert' systems)
   — Time management (appointments diary, reminders, alarms, etc.)
   — Project scheduling and monitoring

□ *Team communication*
   — Conferencing between multiple participants
   — Messaging
   — Performance monitoring

The workstation approach is application-driven — it has to meet the current and possible future requirements of the user's job and it has to insulate the user from the technological attributes of the devices being used.

So the workstation need not provide all possible functions: full-scale word processing, for example, will not be required by the average line manager. Equally, the workstation must be flexible enough to include the most useful functions. The key requirements are:

□ The starting point must be the needs of the user — in particular, how the user can best match the goals of the organization — rather than the exciting sophistication of available technology.

□ Information systems must be easy to use — or they won't be used at all.

□ Executives do need information, but the prime requirement is for information in a consolidated, packaged, presented form that is not open to misinterpretation. The answer may *not* be a desktop workstation.

A computer, any computer, is basically a fast rule-following idiot.

- It is fast because it works electronically.
- It follows rules with rigid single-mindedness. The 'rules' come in the form of instructions that tell it what to do, and those instructions come as 'programs' or 'packages' or 'software' — three words that mean the same thing.
- It's an idiot because following rules is all the computer can do. It can't guess what it ought to be doing in particular circumstances.

In practice this means a computer can be made to do any kind of job that can be formalized with rules and procedures. It does that job the same way each and every time: it will not make mistakes, and it won't bodge over things 'because it's simpler'.

This puts the onus on the software supplier, who has to provide the right instructions for the computer — and enough of them to cover every likely situation in a particular job.

It also has implications for the user: the speed and apparent sophistication of the system can blind you to its restrictions and produce a false sense of security.

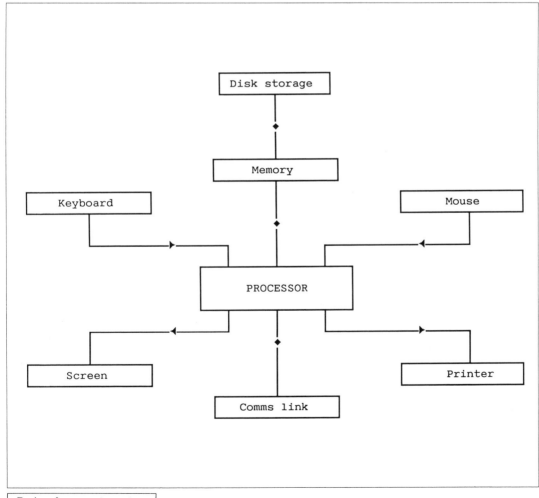

Basics of a computer system

Microcomputers versus microprocessors

A *microprocessor* is a single component; on its own it can't do very much. It needs some means of acquiring data to act upon, some way of storing its instructions, and some method of acting on them.

A *computer* has all those extras. So a microprocessor isn't a computer as such. Inside the microcomputer there is likely to be at least one microprocessor — but there will also be several dozen other components.

How computers work

The *processor* (which these days usually means the miniaturized circuitry called a microprocessor) sits at the centre.

It operates under the control of instructions that it is reading from the *operating system* in its *memory*. The operating system controls the operation of the computer and decides how it handles *applications programs* — the operating system in fact decides which programs can be used on a particular computer.

Those programs may be purpose-written or 'applications packages' (ready-to-use programs available off the shelf for particular tasks). Instructions in those programs are passed through the operating system to the processor for execution.

Commands and fresh data come in from the *keyboard*, from another computer via a communications link or from some other external source. Those commands might tell the computer to load a program from the *disk storage* and start running it; or they might tell the computer to fetch a file or some other data from the disk and then do something with it.

More commands from you and/or from the program instruct the computer to do something with the results of its work. That could mean displaying it on the *screen*, printing it on the *printer*, sending it to another computer over the *communications link*, or just saving it on *disk* again.

Memory

All computers must have some kind of memory in which to store programs. The memory comes as one or more chips which look rather like the microprocessor itself; internally they are very different, though, for the memory chip is purpose-designed to do no more than store instructions.

Read-only memory (or ROM — sometimes ROS, for 'read-only storage') is a type of memory chip that can be filled with programs — but once the programs are in there they cannot normally be altered or erased by a user. ROM does not lose its contents when the power is turned off. Computer manufacturers tend to use ROM in three ways:

☐ A *bootstrap* program starts up the disk drives automatically and loads in something (usually an operating system) so that the computer is ready for use.

☐ *Diagnostics* — small programs that check out the components of the computer when it is started.

☐ Some of the key elements of the *operating system*, particularly those that customize the operating system for the particular set of computer hardware, may be held in ROM.

Read-write memory (or RAM — an anachronistic, inconvenient and inaccurate abbreviation that has settled into popular usage) has no fixed contents. It comprises the bulk of memory provided in the computer; it is available for programs and data to be loaded in, and successive loads will overwrite the previous contents. RAM loses all its contents when the power is switched off.

Some programs simply require a good deal of memory to work at all. In general, though, more RAM means software writers can apply more sophistication to programs:

☐ *Fast operation*. If there is insufficient memory to fit the whole program or all of a work file into memory, the processor will have to pause every so often to fetch in the next part from disk.

- *Memory-resident programs*. Given enough memory, the whole of a program may be able to fit into memory — and stay there while other programs are run. Memory-resident programs are sometimes called TSR or 'terminate-and-stay-resident' programs after the operating system function that allows this to happen. Such programs are loaded just once and sit there quietly in memory to be called up when required — without interrupting the current task fatally, which is what normally happens when one program is loaded after another. These programs are generally utilities of one kind or another, such as spelling checkers or comms packages.
- With so much memory to play with the programmers can also afford to build in more *user-friendliness* — information to guide the user, 'help' displays, simplified methods of operation.
- *Capacity*. Increased size for spreadsheets, for example.
- *Concurrency*. If the operating system can handle it, two or more tasks can be run simultaneously if sufficient memory is available.

Bytes, KB and MB

The amount of information that can be held in any form of computer storage is counted as 'bytes', one byte being equivalent to one character (which may be a single numeric digit, one letter, a punctuation mark or a special 'control' character that means something specific to the computer).

Given the large storage capacities available on computers, you are more likely to come across 'kilobytes', abbreviated to 'KB' — meaning 'thousands of bytes'. In fact 'K' is a mathematical constant, like *pi*, and actually means '1024'. For practical purposes you can assume it denotes thousands. So '8KB' is 'eight thousand bytes'.

Similarly, a 'megabyte' (or 'MB') is 'millions of bytes'. Here the 'M' *does* mean 'millions'. So '1MB' or 'one megabyte' is a million bytes, more or less equivalent to a million characters.

Processor speeds

The overall performance of a computer system depends on a good many factors, and their importance varies from one application to another. They include:

- Disk read/write operations
- 'Wait states'
- Processor clock speed
- Memory access speed
- Performance of the operating system
- Speed of operation of any 'front end'

And ultimately it depends on precisely what applications packages are used and how well they have been written.

It is, however, possible to get a likely indication of overall performance from the hardware specification.

- *Processor clock speed*. Microprocessors operate at a regular, fixed rate — the 'clock rate' — in performing their operations, and up to a point it is the system's designers who decide what the optimum speed should be. The clock rate applies to everything the microprocessor does, but as a point of reference it is quoted as how long it takes the processor to access any one memory location. Processor clock speeds are measured in megahertz (MHz).

Obviously the faster the processor can operate, the quicker it will get through programs. And when a program has to be decoded by the computer a line at a time before it is executed, the speed of the processor becomes a major factor in the overall run time (though by no means the *only* factor, or even the most important).

- *Wait states*. A car performs better when the ignition timing is properly adjusted, with the spark being delivered at the optimum point for the cylinders to be full of petrol and air. Similarly, a computer will work faster when the processor clock rate is synchronized with the clock rate for memory. A 'wait state' is the processor pausing for one clock cycle each time it accesses memory because otherwise the memory might not be able to deliver the goods in time. 'Zero wait states' means that the processor clock is completely synchronized with memory access.

☐ *Hard disk access time*. In fact the access time measures only how long it takes on average for the disk's read/write head to move to the required point on a disk. Other factors affect the overall disk read/write task — how long it takes for the computer to start the head moving, how fast data can be read from or written on to the disk, how quickly data is actually moved between disk and processor. Access time is a reasonable guide to performance. It is rated in milliseconds — 85ms is relatively slow, 28ms is relatively fast, most hard disk units are 40 to 65ms.

Expansion slots

These are sockets for the 'edge connectors' on a circuit board, and additional circuit boards can be plugged in there. The contacts inside the slot link to the computer's 'bus', the electrical connections that carry signals and power between the computer's components; so plugging a board into an expansion slot effectively makes it part of the computer.

Expansion slots are typically used for adding memory, local area network controllers, alternative displays (for colour and graphics, usually), and so on. Entire hard disks, modems and other devices can also be mounted on circuit boards and sold as optional extras for a basic computer.

How big a computer?

What computer will run the software?

Most packages will run only on one design of computer and they may not run effectively with some variants of that design — in particular, the speed of the processor and the amount of memory may be inadequate for all but the most sluggish performance.

There may be no options on processor speed, but as a rule-of-thumb approach all computers should have as much memory as they can (or as much as the organization is prepared to afford). More memory means the widest possible choice of programs and the best chances of obtaining maximum performance from them.

What kind of disks?

Files are stored on disk. So in theory the size of the largest file will determine the capacity and type of disks on a desktop computer. In practice, a variant of Parkinson's law applies — files and programs tend to fill the disk capacity available for them. For optimum performance, floppy disks should only be used for loading material and for backups; the hard disk should be as fast as possible and as big as it can economically be to maximize the options and cater for future demands.

Styles of computer: the classic three-box approach on the left — and users apparently get accustomed to the Apple Mac's two-box sit-up-and-beg styling seen on the right

'Computerphones'

Since a modem can be installed in a small computer, it is feasible to package many of the tools a manager might require into a 'computerphone' — a desktop computer that includes:

- Screen
- Keyboard
- Disk drives
- Telephone handset
- Modem

... and software for:

- Dial-up access to information services, e-mail services, and the organization's other computers
- Spreadsheet with on-screen graphics
- Personal filing system
- Word processor

The attraction is the marketing man's ideal of getting a computer on to the manager's desk instead of leaving it to the secretaries — of changing the manager's attitude to information technology. The computerphone is intended for managers, for occasional access to other systems and limited computing. As such, it features:

- *Neat design* and a small footprint. It should look like a status symbol rather than a threat.
- *Ease of use* with ready-made menus, one-key selection of facilities, ready-to-go dial-up and log-on facilities.
- *Introductory personal computing* with a strictly limited but accessible set of capabilities (not full-function WP, restricted spreadsheet size and functions, simple filing system).
- *Immediate appeal* that means something to the user — such as short-code dialling from a very large telephone directory.
- *Demonstrable benefits*. Electronic messaging, access to useful dial-up information.

A system like that might be everything the manager needs. In practice, it seems that many such users have actually put the computerphone on a *secretary's* desk.

And despite all the theoretical attractions, sales of such computers have been poor. In terms of a mass market, a basic problem is cost: ICL's OPD, for instance, sells for £1300. It may be custom-designed for the manager's desk, but the same money buys a great deal more function from a conventional desktop computer with similar equipment.

Two approaches to computerphones: ICL's One-Per-Desk and BT's QWERTYphone

Types of computer

There are no hard and fast definitions when it comes to identifying types of computer. What follows is a pragmatic distinction.

Microcomputer. A small computer based on a microprocessor, usually with all electronics on a single circuit board, and designed for use by one person.

Hand-held computer. A microcomputer in a package small enough to be held in one hand and operated with the other. It will have a narrow display and a compact (probably non-QWERTY) keyboard layout. Typically uses include stock recording and other data capture, though at least one is sold as a 'personal organizer' with diary functions, address book in memory, etc.

Laptop computer. A microcomputer with a full-size keyboard and a screen large enough to display readable text (eight lines of 40 characters is common). Modems and cassette or disk storage may be plugged in. Typical applications are for electronic mail on the move or peripatetic journalism.

Briefcase computer. A microcomputer compact enough to fit in a briefcase. This is more an advertising copywriter's expression than an accepted product group — both laptops and portables are often called 'briefcase' computers.

Portable computer. A microcomputer with all the capabilities of a desktop computer (including large memory, full-size display and one or more disk drives) that is light enough to carry. Flat screens are used, battery power is the norm.

Transportable or **luggable computer.** A full-function desktop computer that can easily be moved — not too heavy, all system units close up to provide a box the size of a sewing machine. The weight and the requirement for mains power precludes such computers being used as true go-anywhere portables; luggables are attractive for occasional movement and the minimum footprint.

Desktop computer. A full-function microcomputer intended for more or less static use.

PC or **personal computer.** Same as 'desktop computer'. IBM's use of the name PC has led to its adoption as a generic term; it indicates that the user loads and runs applications directly, rather than employing a link to a central computer facility. In practice, of course, such computers are no more 'personal' than any other microcomputer type listed here.

Workstation. Broadly, any working microcomputer system — including ancillaries such as a modem, printer and software — and especially one that is part of a local area network. More rigorously, the term should probably be reserved for extra-powerful special-purpose microcomputers for research and 'number-crunching' applications like computer-aided design that place a premium on raw processing power.

RISC. Reduced Instruction Set Computer — a brand new approach to processor design that overcomes the tecnical limitations in current microprocessors to give ever higher performance. The cost and present state of the technology combined with the limited requirement for that much power restricts RISC to special-purpose workstation applications for now.

Supermicro. A microcomputer version of a minicomputer — a substantial microcomputer intended for multi-user operation.

Minicomputer. A computer that services several users at terminals connected to it. Technically, there was a genuine distinction in that micros utilized a higher level of integration in circuitry (more functions crammed into fewer chips) while minis featured a reduced level of integration (which in theory enabled them to operate rather faster). In practice this no longer applies, and the only safe definition is to describe a mini as a smallish computer that is made by a minicomputer manufacturer. Not a lot of help.

Supermini. A high-powered minicomputer, often used in technical applications where raw processing power is required.

Mainframes. Large, complex computers often supplied as a collection of boxes rather than a single unit and usually requiring special computer rooms with air conditioning, their own high-quality power supply from the mains and a team of specialized acolytes.

Supercomputers. High-performance mainframes for fast number-crunching work like weather forecasting and nuclear accident simulations.

The first portable computers appeared at about the same time in the early eighties. Some were 'luggable' — the size and weight of a sewing machine, but otherwise similar to the standard desktop computer and still needing a mains socket.

Simple laptop computers

The first *true* portables, those that did not need mains electricity, were called 'briefcase' or 'laptop' computers because of their size. The same basic layout is still used today for some laptops:

- About the size of a large paperback.
- Driven by an eight-bit chip.
- Provided with some simple built-in software for word processing, address lists, appointments diary, and communications.
- Between 8 and 64K of 'non-volatile' memory (which doesn't lose its contents when the power is switched off, unlike conventional memory chips).
- Flat display showing eight lines of 40 or 80 characters apiece.
- QWERTY keyboard — tightly packed but full-size keys.
- No built-in disk drives (there is usually a socket for an externally-connected disk drive and/or a cassette player for storing information when the memory gets full; or the laptop can be plugged into a desktop computer back at the office to unload its memory).
- Rechargeable battery.

Their compactness, lack of complication and low cost mean that such machines are still useful in many applications — sales and stock recording, note-taking on the move. But the absence of a full-size screen, disk storage and (crucially) IBM-compatibility all restrict their appeal. It is not possible to do serious general-purpose work on such computers, and it can be difficult to integrate that work with anything running on the computers back at the office.

Clever laptop computers

A slightly larger package and cleverer electronics provides a much more useful tool:

- About the size of a (flattish) portable typewriter.
- Driven by a 16-bit chip, probably the same variety used in desktop computers.
- Provided with a real operating system, an up-to-date version of the MS-DOS used in the office.
- Between 256 and 640K of non-volatile memory, or ordinary memory with battery power to prevent it losing its contents.
- Flat full-size display showing 24 or 25 lines of 80 characters (and perhaps with an option for graphics too).
- QWERTY keyboard plus IBM-compatible control and function keys.
- At least one built-in floppy disk drive (usually for 3½in disks), more likely two, and possibly a hard disk of 20MB or more.
- Rechargeable battery with mains adaptor.

In short, these computers are functionally similar to the office machines; they differ only in physical appearance, the display technology employed for the screen, the probable use of 3½in rather than 5¼in disks, and the absence of extra slots for expansion.

They can certainly be used for exactly the same kind of work — the packed keyboard and the unusual screen may take some getting used to, but all IBM-compatible software will run and the capabilities are all there.

Those capabilities are needed because the classic users for such computers are business executives; the classic uses are in data analysis (using a spreadsheet, for instance) and word processing (writing reports and the like). These laptops are also used in harness with conventional machines back at the office, so they must be able to take information easily from the desktop computers and pass it back.

Laptop (or 'briefcase') portable

The other style of portable computer does not use a flat-screen display. Instead a small CRT monitor (usually 9in diagonal) is employed in a box the size of a small suitcase. Typically the unit offers much the same as a conventional desktop computer

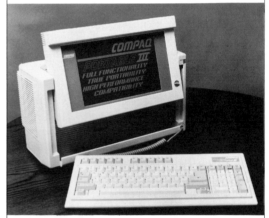

Different styles in true portables

When no significant compromises are made in capability, however, miniaturization comes at a premium price.

☐ *Robustness*. A computer designed to be moved around has to be carefully and solidly constructed, especially when the designers can't build in a lot of weight to maintain stability.

☐ *Electronic complexity*. Packing everything into a physically small space demands careful and clever design. This is particularly important as electronic components heat up when they are working; too much heat will cause them to malfunction intermittently and then to fail. The best components and the most precise design and manufacturing have to be used.

☐ *Component cost*. Not only do the components have to be smaller and more robust than their equivalents in a normal desktop computer, they may also have to be different: non-volatile memory chips, for instance, cost more than the conventional variety.

☐ *The display*. Flat-screen displays are electronically no more complex than the TV-type CRT screens utilized with most desktop computers, but because production runs are shorter they are inevitably much more expensive. This is particularly so for 'backlit' or 'supertwist' screens, which get over the legibility problems of other flat displays.

☐ *Rechargeable batteries* of sufficient life and power are costly.

and uses basically similar components. There will be a full-size keyboard, normally clipped on to the computer in transit to form a 'lid'.

A certain amount of clever packaging is involved, but the scale is not great and machines such as these do not carry a substantial price premium.

These portables are not really intended for use away from the office; they run off the mains, for instance. Instead they appeal as straight alternatives to the desktop computer because of their small footprint. They can also be carried comfortably from one office to another ... but probably not much further.

Nickel-cadmium batteries are normally used in portable computers. They are rechargeable and typically last for up to five hours. You may need an external battery charger, a version of the kind of thing sold for recharging torch batteries; not all machines come with a recharger. Some portables have a trickle charger built in for overnight connection to the mains.

Portable comms

One of the obvious uses for a portable computer is for work in transit — to collect information and store it on the computer while travelling on business. It will probably be necessary to get that information back to the office somehow. The travelling businessperson may need to send and receive information, to check facts, to send and receive electronic mail messages.

The portable computer has always looked a natural for that kind of application, and early models were often sold with 'acoustic couplers' — practically any telephone handset in the world can be pushed into the rubber lugs of the coupler, the user dials the number for the home-base computer or the information service and a small program in the portable takes over to send and receive information.

On a few models, such couplers were built into the portable. On most, they were sold as cable-connected extra-cost additions.

There are problems with acoustic couplers, however — they are limited to very slow data transmission and they are prone to pick up interference that garbles the data. The preferable option is a true modem, which by-passes the handset to connect directly to the telephone wall-socket via its own plug and lead.

Such modems may again be external boxes wired to the computer, but for the traveller, a built-in modem is preferable; they come as slot-in circuit boards with a telephone lead that emerges from the back of the computer. Data transmission speeds can be much higher with such modems and the internal version means very little fiddling about to use it.

The drawback for the overseas traveller is the variation in national standards — not all modems work in all countries (Europe should not be a problem, but North America, for instance, follows totally different data comms standards) and the plug at the end of the modem's phone lead is most unlikely to fit any socket outside Britain.

Cellular modems: comms from your car?

A Logica report on *Mobile Communications in the UK* forecasts major growth in the public mobile comms market — over 800 000 cellular telephones and nearly as many wide-area pagers in use by 1992. For mobile data comms, Logica sees little take-up until digital cellular networks become available and integrated with ISDN during the nineties.

But given that many users of portable computers will also have a portable phone, particularly a cellular carphone, it may be worth considering a modem to work on the cellular network.

There are only so many Yuppie managers with a taste for technology, and much more important sales targets have appeared for the mobile computing/communications vendors: the sales team, the maintenance engineer, the surveyor, the doctor. These and others like them often have a genuine need to talk to base wherever they may be, and increasingly they want to send or receive rather more information than can be handled by a casual phone call.

The national UK cellular radio networks (CellNet and Vodafone) and a number of specialist suppliers have done much of the groundwork for standardization. They have also developed protocols for cellular communication (protocols rather than protocol, of course; wheresoever two suppliers are gathered together, there can be expected two — or more — protocols).

Different approaches in this particular area are perhaps understandable since applications are varyingly fastidious about quality of transmission, and there are also many different approaches to handling the medium of cellular radio — which is fundamentally hostile to data transmission.

For example, sending and receiving electronic mail messages through a setup involving portable computer, modem and carphone is not going to suffer too much if radio interference corrupts the odd character with a single-user text-based application. But a system for peripatetic staff to transmit data back from sites and receive complex material from the mainframe will be considerably more sensitive.

All the early players in this field have rejected existing error-correcting protocols and conventional modems. None were too good at handling, say, 20-millisecond signal deteriorations as you move from one cell to another. Signal fading, co-channel interference, 'line dropouts' (temporary disappearance of the connection, which could even be the effects of juggernauts lumbering along the motorway) — all add to the problems of fast and fault-free reception for cellular data; blocks rather than bits or bytes had to be the medium for retransmission to provide a degree of security.

Racal came up with CDLC, cellular data link control; it is in the public domain now and on its way to becoming one of those *de facto* standards so prevalent in computing. The company offers a 1200bps modem using CDLC, and its colleagues in

the Vodafone network have set up the VMACS service as a gateway from cellular data comms to conventional computer and network links.

CDLC permits transmission at up to 2400bps; in practice the net data rate is about half that, given all the error-checking and retransmission overheads that are still involved in getting past the interference problems. Faster rates are theoretically feasible, but Vodafone considers the price/performance ratio is right for the market at present.

CDLC has been submitted to CCITT for consideration as a European standard; its only serious competition comes from the other major UK cellular network supplier, BT Cellnet, with its KEYSTREAM service based on BT's EPAD error-handling protocols. The car has an interface unit and a Hayes-compatible 1200 bps modem; back at base, a similar modem translates between the cellular data link and conventional data lines.

There is also a new breed of mobile comms system suppliers who use cellular-standard radio transmission throughout, from the remote portable terminal to the computer back at base. With appropriate modems, the car driver can communicate directly with an electronic mail service in this way.

Or how about a fax for the car? The first such portable unit appeared in 1987 at less than £2500, provides Group 2 or 3 facilities, can transmit an A4 page to your car from across the world in less than a minute and incorporates a photocopier to boot.

The 'desktop computer' has come a long way since IBM popularized the idea with the PC back in 1981. Current examples offer considerably more power, more flexibility, and more range of choice. New technologies can clarify the opportunities or confuse the issues. Key technical considerations that can directly affect the operation of the computer as a management workstation are its role in a *local area network*, the *operating system* it employs, and the importance or otherwise of *IBM-compatibility*.

The heart of a desktop computer is the 'motherboard' or 'system board'; this contains all the electronics that drive the computer. It is usually housed along with the disk drives (and the display screen as well, in the case of computers like the Apple Macintosh) in what is called the 'system unit' — the main box.

Externals ...

On the outside of the box, you will see some or all of these:

- □ *On/off switch* for power, often with a nearby *fuse* compartment.
- □ *Power-on indicator* lamp.
- □ A *key lock* which in theory can prevent unauthorized use of the computer (but which is rarely used in practice, because it's inconvenient and usually unnecessary).
- □ *Floppy disk*. Slots, latches and/or doors for one or more floppy disk drives.
- □ *Hard disk*. There may also be a blanking panel that indicates the presence of a hard disk.
- □ *Disk drive indicators* that light up when a disk is being accessed.
- □ *Reset button* (usually at the rear, but a few computers locate it on the keyboard). This will interrupt anything you are doing and return you to the operating system (or in some cases to the start-up menu for your package). You'll lose whatever work you're doing, for in practice a Reset is like switching the computer on and off. To avoid any chance of an accidental Reset, this button should be well out of the way; it should be a different shape to any other button; it should not be possible to touch it inadvertently; and it should need a bit of pressure, so that using Reset is always a quite deliberate act.
- □ A *printer socket*, which is almost always a *parallel* port (sockets on computers are often called 'ports'). This has a characteristic shape to take a 36-pin Centronics-type plug.
- □ One or more *serial ports*, used primarily to attach modems and other output devices (plotters, printers that can't go on the parallel port, output to 35 mm slide-making devices, and so on). These connectors generally conform to the RS-232 standard, but there are several different shapes of socket.
- □ *Sockets* for attaching the mains lead, keyboard and display. Ideally all sockets should be clearly identified, and preferably of different shapes, to prevent you accidentally plugging in the wrong lead.

... Internals

Inside are the disk drives, a beefy power converter (that transforms the mains electricity into the form the computer's components like) and a large circuit board.

- □ *The main circuit board*. This 'motherboard' is generally bolted down to the bottom of the system unit box. There may be one or more 'daughter boards' attached to it mezzanine fashion if the main board is not big enough to hold all the electronics. It contains the main electronic components:
  - — The *microprocessor*.
  - — A block of *memory chips* (more memory can usually be added later, either by plugging in extra chips into vacant sockets on the motherboard or via the expansion slots — see below).
  - — One or more *read-only memory* chips for various start-up and self-testing routines. Some parts of the operating system will also be in ROM.
  - — *Controller circuitry* to drive the disks, the input and output devices and sockets (keyboard, screen, printers, etc.).
  - — *Expansion slots* for plugging in circuit boards containing extra memory, connection to local networks or additional functions (terminal emulation for communicating with mainframes, alternative colour and graphics displays) or devices (hard disks and modems are available for some computers on plug-in boards).

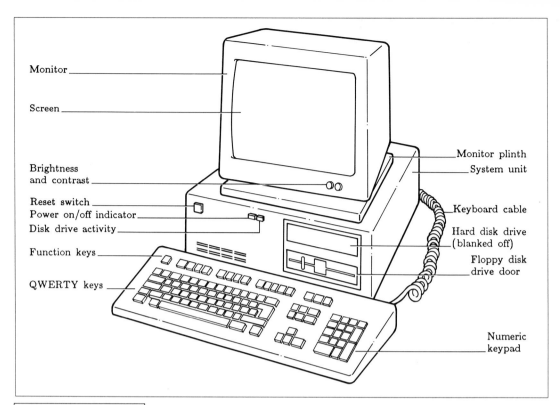

Monitor

Screen

Brightness
and contrast

Reset switch
Power on/off indicator
Disk drive activity

Function keys

QWERTY keys

Monitor plinth
System unit

Keyboard cable

Hard disk drive
(blanked off)

Floppy disk
drive door

Numeric
keypad

Guided tour — externals

Guided tour — internals

On the motherboard there may also be:

— A *local area network controller* to attach the computer to a local area network.

— A small *loudspeaker* and associated circuitry to produce the clicks and beeps of normal operation.

— Special *maths processing chips* that can speed up mathematical operations (useful for spreadsheet and data analysis work, but only if the package in question can utilize the 'maths co-processor' chip).

— *Empty sockets* for extra add-in chips to provide functions that are not part of the basic specification.

— *Special connectors* for attaching external devices that cannot plug into any of the standard ports.

▫ *The 'power supply unit'*. The power supply is a transformer which steps mains voltages down to the levels the computer uses — generally 5, 9 and/or 12 volts — and then distributes it to all the system components (keyboard, disk drives, all the devices on the circuit board). It may also pass power to the display, though many screens have their own power supply unit actually inside the monitor.

The power supply probably includes 'line filters' in the power supply, which shield things from the effects of 'electrical noise' and extraneous radio waves. There will also be built-in protection against voltage and current fluctuations on the mains.

The assembly for this is normally a substantial and heavy unit bolted on to the back panel; power supply units are more prone to failure than most other components in the box, but replacement is generally easy.

▫ *The fan*. Most computers include a small fan to cool the electronic components, which can generate quite a lot of heat — especially when packed tightly together. Electronic components will misfire and eventually fail if they get too warm. Fans account for most of the noise from the computer.

Memory chips — electronic memory, 'solid-state' memory — are essential to microprocessors. They allow programs to be read and executed speedily. But it is just not feasible to put all the computer's programs and all the data it needs into memory:

- ❑ *Cost*. There are cheaper ways of holding programs and data.
- ❑ *Capacity*. Though the storage capacities are increasing dramatically, you cannot get enough information into memory chips — not without having a great number of them.
- ❑ *'Volatility'*. Most types of read-write memory chip (the most economical of them, in fact) lose their contents as soon as the power is turned off. Next time the computer is switched on, that memory will be empty until something is transferred into it.
- ❑ *Non-removability*. Information and programs should be kept away from the computer. It makes sense to do this for reasons of security — not keeping all the eggs (computer *and* programs *and* data) in one basket. The computer will probably have more than one program to run and the separate programs will have separate files of information to work with.
- ❑ *Distribution*. There has to be a simple and easy way for programs to be sold and for programs and data to be transferred to another computer. You can't open up your computer to solder in another chip every time you need a new software package.

For all these reasons, most computers come with disk drives. There will be at least one of these on any personal computer; the 'drive' is a box that reads from and writes on to a disk, a bit like a record player or a tape cassette deck.

Floppy disks

Floppy disks really are floppy (though they may come in stiff card or plastic envelopes to protect them). They are made of a coated plastic: the coating is magnetizable, and the information on a disk is actually put there as a series of tightly packed dots or spots of magnetization.

You may come across the older 8in diameter floppy disk, though that is a dying breed. More common is the 5¼in variety; these can generally hold between 360KB and 1.2MB of data.

Access time

'Access time' indicates how quickly the computer can get at the information on the disk — specifically, how long it takes for the read/write head to locate the required point on the disk.

This is partly a function of the electronic componentry that controls the disk drive, partly down to the capability of the drive itself. A fast hard disk will have an access time of something like 28 milliseconds, though between 40 and 80ms is more usual for cheaper drives. By contrast, floppy drives are doing well if they manage 200ms.

Access time is not as important with floppy disk drives, since most desktop computers will not be using floppies for actual day-to-day work — backups and program or data transfers are the more usual application.

It is obviously more important for hard disks — the faster the drive works, the faster the computer will be. On the other hand, access time is only one factor in overall throughput. For instance, the read/write head may be able to get quickly to a specified point on the disk, but the software may not be particularly quick at telling the disk drive exactly where that point is.

Anatomy of a 5¼in floppy

Into the envelope are cut:

- ☐ A central circular hole that exposes a rim of disk (the hub of the disk drive fits into that to spin the disk).
- ☐ A longish slot showing more of the disk's surface. This is where the read/write head actually makes contact with the disk to transfer information to and from the computer.
- ☐ Near the central ring may be a smaller 'index hole', which provides a reference point for the read/write head to enable the controlling software to find the correct point on the disk.
- ☐ The squarish cutout in one edge of the envelope is the 'write-protect' notch; if it is covered you cannot 'write' on to the disk, which means you can't overwrite anything on it or add new files or programs.

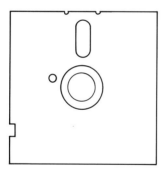

Both 8in and 5¼in disks are normally encased in a stiffish card envelope. The preferred alternative these days is the 'microfloppy', a disk that is only 3½in in diameter but still holds at least 315KB and possibly a megabyte or more of information (standard capacities are 720KB or 1.44MB, in fact). These small disks are the ones that come in rigid plastic packages. They do not need such a large disk drive, so the computer can be more compact, and the robust casing makes it difficult to damage the contents of the disk inside it.

Because floppy disks are cheap, convenient and relatively safe, they have become the standard method of selling or transferring programs and data. They are also convenient for taking safety copies of work — 'backups'.

Floppy disk drives are still occasionally 'single-sided', which means data can only be stored on one side of the disk. More usually, they are 'double-sided' — the drive includes read/write heads for both sides of the disk surface. Predictably enough, double-sided disks have twice the capacity of a single-sided equivalent. Single-sided disks can be read from and written to in a double-sided disk, but not *vice versa*.

Floppy drives are usually built into the system box. It may be possible to add additional drives in an external cable-connected box.

Anatomy of a 3½in floppy

- ☐ The central hub is not exposed — instead it is gripped by the disk drive mechanism to spin the disk.
- ☐ The read/write slot is covered by a shutter that is moved aside automatically to expose the disk's surface for the read/write head. This is done automatically when the disk is inserted correctly into the drive.
- ☐ Write-protection is provided by a sliding or snap-off tag.

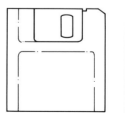 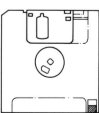

Buying floppy disks

There are dozens of brands of floppy disk on the market, and dozens of suppliers with different prices on the same brand. In fact there are only a handful of manufacturers of the disk surfaces themselves; they tend to supply in bulk to the people who put the disks into envelopes and check them out.

Disks are not generally manufactured for a particular capacity. What happens is that all disks are tested to see if they will be suitable for the maximum likely capacity; failures are then tested for successively lower capacities. Thus a single-sided 180KB IBM-type disk may be one that didn't make the grade as a 1.2MB or a 360KB disk.

Buy in bulk and the disks will be cheaper; disks are usually sold boxed in tens, with discounts starting at five or ten boxes per order. Buy from a specialist disk supplier, too — computer dealers mark their prices up because they do not deal in volume (and because they don't particularly want to get into that cut-throat market).

As for which brand to buy — avoid the cheapest, avoid the most expensive, try a few different brands in the middle until you get a satisfactory combination of price, performance and frills.

'Hard' disks

Now these really *are* hard. They use exactly the same principles as the floppy disks, except that the magnetizable coating sits on a rigid aluminium base. The main attraction of these disks is simply their large storage capacity, typically between 10 and 70MB.

They are not usually removable, however, because the disk is sealed inside the drive. For technical reasons — principally the lack of friction and the absence of stray dust and other particles — this means the manufacturer can cram a lot more storage capacity into a disk drive box that is the same size as a floppy disk drive (the hard disk itself is likely to be 3½ or 5¼in in diameter, just like a floppy drive). It also allows the disk to spin much faster, so that getting information to and from the disk is generally much faster than with floppies.

Their speed, capacity and convenience have made hard disks the norm for storing programs and data; floppy disks are used then only for backups and for loading the original program on to the hard disk.

Again, these disk drives are usually built into the system box. In many cases it is feasible to gain extra capacity (and perhaps a faster access time) simply by swapping one drive unit for another.

It is also possible to add a hard disk to a floppy disk computer, or as a second drive to a computer that already has one hard disk. This can be done by connecting an external box; or, for some computers, a complete disk drive unit sitting on a circuit board can be plugged into one of the computer's expansion slots.

External hard disk on a floppy disk machine

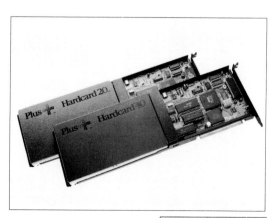

Internal hard disk

Removable hard disks

These come in the form of solid cartridges or packs, sometimes as an extra-cost option connected by cable to the computer but now more frequently built into the computer. They offer all the extra storage space and speed of non-removable disks, but because you can take out the disk there is an added element of safety. Such disks are very robust.

You may come across 'Bernouilli boxes', a variety of removable disk that does not actually use aluminium-based platters. Instead they feature an advanced floppy disk technology, utilizing 8in floppy disks as a rule. The disks still come in rigid plastic cartridges.

You pay for the virtue of removability, though: these disk units are pretty expensive. They are generally used as backup devices (to provide an exact copy of the contents of a hard disk) but are fast enough to work as normal day-to-day information and program storage.

External 'Bernouilli box' removable disk

Disk formatting

Just because a disk is technically capable of holding a lot of data does not mean that it will do so in practice. Also, a disk containing programs or information for one computer may not be usable on another.

Both of these are functions of a disk's 'format'. Blank disks straight from the factory are generally sold for any computer into which they can fit; formatting is a customization process that sets the disk up for use on a particular computer — or, more accurately, for use with a particular computer's operating system. Any blank disk has to be formatted before it can be used, and the operating system will include commands that enable a user to do this.

☐	160KB	the original PC single-sided format for 5¼in floppies
☐	320KB	the original PC double-sided format for 5¼in floppies
☐	180KB	the revised PC single-sided format for 5¼in floppies
☐	360KB	the revised PC double-sided format — the most common format for IBM-compatibles now for 5¼in floppies
☐	1.2MB	the standard AT format for 5¼in floppies
☐	720KB	the standard IBM format for 3½in floppies
☐	1.44MB	the PS/2 format for 3½in floppies

Formatting generally has to be done just once, when the disk is new. Subsequently it might have to be reformatted for use on another computer or with another operating system, or because some disaster has scrambled its contents. Formatting has the side-effect of completely erasing anything that is currently on the disk.

Part of the formatting process will determine the maximum usable capacity of the disk, on the basis of the capabilities of the disk drive installed. For instance, an IBM computer may be able to format a blank floppy with any of these different capacities for use on different drives and with different operating systems:

In practice, a computer cannot format a disk for a higher capacity than its own drives can manage. But it will be able to format (and read from and write on to) floppies of a lesser capacity — which may be required if disks from one machine have to be given to another user with those drives that store less data per floppy. So a PC-compatible with 360KB drives can't format AT-type 1.2MB floppies, but it will probably be able to format 180KB disks. An AT-compatible will be able to format and use all three disk formats.

Backups

If the computer is going to become an essential tool, it pays to take a circumspect attitude to the information it uses. The computer can malfunction or simply die on you; component failures are unlikely, but a power blackout or a sudden dip or surge in the mains supply are by no means uncommon. They can wipe out anything currently in the memory and may also corrupt the contents of your disks.

The only safe option is a regular and rigorous backup procedure to take copies of all programs and data residing in the machine.

☐ The simple option is *copying on to floppy disks*. With a whole hard disk to copy, this may take some time and will require a lot of floppies.

☐ *Selective copying* is one answer — only files that have changed since the last backup are copied. All operating systems attach a time and date 'stamp' to files on disk; this shows when they were last updated, so that information can be used by a special backup program to take only those files with a time and date more recent than the last backup.

☐ *Compression* is another alternative. There are techniques for 'squeezing' large files so that they take up less room; in the event that the backups have to be copied back, they are 'unsqueezed' so that they can be used. Most computers come with a backup utility of some kind that will do this kind of compression.

☐ Even a compressed data file may not fit on to a floppy, and in any case the transfer will be limited by the access speed of the floppy disk. Special high-capacity fast-transfer backup devices are

available, often with their own software utilities to control the copying (and probably to provide selective and/or compressed backups as well).

The commonest of these devices is a '*tape streamer*', which uses slot-in tape cartridges; some computers have a tape unit built in, others can attach an external tape streamer via a cable connection. *Removable hard disk* units also have a good deal of appeal as backup devices, because they will be faster still. For large capacities, removable *laser disks* like CD-ROM disks should be considered.

Tape streamers may be integral ...

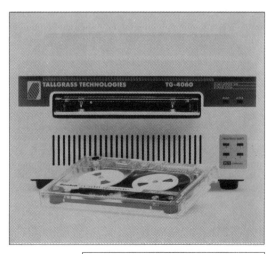

... or external cable-connected units

Portables and other computers with an integral screen will be wired up internally. With the three-box approach, a lead at the back of the monitor will plug into the side or rear of the computer; the same cable may provide power as well as video signals, but there may also be a separate power lead going direct to a mains socket or to another socket on the system unit.

A brightness control is normal, and most screens have a contrast control as well. In a few cases, brightness and contrast are controlled by software using the keyboard (combinations of the ALT key with the cursor arrows, for instance) rather than by knobs.

The display

The screen on most desktop computers can display up to 24 or 25 lines of 80 characters each.

Most screens measure 11 or 12in across the diagonal; a few are as large as 15in, some as small as 9in. A common rule of thumb among designers is that the diagonal should be at least one-eighth the average viewing distance, and with most computers the user will be a maximum of 30in from the screen.

On larger screens, text characters will obviously be fatter and more legible. More important, bigger screens will be useful for dense displays that utilize a lot of the available area for graphics.

Monochrome displays

A monochrome display typically shows white, amber or green characters on a charcoal background, though there are alternatives — the so-called 'paper white' screen has black characters on white, and yellow on brown is featured by some suppliers.

In principle, the key consideration is ergonomic: what gives the most restful and the most legible display that suits the type of

work at hand? The yellow/brown combination is preferred by some North European suppliers on the basis of ergonomic research; the paper-white display suits the 'what you see is what you get' requirement of some desktop publishing tasks.

In practice, most manufacturers buy displays as off-the-shelf components; and provided the image is acceptable, they will take what they can get at the best price. The white-on-black and green-on-black displays may have come in for some criticism from ergonomicists, but they are usable — and production volumes are high enough for savings of scale to be reflected in the component price the computer supplier has to pay.

Such displays will include various highlighting options — extra-bright, reversed, underlined text. This is usually applied to parts of the displayed text under the control of a program, with the user not knowingly participating at all.

Colour screens

Desktop computers generally come as standard with the circuitry to drive a monochrome display. To handle colour, a special colour monitor is required along with a colour graphics controller; that normally comes in the form of a plug-in circuit board which fits into one of the expansion slots and will have a socket for the monitor lead.

Colour monitors display several colours at a time. Up to 16 colours is normal, some manage 64, a purpose-designed colour graphics system will provide several hundred hues and shades.

Colour can be useful for presentation (a pie-chart, say, or share movements) and for highlighting options on the screen (to distinguish between messages from the computer and actions you have to take, for instance).

Character sets

Most computers will be able to display a total of 256 different characters. Those will include all the characters the keyboard can produce with or without Shift. Exactly *which* characters will depend on the computer and the software; they will include all the familiar typewriter characters — the normal upper- and lower-case alphabet, numerals, punctuation marks and mathematical symbols.

That is the basic set of 128 characters defined by a US standards body and known as the ASCII character set; it specifies what bit combinations relate to what characters. Because virtually all computer designers follow the standard, software writers do not have to customize their packages too much to fit different computers.

On the other hand, for technical (and largely historical) reasons a total of 256 characters can normally be provided on the display. The ASCII code doesn't specify what the extra characters should be, so different designers came up with their own collections of miscellaneous symbols and characters to fill out the 256 available. And in any case many programs will replace some of the standard symbols supplied, giving instead some special characters or foreign-language characters relevant to the package's operation.

Provided the software limits itself to the basic 128 characters, and provided it can persuade the computer to display them, there's no problem. If it wants to display extra characters, it can tell the computer to do so; the drawback is that other packages may have a different use for the extra codes, so output from one package may look a bit garbled when it's used with another. The nearest thing to a standard for all the 256 character codes is IBM's usage, which includes among the extras some simple block graphics characters and other symbols (funny faces, playing cards and the like).

On the other hand:

- □ Colour can be very distracting.
- □ Looking at a screenful of colour at such close range can become tiring.
- □ Colour adds to the cost of the computer, necessitating a colour controller board and a special monitor.
- □ By no means all software packages can utilize the availability of colour — and those than can display in colour will normally have a perfectly readable monochrome option.
- □ Text displayed is usually less crisp than on a monochrome screen and characters appear slightly blurred.

Video controllers

The display on a computer is usually determined by the controller card which drives it. That controller will determine how the monitor works — the resolution, the refresh rate and the 'scanning frequency'. It will also fetch whatever is to be displayed from a reserved area in the computer's memory and direct it to the monitor.

A controller for monochrome text is often built into the off-the-shelf computer, in the form of circuitry on the main system board. For anything else — for colour, or graphics, or both — a plug-in card may well be required (and in the case of IBM's PC, you even need such a card for monochrome display).

Measuring the performance

'Scan frequency' is often used to describe the performance of a monitor; it's the speed at which each line of dots must be scanned, the product of the refresh rate multiplied by the vertical resolution (the number of lines on the screen). This is determined by the controller, and the monitor must therefore be able to match what the controller requires.

For instance, the basic IBM PC or AT models offer a simple colour graphics controller called the CGA card which requires a monitor with a scan frequency of 15.75kHz. That monitor cannot be used with the higher-specification EGA card, with a scan frequency of 22kHz. But EGA boards can be switched into CGA mode, so any monitor that claims to be an EGA-compatible monitor should be capable of both scanning rates.

The safe bet is also the costliest option — an *auto-sync* monitor is one that can automatically adjust to a range of scanning frequencies, typically between 15 and 35kHz. That should be able to handle anything any video controller will require now or in the future.

Clarity

The clarity and crispness of a screen is indicated by its 'resolution', the number of dots that can appear on the screen. (An individual dot is called a pixel, or sometimes 'pel' — both are short for 'picture element' and defined as the smallest discrete element that can be displayed. Screen resolution is sometimes described in terms of pixels.)

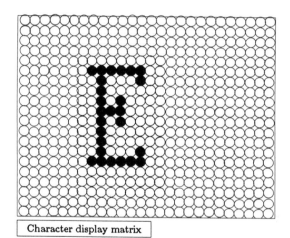

Character display matrix

On the IBM PC and most compatibles, the normal monochrome resolution is 640x200 — meaning 640 rows of 200 dots. Some compatibles do better than this, with resolutions of up to 720x350; the late-lamented Sirius (not an IBM-compatible) had an excellent 800x400 screen which gave an unusually good display.

The number of dots is relevant for the quality of text display, but it is more important for graphics — the more dots, the smoother any curves will appear.

Not all the dots are necessarily used for text characters. Desktop computers usually display up to 24 or 25 rows of 80 characters; the IBM and compatibles build those characters within a 9x14 matrix — that

means there are nine rows of 14 possible dot positions per character that can be lit up or left dark to construct the character's shape. To distinguish each character, the display leaves a 'blank' row of dots on either side of a character and two above and below; so the characters themselves actually use a 7x9 matrix within the block. The Sirius had an 8x10 matrix within a 10x16 box.

How CRTs work

The display unit on most desktop computers is sometimes referred to as a CRT display. Essentially this is a refinement of conventional cathode-ray tube TV technology, with the added bonuses of considerably improved clarity and a total inability to receive *Dynasty*.

Characters appear on the screen because inside the monitor there's an 'electron gun' that fires a stream of electrons at the phosphor coating on the back of the glass. When struck by a beam of electrons like this, the phosphor lights up — in the jargon, it's 'excited' — and you get one illuminated dot on the display (the colour of the dot is determined by the type of phosphor used).

The stream of electrons moves very quickly on to the next dot to excite that one too, moving horizontally across the screen from top to bottom, and eventually you get a pattern of illuminated dots appearing in the shape of the characters to be displayed.

The gun itself doesn't move; instead the stream of electrons is deflected electromagnetically to particular points on the screen. When the electron stream moves on to do another dot, the previously-illuminated one loses its excitement and starts to fade. If the computer uses a 'high-persistence' phosphor, as most do, the illumination decays relatively slowly; in any case, when the electron stream reaches the bottom of the screen it returns to 'refresh' the dots at the top. It all happens very rapidly, too rapidly for the naked eye to observe with current CRT technology.

Glare and reflections

CRT displays do not perform well in bright light, and the glass screen will pick up any reflections. A casing that has the actual screen quite deeply recessed will reduce the chance of damage in transit and also helps to cut out some extraneous reflections — but a deep recess will accumulate dust.

Most screens have an antiglare treatment of some kind, typically a light etching on the surface or as a bonded-on mesh. These work at cutting down reflections, but they will probably have a detrimental effect on the clarity of the display.

If the antiglare treatment is on the side facing you (rare, these days) it may be difficult to clean the screen with conventional antistatic impregnated cloths and liquids (they tend to clog in the etch or the mesh).

Fading phosphors

A high-persistence phosphor means the electron gun in a CRT display doesn't have to work too hard to keep everything bright on the screen, and a high 'refresh rate' means the dots do not have enough chance to fade before the electron stream returns — most CRTs 'refresh the display' at least 60 times a second. So there is no noticeable flicker.

A high refresh rate is no bad thing, though over about 70Hz the eye can't notice any benefit. But there are a couple of potential drawbacks with long-persistence phosphors. For one, when the screen display changes, the previous display retains some of its brightness for a fraction of a second before it fades away completely. That can be irritating; it can also be a (slight) strain on the eye.

High-persistence phosphors are invariably less bright than the normal variety. Users turn up the brightness and contrast, which has the effect of increasing the electron

bombardment. Phosphor coatings do wear out eventually, and maximum brightness will hasten that day.

A 'screen saver' utility will help; these automatically dim the screen to save wear of the phosphor if the display hasn't changed after a preset time interval.

'Paper-white' CRT screens for desktop publishing

Flat screens

There is a limit to how flat a normal CRT display can be — there has to be space for the electron 'gun' to fire at all parts of the phosphor coating. The alternatives are all more expensive, since production volumes are not sufficiently large to produce economies of scale. So they are generally reserved for special-purpose applications where size is more important than cost, notably portable computers.

□ *LEDs*. Light-emitting diodes are like tiny lightbulbs — they illuminate when current reaches them and switch off when the power is removed. Individual points in a matrix of LEDs can be illuminated to create a pattern of dots corresponding to a character. The problem is that each LED has to have an electrical connection; more important, the LED cannot be small enough for fine resolution — and as a result, LED displays are rather coarse, with poor clarity for individual characters when the screen is fairly small.

□ *Gas plasma*. Here the matrix comprises a series of cells, one per dot position, that are filled with a gas which illuminates when power is applied. There have been resolution problems with gas plasma, but the cells can now be small enough to provide CRT-like quality. The main drawback is a voracious appetite for power — gas plasma displays require more than most other display technologies, which is a problem when batteries are used.

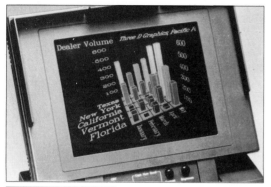

Gas plasma display

□ *Liquid crystal*. The current preference in portable computers is for liquid crystal displays. An LCD is a screen-sized sandwich containing a liquid material that reacts to heat or electricity. Behind this is a web of electrical connections arranged as a matrix of possible dot positions; applying power to one of those positions excites the liquid crystal, which glows as a dot on the display. This is a relatively simple technology, and the screen itself can be fairly flexible — you do not need a thick coating of glass or plastic to protect the LCD elements.

□ *Backlit LCDs*. One of the problems of standard LCD screens is their unreadability in even quite moderate light levels — the dots just can't be bright enough to compete with reflections, daylight, and even office lighting. One solution has been to improve the contrast of the screen by including a light source behind it; that throws the characters into sharper focus.

□ *Supertwist LCDs*. Most modern LCD screens use 'supertwist' displays, a technical approach that adds slightly to the component cost but greatly improves the contrast of the display. Supertwist screens do not normally need backlighting as well, but since they consume more power there is sometimes an option to switch to less effective but less power-hungry backlighting.

The crucial drawback with all current LCD displays is the effect of rapid screen movements — the illuminated dots have a high persistence because the crystals take some time to rearrange themselves when you are moving through text or scrolling a column of figures. Many users find this disconcerting at best, nauseous at worst.

Along with the quality of the display, the keyboard of any computer is probably the most important aspect of what designers like to call the 'user interface' — the way the machine and the human come into contact. It is somewhat surprising then to observe the variations in quality among computer keyboards. Despite a good deal of ergonomic research and the experience from 20 years of electric typewriters, many keyboards are apparently designed with little thought for the user, constructed primarily to simplify production and laid out to suit the requirements of the electronics engineer rather than the typist.

What you get

When the computer is a two- or three-box arrangement, the keyboard is generally attached by cable — it could be two metres of stretchable coil to allow some flexibility in organizing the workspace — and plugs into the side or back of the main box. There have been some less than successful attempts to do away with the cable; key depressions generate an infrared pulse which is picked up by a receiver at the front of the computer. But this limits the options for positioning the keyboard; little variation is possible before the keyboard gets out of range of the receptor.

The main keyboard

The centre section of keys will provide a conventional typewriter-like QWERTY layout. These are the 'printing' keys — they put characters on to the screen. None of them should have system control or editing functions.

For the standard set of typewriter characters, all the usual symbols are present plus some extras (in addition to any other symbols that a particular package provides). The characters appear as expected, except that zeros may have a slash through them to distinguish a nought from a capital 'O'.

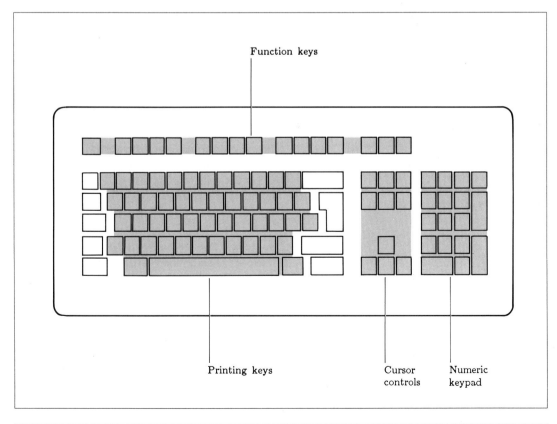

Function keys

Printing keys

Cursor controls

Numeric keypad

Formatting keys

Around the periphery of this arrangement are the 'typewriter' controls, like tabs and shifts; the return key is there too. International symbols are normally used for Tab, Shift and Backspace; US-derived keyboards may show Caps Lock as a dot in a circle.

While CAPS LOCK is engaged you cannot type lower-case letters at all.

The Backspace key may cause some problems. On some computers and with some packages, this key does not just move the cursor left (back along a line); it also erases as it goes.

The 'Return' key

This is often (and more accurately) referred to as the 'Enter' key. The descriptor 'Return' obviously dates from typewriter days, when hitting that key did actually return the print mechanism to the start of the next line. 'Enter' is better suited to computer use, since the computer will not actually act on anything you have typed until you hit that key to 'enter' the command or text.

Control keys

One or both of the ALT and CONTROL keys may be provided — they act as extra Shift functions. On some keyboard arrangements there will be alternative symbols on particular keys, perhaps engraved on the side rather than on the top of the keys; ALT or CONTROL are held down while the relevant key is pressed to produce that symbol.

ALT and/or CONTROL may also be used in combination with other keys for system functions. Holding down CONTROL and pressing C, for instance, will often have the effect of aborting whatever the computer is doing at the time.

ESC is another undefined key that can be set up by a programmer for particular functions. 'Escape' implies quick and easy exit from something, and in some situations does just that — usually by cancelling the operation you are currently performing. It is rarely employed by packages, however; its principal use is in programming, to key in special 'escape codes' in the form of a number preceded by an ESC character generated when the programmer touches the key.

Function keys

Along the top or to the right of the main keyboard may be ten or more 'function' keys. Their use is generally defined by a particular program and so varies from one package to another; they might include:

☐ Selection of options from a menu displayed on the screen or printed in the handbook.
☐ Calling up on-screen help.
☐ Single-keystroke entry of commands that might otherwise take several key depressions.

Programmable keys

The function keys can be given a specific meaning by a program. On some keyboards, all other key depressions automatically generate specific codes that are recognized by the computer. On others, the meaning of *any* key can in fact be specified by a programmer for a particular program — the keystrokes are detected and converted into the appropriate codes by software, so that different packages can assign different meanings to the keys. It is normally only the function keys and one or two others that are given special meanings like this, but some packages do assign special effects to just about every key outside the main QWERTY and numeric keypad layouts.

This necessarily applies for the different keyboard layouts required for different national expectations. Thus there is a French AZERTY layout, a British version with the Sterling sign, an American one with a cents symbol, a German keyboard with umlauts, and so on. The keytops can be levered out and replaced, so what appears on them has no inviolable relationship to what a key depression will produce; the software in the computer generally decides what each keypress *means*.

The ideal keyboard

Weight

The keyboard should at least be solid enough not to slide around the desk as you type on it.

Distinction

A computer may need all kinds of control keys in addition to the normal typewriter layout — there could be over a hundred keys. They should be arranged such that the keyboard does not feel overcrowded or intimidating; groups of keys should be logically distinct. Different colours for the keytops can help, though too many visual alternatives can be confusing.

Palm rest

There should be a wide lip below the space bar which can be used comfortably by touch-typists who like to allow the hands to rest.

The Return (Enter) key

The Return key is a much-used and therefore important key, so it should be large and unmissable. That applies to all the 'typewriter' controls like tabs and shifts as well; they should be the size that a touch-typist would expect.

Left and right

The least-used keys should be positioned under the least-used hand, which for most people is the left. Frequently-used controls like those that move the cursor should get the 'preferred' hand of most typists.

Numeric keypad

For fast and simple entry of numbers, for instance when using a spreadsheet, a numeric keypad is useful. These too should be located under the right hand. (A drawback of the IBM keyboard layout is the way the numeric pad doubles as the cursor controls; a 'numeric lock' is provided to switch operation to number entry, in which case the cursor movements become inoperative until the NUM LOCK key is pressed again.)

Rake

A keyboard that lies flat is uncomfortable to use. The keyboard should have a slight slope from top to bottom, and it should also have the option of increasing the slope with short pop-out legs.

Curve

Seen from the side, the keytops should appear dished — there should be a curve from the top row of QWERTY keys to the bottom, and those in the middle should be marginally lower. This is demonstrably more comfortable for typing.

Dished keytops

The individual keys should also be dished slightly to take the fingertip more comfortably.

'Feel'

The tactile sensations of actually using the keyboard can be a matter of personal taste, but in general the more solid the feel the better. The keyboard should not feel light and clacky, with no 'feedback' from the keys when they do make contact.

Key-click

Some or all of the keys should click when contact is made. This certainly applies for 'lock' keys like CAPS LOCK and NUM LOCK; for other keys it can probably be left to the user's preference, in which case there should be a setup option to select no click or to adjust the loudness — on most modern keyboards the click is produced by the computer's loudspeaker rather than by the key mechanism itself, so it is under the control of software.

Space bar

The space bar should work along the whole of its length, not just when it is pressed in the centre.

Indications

There should be some indication of when the 'lock' keys are engaged — a small indicator light, for instance.

Compatibility

The keys should generate the characters and the control effects expected by the package being used.

Editing

Backspace may delete characters as it moves from left to right, but there will also be a 'delete character' key. This will delete whatever character is under the cursor at the time (or maybe the character immediately to its left); text is usually 'closed up' after the deletion, so that the character which was immediately following the deletion is then the one under the cursor.

There may be a 'delete line' key as well that erases the rest of the line from the current cursor position or wipes the whole line that the cursor is on.

Also in the editing category, you are likely to find an INS or 'insert' key. Depending on how the package uses it, this may have the effect of splitting the line so that a gap appears in the middle of the screen for the insertion; or the cursor might change shape to indicate that you are in 'insert mode', with new text being entered at the cursor and everything to the right of it on the original line shuffling rightwards to accommodate the insertion. Pressing the Insert key again usually turns off the insert mode.

Cursor controls

Most keyboards include five keys to move the cursor around — up and down one line, left and right one character and 'home'. The precise operation of a key labelled HOME or CLR will depend on the particular package; it will probably have the effect of taking the cursor immediately to the top left corner of the display — the 'home' position — but it may also clear the screen as it does this, which means you lose anything that happens to be on the display at the time.

IBM-compatible keyboards also have keys to move the cursor a whole 'page' at a time — a 'page' being a screenful of text. These keys will take the cursor forward or back 24 or 25 lines at a time.

Numeric keypad

If present, the numeric keypad duplicates the numerics on the top QWERTY row and usually has the arithmetic symbols as well (plus sign and dash for addition and subtraction, asterisk or 'x' for multiplication, slash or '÷' for division).

The arrangement of keys will be familiar to calculator users; an oversize zero is normal.

The numeric pad is not affected by the use of the standard Shift key, but there may be a separate 'numeric Shift' or NUM LOCK key to allow extra functions — notably in the case of IBM-compatibles, where the keypad doubles as the cursor controls.

Most desktop computers have expansion slots that take additional circuit boards. What the plug-in boards actually do is to extend the basic system; the contacts inside the slots link directly into the 'bus' that connects all system components.

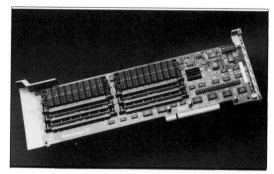

Memory board

Expansion slots on the motherboard

Add-in circuit boards are often called 'cards' for no particularly good reason. You may also see the abbreviation 'PCB', for 'printed circuit board' — they used to be 'printed' with fine lines to connect their components in just the same way as paper is printed, only metal was used rather than ink. Today the connecting lines are actually etched on to the board using acid and a photographic technique for the template.

There are broadly two kinds of extension possible: you can add memory or extra functions.

Adding memory

Some computers come with as much memory as the operating system can handle, provided in the form of chips soldered on to the motherboard. Many do not, and where an alternative operating system is available on the computer, it may be necessary to add memory.

Extra functions

A slot-in board can fill some of the gaps in the computer's standard specification by providing extra functions. This particularly applies to control of peripherals — a 'peripheral' is in theory any externally connected device, though in practice the word is used to mean anything that is not there on the main system board.

For many such devices it is simply a question of plugging into the appropriate socket already provided. Others, however, will need a special controller in the form of a plug-in circuit board; connections to local networks and use of a colour monitor are likely to require this extra hardware.

In some cases, just about *everything* attached to the computer needs a controller card in one of the expansion slots — even standard items like monochrome display and a printer. Internal disk drives may also need a controller board. On such computers it is easy to run out of slots just in order to run a pretty basic system.

The board may provide the connection for external devices, but the device itself may reside on the board — this is the case, for instance, for some internally mounted modems and disk drives.

Multi-function cards cram a variety of extras on to a single board. This one provides memory expansion plus additional printer and serial ports and a battery-powered clock/calendar function.

Paper is cheap and familiar. You cannot accidentally format a piece of paper. You can see where text has been altered. Paper is portable. You do not need electricity or any special equipment (other than a writing implement) to use it.

So all computers need a way of getting information on to paper. And despite the promise of the all-electronic new-technology office, computers can generate a very large amount of paper.

Impact dot matrix printers

The dot matrix printer currently provides the best balance between price, reliability, physical size and print speed for day-to-day work where perfect quality is not the key consideration.

These printers have a single print head that contains a collection of metal needles (sometimes called 'pins' or 'print wires'). By selecting a particular pattern of needles and pushing them against the ribbon on to the paper, the printer can produce a collection of dots that resembles a character.

The needles are usually arranged in a vertical row. The printer will print all the dot positions in the first column of a character, then move on to do the second column, and so on. Some printers have two or more columns of print wires for extra speed or to provide extra dots per character.

In addition to their standard mode, nearly all such printers have an option for correspondence-quality printing (or 'NLQ' — near-letter-quality) at slower speeds. NLQ involves printing more dots per character to form a crisper, denser image. This can be done by moving the paper or the printhead slightly and printing the character a second time, so that the dots overlap slightly. That obviously slows down the printing by comparison with the single-pass 'draft' mode; in this style the

printer is usually at least 25 per cent slower.

For NLQ print, it is a case of the more print wires the better; a nine-pin matrix printer can produce a reasonably solid impression, but the output from a 24-pin printer will be acceptable for any but the most demanding applications. As well as improving the image of normal English characters, a 24-pin printer will also be better able to handle unusual printing such as accented foreign characters and graphics symbols for which any fewer print wires could not provide adequate precision.

Print styles from an impact dot matrix printer

Paper feed options

The two standard methods of using paper in printers are 'friction feed' and 'tractor (or pin) feed'. In the case of friction feeding, the paper may be delivered by a 'single-sheet feeder'.

Tractor feeds require the stationery to have sprocket holes down the edge. These engage in rubber or plastic teeth in the paper feed mechanism, and when these 'pins' are turned they drag the paper through. Paper for tractor feeds is 'continuous' or 'fanfold' stationery, long strips of paper perforated horizontally at the equivalent of a page's length. There is normally a perforation down the edges too, so you can tear off the bit with the sprocket holes.

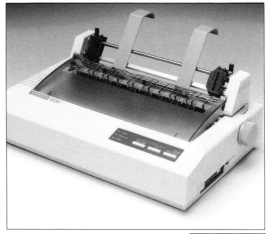

Tractor feed

For a fairly modest price premium you can have continuous stationery ready-printed with a letterhead, which gets over the somewhat utilitarian look of the plain stuff. It is also possible to buy heavyweight continuous stationery sized so that when you tear along the perforation you end up with an A4 sheet; the tear lines are barely noticeable, so this can be used with a tractor feed for correspondence-quality work.

Matrix printers tend to have a tractor feed built in, and many do not have a platen at all — so you do not get the chance to use single sheets. Daisywheel printers use friction feed, but you can generally get a tractor feed attachment for extra cost.

Friction feed

Friction feed works just like a typewriter. The paper is held against a rubber-covered roller called a platen; when the platen turns, the paper rolls with it. Ordinary typewriter or photocopier paper can be used. A variant of this approach is used in laser printers.

Sheet feeders are trays that automatically deliver the paper a sheet at a time; they are available for most printers with a friction feed, but are generally used for bulk printing on headed notepaper by a daisywheel or other letter-quality printer.

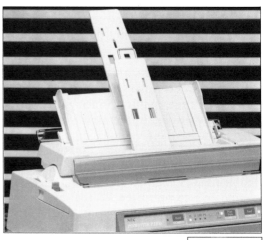

Sheet feeder

For most day-to-day office work the matrix printer is fine. It is relatively cheap, fast, pretty robust, fairly quiet, compact and easy to use. The printing is legible. Ribbons are inexpensive and easily replaced (though even today some printers do require you to cover your fingers in ink before you can do that). The print element itself lasts a long while — 30 million characters is normal — and is also replaced easily.

However, such printers can seem prone to mishaps like sticky labels jamming under the platen and the paper getting caught in the ribbon or under the printhead. And printer manuals — particularly for the smaller, cheaper models — are often written in a kind of Oriental American that impedes comprehension.

Daisywheel printers

The best print quality for correspondence purposes comes from a preformed type element. Daisywheel printers produce a good-quality print image because they use fully-formed characters, rather as a typewriter does (indeed, some typewriters these days use a daisywheel element).

The 'daisywheel' itself is the removable print element, the equivalent of a Selectric typewriter's golfball; it is a flat disc with radiating spokes, usually between 96 and 120. (A less successful relation uses a print element that looks like a daisywheel whose spokes have been bent upwards to form a kind of cup; because of the vague resemblance the manufacturer, NEC, calls it a 'thimble'.) On the end of each spoke is a character; the print wheel is turned so that the relevant character faces the ribbon, and then that particular stalk is pushed forward to press the ribbon on to the paper and so leave the impression of the character.

The print elements are easy to slot in and out; the printing can match a typewriter's; daisywheels are available in a variety of typestyles; and ribbons are cheap and easy to replace.

On the other hand, being pre-formed means the printing is limited to the characters provided. By comparison, other types of printer can be used to build a variety of printed shapes.

The other problem is that daisywheel mechanisms have to be relatively complicated: they involve many more moving parts than a matrix printer. Moving parts inevitably wear, so there is a greater risk of failure. This also means the print mechanisms cannot really go very quickly — the fastest speed for daisywheels is presently about 80 characters a second, and that is for high-priced examples. The hammer impact also generates a good deal of noise.

Daisywheel

Thermal printers

These use a ribbon coated with wax-based ink; the print element heats it from behind, the ink melts and the image is transferred to the paper again as a series of dots.

The results may not appeal; the ink tends to have a shiny finish and the resolution will not be high enough for letter-quality work. Ribbons can be expensive, and special paper may be required. There are also limitations on paper width, for the matrix of heating elements is arranged as a non-moving strip the width of the line.

On the other hand, such printers can be technically quite simple and very compact. They are also virtually silent in operation. As well as some special-purpose applications, thermal printers may have applications in portable computing — where a small, draft-quality printer is all that is required.

Inkjet printers

Inkjet printers can deliver the same kind of quietness, compactness and speed — with rather better print quality.

Inkjet printer technology is by no means new, prototypes having been shown in the mid sixties, but it has received something of a boost thanks to the requirement for low noise levels (in offices and with travelling portables) plus the reasonable print quality and the use of plain paper. Most of the other more or less silent printer technologies demand special paper; apart from the extra cost, such stationery has not generally proved acceptable (or in some cases sufficiently durable) for correspondence and documentation.

This technology features a reservoir containing special ink under pressure; very small droplets are ejected from one or more nozzles on a moving head. As they squirt out, they pass through electrically charged fields which attract the droplet one way or the other and so steer the drop into the correct position to form a dot on the paper.

It has taken some time for inkjet printing to catch on. Hitherto the disadvantages have included nozzle clogging, spatter and poor character definition, speed limitations and the cost of the ink (it requires a special formulation, otherwise it dries up after two or three passes).

Most objections are being met in current inkjet products, however, and markets are emerging. Currently the major impact of inkjet is probably in labelling and industrial marketing, with a lively runner-up in inkjet addressing machines. One newer area where inkjets might have some application is in colour printing; and at present, inkjet printers certainly look the best bet for portable computing.

But while other technologies are either predominant or can offer rather more presentation options, applications for inkjets will remain somewhat specialized and the consequent scale of production will not permit prices to drop very far.

Diconix 150: portable inkjet printing

```
PRINTER SETTING USING PR.bat

PR PP (Pica Proportional)
This is a test for the printer.  It i
has 80 characters, two has 76 and th
QWERTYUIOPASDFGHJKLZXCVBNM^!@£%$&*()

PR PC (Pica Condensed)
This is a test for the printer.  It includes two typ
has 80 characters, two has 76 and three has 79 (SOME
QWERTYUIOPASDFGHJKLZXCVBNM^!@£%$&*()_+qwertyuiopasdf

PR PCS (PC Superscript)
This is a test for the printer.  It includes two typ
has 80 characters, two has 76 and three has 79 (SOME
QWERTYUIOPASDFGHJKLZXCVBNM^!@£%$&*()_+qwertyuiopasdf

PR ES (Elite Superscript)
This is a test for the printer.
```

Print options from the Diconix

Electrostatic page printers

This catch-all heading covers a number of new-technology printers that assemble a whole page (rather than a single character or a line) before printing.

They also derive from photocopier technology. At the heart of an electrostatic page printer is a drum or belt coated with something that can develop an electric charge when exposed to light. A light source 'writes' an image on to the photosensitive coating one row of dots at a time; the drum then rotates to take the next line.

As it moves, it is passed through a bath of containing toner (usually in the form of a dry ink powder); this is attracted to the charged areas on the drum, which then comes into contact with a sheet of paper and transfers the ink.

The paper passes over a heated element that fuses the toner on to its surface and is then ejected into an output tray; the roller meanwhile continues its rotation past cleaning and scraping mechanisms so that the surface is ready for the next page's worth of image.

In the case of a copier, a light source behind the original document is used to energize the photosensitive coating; the toner sticks to the areas that the light did not reach — the bits corresponding to the dark areas on the original.

The page printers replace the light source and the original document with a light source that 'writes' directly on to the photoreceptive surface. For each unoccupied (blank) dot position on the page in memory a flash of light is fired on to the equivalent position on the drum. In this way a charged/uncharged area is constructed on the photosensitive surface from the bit map to produce what will be printed as a light/dark image.

This is controlled by character codes received from the computer. As with photocopiers, these printers can print anything that is 'written' on to the photosensitive surface. This includes just about any dot pattern that can be reproduced within their (high) resolution — text in a variety of styles and fonts, rules and borders in varying thicknesses, shaded areas in different weights, size and shape, any graphic image at all that can be converted into a series of dots. And all of these can be mixed on the same page.

This is because the print style used is not preset. Electrostatic page printers include their own microprocessor with its own memory, and into that memory you can load one or more different typestyles and images. The result is akin to typesetting, which uses the same approach (though only for text and simple graphics) at much higher resolutions.

Laser printers are now common, but there are a number of alternative types of electrostatic page printer, using different light sources to get the image on to the drum.

Interfaces

The easiest and safest way of connecting any printing device is via a Centronics-type parallel socket; 'parallel' refers to the way the computer delivers data to the socket, Centronics was/is a printer manufacturer whose plug-and-socket connection became a *de facto* standard for deciding the shape of the plug and the use of the wires inside it.

The alternative, the serial or 'RS-232' port, is much more tricky to use. The shape of the plug varies, and so does the meaning of the connections — different manufacturers have different uses for the wires in the RS-232 link.

In short, there is much that can go wrong. The data centre engineer who has to connect the printer will usually need a collection of manuals and a tool called a breakout box that indicates more or less what is happening on the link between computer and printer. Connecting up via an RS-232 interface can often involve a lot of solder — and de-soldering, for trial and error is sometimes the only way to do the job.

Sometimes the RS-232 connection is the only option. If there are problems with printing in that case, the RS-232 link is the likeliest culprit.

Characteristic shape of the Centronics plug (above) and one of the common RS-232 plug shapes

Laser printers

The best-known and most widely used type of electrostatic page printer uses a moving laser as the light source.

Laser printers are getting smaller and cheaper. They probably will not become small enough or cheap enough for some years yet to threaten the dominance of traditional printer technologies for everyday work. But they are unrivalled for applications that can utilize the excellent print quality and the ability to use a variety of typestyles and graphics — particularly when the cost and capability can be shared between multiple users. Indeed, laser printers have made possible a whole new class of applications in desktop publishing: you are holding an example of this.

There is an inherent drawback with laser printers. To work properly, they have to use a complex optical system — the laser beam must be equally strong and equally well focused at every possible point along the row of dots. The problem is that the beam will inevitably be weaker and more diffuse at the edges of the image, and laser printers have to use a complex lens system to compensate for that.

Further, the whole optical system has to remain precise and stable — minute vibration or misalignments can ruin the print quality. Building in that sturdiness is one of the reasons for the weight of laser printers (the other is the beefiness of the power supply transformers for the high voltages needed by the laser gun).

LED and LCS printers

With LED printers the light source is an array of miniature lamps, one for each possible dot position in a row; pulses of electricity switch an individual LED on and off as required to produce a dot.

The LCS (liquid-crystal shutter) printer is another up-and-coming alternative to lasers that is similar in principle; there is a powerful light source from a fluorescent bulb, and pulses of electricity open and close a row of shutters (one per dot position) to create the image.

With both of these newer technologies, the light source for each dot position is the same fixed distance from the target points on the drum. As a result, the optics are considerably less complicated. There are fewer moving parts to wear out or fail, it is easier to maintain alignment and replacing faulty parts is greatly simplified.

On the other hand, the electronics are more complicated because each of 300 or more light sources has to be controlled independently. Until recently, it has been difficult and/or expensive to pack the dot-producing elements tightly enough to achieve a resolution as good as that from laser printers.

Ion-deposition printers

Sometimes called 'iconographic' printers, these use a related technology that employs a rotating drum or belt but fires charged particles (ions) rather than light to write on to a receptive coating. The latent image attracts toner in the same way, but when it is transferred to paper it can be fused by pressure rather than by heat. Because heat is not required and because the drum can be harder than the photoreceptive equivalent, ion-deposition printers can claim advantages of durability — 500 000 copies per drum is very good for a laser printer; an ion-deposition printer should give double that and maybe as many as three million copies.

Ion deposition is expensive, though, and cannot compete on price with small-volume printers. The pressure on the paper also gives it a shiny feel that some people find objectionable.

What users want from lasers

As is usual with computer (indeed, any) equipment, the demand is for lower costs and higher performance.

Prices of page printers will fall in the next few years. Economies from advances in electronics are somewhat offset by the more or less static cost of the electromechanical components in page printers required to move the drum and the paper. But increased demand will lead to increased production and economies of scale that can be passed on to the price-tag — to fuel demand further.

This is already happening with laser printers; LED and LCS printers are at the start of the market-acceptance curve that will drop their prices too.

In the case of electrostatic page printers, especially lasers, improved performance initially means a better resolution. The 300 dots per inch produced by most laser printers may be superior to any other computer printing, and it may be good enough for some desktop publishing applications. It does not compare with the 1200 or more dots per inch produced by phototypesetters; that means that large characters can look distinctly notchy on curves, and half-tone reproduction of photographs is imprecise. (Half-tones are produced by converting a photograph with variations of grey into a matrix of dots. Only white and solid black are used, but the black dots are printed in different shapes and sizes such that the result includes approximations of grey scales.)

The answer is to increase the resolution — 600 dots per inch would be good enough for most applications. The problem is cost.

- Individual dots have to be smaller and their placement more precise. This means higher quality in the optics — the light source and the lenses.
- It also demands greater precision from the stepper motors that rotate the drum and the electronics to control the movement of the drum and the light source.
- Current toner technology may be inadequate. The smaller the dot, the smaller the toner particle has to be; and the smaller the particles, the harder they are to control — they like to stick to each other and to the drum, and they become more susceptible to stray electromagnetic influences.
- Ordinary plain paper is not smooth enough to take a high-resolution image. Apart from the extra cost of supplies, a super-smooth paper requires a more sophisticated paper-handling mechanism like vacuum suction — the friction rollers in present laser printer mechanisms rely on the roughness of the paper's surface.

- More dots per inch means more electronic componentry — notably more memory to handle the same overall size of page image.
- To keep up throughput speeds, the controller has to work faster to lay down the extra dots.

Print buffers and spooling

Most printers include a small chunk of internal memory called a buffer. A similar buffer might also be provided inside the computer, and it is possible to buy an external buffer of some kind.

A buffer effectively compensates for the performance difference between the computer (which can deliver characters for printing at high speed, typically 960 or more per second) and a device like a printer (which cannot print those characters at anything like that speed). Without a buffer, the computer would simply have to wait for some printing to be done before it could send the next lot to the printer.

The buffer provides a partial solution — the computer can send characters into that memory at its own speed, and they are taken out at the printer's speed. So the user should regain use of the computer that much sooner.

In practice, print buffers may not be large enough to make much difference — the computer still has to hang around waiting for the buffer to empty before it can send on the next chunk of printing.

Multi-tasking computers or those provided with a 'spooling' capability are able to get on with printing while the computer works on something else.

The print facility on a multi-user system or a local network will probably use both techniques. Here the user passes the output for printing on to a 'print server' on a LAN or a 'spooler' in the host multi-user computer; these will queue the print jobs and output them in sequence.

Sharing printers

It makes sense to spread the cost and capabilities of a page printer among several users. A print server on a LAN will do this efficiently, queuing jobs as they arrive and printing them in sequence. However, there are also simpler methods enabling a small number of desktop computers to share a printer.

The simplest and crudest is a switchbox: several computers plug into the box, output goes via a single line to the laser printer, and a switch or buttons on the front select which computer gets the printer.

The drawback is that someone has physically to operate the switch, and it is all too easy to do that inadvertently while someone else's job is printing. More dangerous is the sudden surge of current that might flow up the line to the laser when the switch is moved; this can damage the printer's somewhat delicate electronics. Some manufacturers recommend that the printer be turned off before the switch is used and on again afterwards; most simply advise against mechanical switches.

The alternative is a more expensive electronic switch, which will include a microprocessor and a degree of intelligence that provides greater control over the switching. Such devices will usually include a print buffer as well, which helps smooth the workload.

Page description languages

Laser printers typically include their own microprocessor (often one that is more powerful than the desktop computer's) and a good deal of memory — half a megabyte is the minimum, 1.5MB or more is common.

Straight text and simple graphics like boxes and rules do not need so much memory, because the character shapes are predetermined and can be held separately as a character set 'library' which does not take so much space. But a lot of memory is required for graphics work, for a 'bit image' of the page to be output is built up in the memory — with one bit corresponding to one dot on the page.

In both cases, though, some of the memory is needed to hold a 'command language' which interprets the data coming in from the computer and decides precisely what the printer should print.

The simpler laser printers use the simplest command languages — those that offer the fewest options: a limited number of fonts, a limited number of character sizes, no easy way to build complex graphics shapes like logos and artwork.

The bottom of the scale is usually mere emulation of the output from a Diablo daisywheel printer or an Epson matrix printer, with the print quality much improved but restricted to their size and style options.

Most low-end laser printers offer rather more than that; they can also emulate one of the early market leaders in laser printers, the Hewlett-Packard LaserJet. HP's command language provides for a variety of fonts in various sizes and styles, plus block graphics like rules and shaded areas. Nearly all software that can output to lasers assumes that the HP commands are available, so this has become a *de facto* standard.

To produce graphics on such a printer requires an advanced command language, what is termed a 'page description language' or PDL. In essence, this will accept incoming commands that describe the appearance of a page — including images as well as text and line graphics.

Obviously, the software must send the correct PDL control codes; and the printer must recognize the same codes. The PDL is usually embedded in circuitry inside the printer or on a controller board inside the computer.

There are a number of PDLs available for software developers to follow and printer manufacturers to build into their products, but the early market leader (and the *de facto* standard for now at least) is Adobe Systems' POSTSCRIPT. It has been adopted for many desktop publishing and word processing packages, and it is featured on several laser printers and some phototypesetters. POSTSCRIPT has the merit of being device-independent; if the software send a command to draw a solid circle one inch in diameter, the result would be a circle with that diameter on any POSTSCRIPT-compatible printer or typesetter — though the printer might use 300 dots per inch while the typesetter uses 2540dpi.

POSTSCRIPT-compatibility is not necessarily required in a printer or a software package. Many quite sophisticated desktop publishing applications can be done (at a lower price) without POSTSCRIPT. But POSTSCRIPT, or something like it, will be required to take full advantage of the laser printer's versatility while giving the user the maximum possible choice of hardware and software.

Colour printing

Colour can greatly improve the effectiveness of a report or presentation — not only to impress the audience but also to aid comprehension. There are a variety of options.

Dot matrix printers

These provide most coloured printing at present. A multi-coloured ribbon with horizontal bands of coloured ink is used; the printhead is moved to the appropriate colour before it fires a pin forward. Four colours are usually provided — black, yellow, magenta and cyan, or black, orange, green and blue. Other colours can be produced by a second pass of the printhead to mix two hues.

For colour printing, there are attractions in using a proven technology with a lot of support from software packages in the

Coming soon

It is likely that the market for page printers will stratify into four broad areas:

- *Low-cost daily-use printers*. These will probably be compact replacements for matrix printers. As such, they will be relatively slow (8ppm or less), limited in paper handling (A4 and envelopes only) and aimed at text rather than full-scale graphics work — no more than 300dpi, none of the extra memory required to build up a graphics image, no built-in page description language.

- *Mid-range DTP-oriented printers* will be refined versions of today's laser printers — probably printing at between 8 and 12 pages a minute, provided with enough memory and a page description language for graphics work, offering a variety of paper-handling options, and aimed primarily at in-house desktop publishing applications. They will probably stay at 300dpi.

- *New-generation high-resolution printers* will be much the same — except that they offer 600dpi, and so will become the norm for commercial desktop publishing (at commensurately higher prices). Speeds of 15 to 25ppm may be feasible.

- *Colour laser printers*. It is unlikely that colour printing will find a large market in DTP (it will be impossible to match the reproduction quality of photographic 'colour separations') or ordinary organizational use — prices will have to be high because of technical complexity and the limited production runs, and in-house photographic techniques like slide production will be simpler, cheaper and give better quality. For specialist applications at reasonable cost — e.g. short runs of original documents like market reports — the colour laser may find a niche.

form of printer drivers. OHP transparencies cannot usually be printed, however, and when that option *is* available the image looks faded. Except with expensive units, the colour lacks brilliance even on paper, 'solid' areas tend to look streaky, and the resolution will never be too good because the printhead wires must be fairly large (in these terms, 0.007in is 'large').

Inkjet printers

Inkjet printers are probably the best of current offerings. They use transparent, dye-based inks (usually black, yellow, red and blue, though some have seven or more ink cartridges) and, provided the software involved will cope with the possible, these printers can mix their inks — typically into 300 or so possible shades and hues from four inks, over 4000 from seven. The ink comes in disposable cartridges with a life over a million characters, about 1100 pages of text or 180 of graphics.

Inkjet colour can be printed in a single pass of the printhead because multiple nozzles can spray different colours at the same time. That means a decent print speed. The amount of plumbing required keeps the cost fairly high, though, and adds to doubts about reliability. Still, the prices are reasonably competitive with those of small pen plotters and the colour inkjet certainly produces better-quality colour than matrix printers.

Thermal printers

These use a wax-based ink that is melted on to the paper. For colour printing, different ribbons or (more usually) a single ribbon impregnated with multiple colours will be used; shades and hues are built up from primary colours by several passes of the print head.

The basic deficiencies of thermal printing are exacerbated for colour work, however. The output may be shiny and supplies are expensive.

Plotters

Pen plotters work by taking commands from the software to draw continuous lines in a specified shape. Those commands can include pen selection, and most low-cost plotters aimed at a market in business graphics provide four or six penholders.

The attraction of a pen plotter lies in its ability to draw quite precise graphics and text (often with a resolution equivalent to over a thousand dots per inch) in a range of bright, dense colours of the user's choice — on a variety of media (OHP foils are usually no problem, for instance), at modest cost (plotters start at the same price as a medium-to-low-cost matrix printer) and without taking much desk space (as small as 250x360mm and weighing from just 4kg up).

Disadvantages include the difficulty of producing solid areas, since the thickness of line is limited to the pen's width. It may be impossible to produce hues by mixing colours, and shades are difficult.

Plotters are not quick — a display mixing text and graphics on an annotated spreadsheet output might take ten seconds or so to appear completely on the screen; plotting the same picture could take at least four minutes and as much as double that on the cheaper plotters. A lot of text and shading on the chart will also slow things down.

Colour laser printers

The same technologies used for colour photocopiers can be applied to computer output from laser-based printers: a four-pass operation may be required, with the paper passing through four separate colour toner baths.

Lasers are quiet, provide a better resolution than any other output device apart from plotters and have no competition in their ability to build up solid, shaded and toned areas.

Supplies for the colour laser should be fairly cheap, though the toner cartridges will not be inexpensive. The resolution should be at least as good as that from monochrome laser printers; with early examples, however, there have been 'registration' problems (making sure the colours print in exactly the right place and do not overlap). Throughput should be acceptable at the same kind of rates as ordinary lasers, from 8 pages a minute up. The units themselves will be pretty expensive, however. Until the quality of the colour toner improves, colour laser printing will suffer from the same faults as colour photocopying — a shiny and somewhat 'unreal' image.

Colour printing options

Type	Strengths	Drawbacks
Impact dot matrix	Low capital costs Low running costs Software support Well-understood technology	Limited range of colours Uneven ribbon wear Smudging and streaks Uneven ink density Lack of clarity and depth in colours Limited resolution Possible deficiencies for OHP foils
Inkjet	Good range of colours Good colour quality Low noise levels	Fairly high capital costs Fairly high running costs Doubts about reliability Limited resolution
Thermal transfer	Good range of colours Good colour quality Low noise levels Fairly low capital costs	Uneven ribbon wear Fairly high running costs Doubts about reliability Limited resolution Shiny print
Plotters	High resolution Good range of colours Good colour quality Easy colour selection Modest capital costs Modest running costs	Slow Restricted options for text Problems on solid areas Difficulty in producing hues and shades
Laser	Good resolution Quiet Good at solid areas	High capital costs High running costs Fairly slow Registration problems Shiny print Currently unable to print right to the edge of a page Unsuitable for paper with thermographic or other embossed letterheadings

Printer drivers and compatibility

In theory there are several methods of getting information out of a computer and on to paper. In practice, the limitation will be what your software can use for printing its output.

The actual operation of a printer — producing characters in different styles, starting new lines, ejecting the paper at the end of a page, and so on — are determined by a set of internal commands. In many cases (like those mentioned) these are more or less standard; the printer will do what it is told when it detects the arrival of one of those commands — nearly all printers follow the ASCII character code set, which includes codes for some controls as well as for alphanumeric and other characters.

But for extra facilities, such as print size selection, underlining, emboldening, and the like, there is no formal standardization. Different printers have their own unique commands to produce these effects.

These will be listed somewhere in the printer's manual, usually as 'escape codes', and it is possible (though usually awkward) to type these at the keyboard to switch individual functions on and off. On the other hand, that is hardly very useful when the printer is trying to produce output from a program.

So most programs use a piece of software called a 'printer driver'. In effect these convert the controls used internally by the package into the equivalent commands for a particular printer. As there are several hundred printers on the market, many packages include a variety of alternative printer drivers; typically the user is invited to 'install a printer' — to specify the make and model of printer that will be utilized — typically by selecting from a menu of the available options that appears when the package is first run.

If your printer does not appear on the option menu, you could be in trouble; not only might all text enhancements like underlining be absent but the printing could also ignore formatting like tabs and indents. New printers with new facilities appear all the time; it is not reasonable to expect *every* package to accommodate *every* possible printer.

Fortunately, there are at least three *de facto* standards that printer manufacturers tend to follow. Unfortunately, as is common in the computer business, they may not be followed too rigidly.

- *Epson*. A printer described as 'Epson-compatible' will follow the controls used by Epson, the world's leading supplier of dot matrix printers.
- *Diablo*. A similar market position was once held by Diablo in the daisywheel printer field.
- *HP LaserJet*. Again, Hewlett-Packard's laser printer is a market leader.

If a printer claims compatibility with one of these, the implication is that it follows the same control commands. It should therefore be possible for you to use that printer from a software package by selecting the relevant Epson, Diablo or HP model as the output device.

Checklist: printers

Paper width

Check how wide a printer you need: the price goes up with the width. The narrowest matrix printers print 80 characters across a page and are called '80-column' printers: 132- and 136-column versions are common. Most daisywheels can print 120 or 132 characters across their width.

Print speed

Actual throughput will be affected by factors other than the quoted print speed, not least of which is the amount of work that the printer itself has to do in decoding the commands and data arriving from the computer as material to be output. Look for facilities in the printer that speed up the throughput — especially a print buffer.

Noise

Daisywheel printers can be very loud, matrix printers can screech irritatingly. The maximum noise level that should be tolerated in offices is 55dBA — this is a requirement in some European countries.

Paper loading

On some tractor-feed printers it can be quite difficult to feed the paper through. Stacker feeds on laser printers and others often have a limited capacity.

Types of paper

Is special paper required? Or a special *grade* of paper? Can the printer handle all the styles of paper you want to use? Top-quality letterheading is too heavy for some printers. Printing directly on to envelopes is rare. Unusual paper sizes may not fit the printer. The acid test of daisywheels and matrix printers is how well they cope with labels — does the ink smear? (Labels usually have a shiny coated surface.) When a label peels off and jams in the paper path, how easy is it to remove?

Software compatibility

Will the printer work with your software? On different printers, different methods are used to switch functions such as condensed and italicized print on and off; the software has to be set up appropriately for you to utilize the printer's capabilities.

Function switches

Several printer functions can be set by hand; front-panel buttons are infinitely preferable to miniature DIP switches buried somewhere inside the printer. Are the controls easy to understand? Are they accessible?

Ribbons

Some printers use proprietary ribbons or print cartridges that are not widely available. How easy are they to replace?

All computers need an operating system. The term applies to a collection of programs that fit between the human user and the electronic circuitry. An operating system decodes the electrical activity inside the computers, it switches the internal movements of data between different starting points and destinations, it decides just what it is the user and the applications software is trying to *do* with the machine.

What is an operating system?

Operating systems represent one of the more arcane aspects of computing. People who are able actually to *write* the programs that make up an effective operating system are few and far between; they tend to reach guru status quickly. The reason is obvious — operating systems are inherently complicated.

☐ A computer comes with a number of 'peripherals', a catch-all term that encompasses the keyboard, disks, the display, printer and so on. If the computer had no operating system, every programmer who wanted to produce a program to run on it would have to write individual subprograms to allow use of those peripherals.

Instead, all these subprograms are gathered together into a single program (or more often a collection of linked programs) to provide the core of an operating system — a number of *device handlers* that allow programmers easy access to the computer's peripherals.

☐ The next layer is a *file handler*; this makes it easier for a programmer to write programs that manipulate files, again by taking a number of common subprograms and providing them in an easy-to-use package.

☐ The top layer is the part of the operating system that might be seen by the average user, the *command interpreter*. This accepts and implements commands to run programs, copy or delete files, and so on; these may come from the user's keyboard or from a ready-to-run string of preset commands that will be initiated automatically.

Either way it is this part of the operating system that gives the computer whatever 'personality' it has. As far as the user is concerned, the main differences between computers — apart from physical appearance — lie in the messages and commands that have to be used. The whole operating style of the computer is determined by the operating system.

How does this affect the average user? As far as the user is concerned, it is the operating system that determines exactly how the computer works.

More importantly, the operating system also decides exactly what software packages you can and cannot use — all software is written to operate with a particular operating system.

The BIOS

This is another component of the operating system you might come across — 'BIOS' (for Basic Input/Output System) is the term used by Microsoft for its own MS-DOS operating systems, but there will be something like it with any operating system intended for use on a variety of different computers.

The BIOS effectively provides the 'personalization' that mates a generic off-the-shelf all-things-to-all-computers operating system with a particular machine. An operating system like Xenix or MS-DOS may be available on many different computers in practically the same form, but each of them will have a different BIOS that enables the operating system to operate the characteristic (and probably idiosyncratic) hardware elements of the computer — the way it organizes its screen display, for instance.

Because each computer has a different BIOS, programs written to run with a particular operating system will not necessary work with that same operating system on a different computer. It all depends on how much direct interaction the program does with the BIOS — whether it leaves most of the work to the operating system, or whether it by-passes the operating system for some operations such as putting a display on the screen.

Why that program won't run

☐ *Wrong operating system.* A package has to interact with the operating system, so all packages are customized for specific operating systems (but software designed for one operating system can sometimes be used with another).

☐ *Wrong BIOS.* The package also has to include some assumptions about how the *computer* works (or how it is worked by the operating system). Packages are often BIOS-specific; not all MS-DOS-compatible packages will run on all computers that feature MS-DOS as their operating system, because the BIOS will be different in each case.

☐ *Wrong version of the operating system.* Subsequent versions include extra facilities that new packages will utilize. An older package will normally run under a newer version of the operating system, but the reverse is not normally the case.

Multiple users, multiple tasks

The most basic operating system allows one user to run one job at a time. Any more complexity than that requires more memory (to hold the additional instruction required in the extra operating system) and a faster microprocessor (to sort through those extra instructions and perform the required operations with reasonable speed).

Memory is becoming cheaper and more compact, and microprocessors are becoming more powerful; the producers of operating systems can incorporate facilities for more than one user and/or more than one job at a time.

A single user controlling multiple jobs is called *multi-tasking*. A typical example in use would be a mix of 'housekeeping' operations being done at the same time as a package is running — printing one document can go ahead at the same time as a backup copy of part of a hard disk is being taken *and* while the user is running a spreadsheet package on the screen. Or different applications could be running concurrently — a spelling checker might be going through a block of text, a file manager could be selecting names for a mailing list, a comms package could be automatically accepting incoming electronic mail and Telex messages, the user could be working on a word-processed document while referencing a spreadsheet file.

With multi-tasking a single user can run several *tasks* at once: *multi-user* operating systems support several *users*. This is done via 'dumb' terminals, VDUs (visual display units) which do not themselves do any computing but which plug into the desktop computer and utilize packages and files running on it.

A multi-user operating system almost invariably allows multi-tasking as well at the individual workstations.

Common operating systems for desktop computers

Single-user, single-tasking

☐ MS-DOS is the world's most popular operating system for single-user desktop computers. It hails from a company called Microsoft, originally known for its programming language systems (most microcomputer versions of BASIC come from Microsoft) but selected by IBM to provide an operating system at short notice for the IBM PC. In fact things could have been very different; IBM did originally approach Digital Research for an implementation of its CP/M-86, but for a variety of reasons (including a conflict of personalities, by all accounts) the IBM design team opted to look elsewhere for an operating system.

Having developed that operating system specifically for the PC, Microsoft produced a parallel version of a more generalized nature; this was known as MS-DOS. This was an improvement on the then-available options in some aspects; more important, IBM's commitment legitimized MS-DOS as the *de facto* standard, and the result has been a huge selection of good-quality software packages that run under MS-DOS.

☐ CP/M-86, produced by Digital Research, is no longer used widely. A development of an extremely successful operating system originally called CP/M (now renamed CP/M-80 or CP/M-Plus) that became the *de facto* standard on eight-bit microcomputers, CP/M-86 has been eclipsed by the popularity of MS-DOS (and IBM's espousal of MS-DOS). There are not any intrinsic technical reasons for this — CP/M-80 was successful because it happened to be in the right place at the right time, and the same is true of MS-DOS for 16-bit computers.

☐ BOS Software's Business Operating System BOS is a British-developed product with some international acceptance. BOS provides a set of tools and a working 'environment' in which programs can be written to run with few if any changes on a whole range of different computers; all the facilities it provides are geared to the production of *business* programs. BOS can run as an operating system in its own right or overlaid on to another operating system.

☐ The UCSD p-System has not achieved much popularity. Something of a technocrat's choice, it came from an academic environment ('UCSD' is the University of California at San Diego). On desktop computers it is, however, unwieldy, memory-hungry and not supported by many applications packages.

Single-user, multi-tasking

☐ OS/2 is the multi-tasking operating system Microsoft produced for the IBM PS/2; it is available to any microcomputer manufacturer who needs an operating system for a machine featuring the Intel 80286 or 386 processor and a megabyte or more of memory. OS/2 retains the ability to run MS-DOS programs, but has many more capabilities and is primarily intended for a new generation of software packages. Multi-tasking on desktop computers is in its infancy, but OS/2 is likely to become the *de facto* standard, just as MS-DOS is.

☐ Digital Research now has a family of 'multi-tasking' operating systems derived from CP/M-86 but able to run MS-DOS programs. Early versions were known as Concurrent CP/M-86 or CCP/M-86; the current implementation is called Concurrent DOS.

Multi-user, multi-tasking

☐ Unix and its derivatives (notably Xenix) are already the *de facto* standard for multi-user, multi-tasking operation — the Unix user base shot up from under 18 000 in 1980 to nearly two million now, and the best estimates suggest this will double by 1990.

Unix is a large, feature-filled operating system. It can offer good performance (meaning the individual users notice no delays as the system processes their commands, and the run-time for separate tasks does not suffer either). Unix is also available on several different machines, providing a degree of integration between disparate office systems.

On the other hand, Unix is enormous by comparison with other microcomputer operating systems; it definitely demands a lot of memory and a fast processor to accommodate all its capability. It can be difficult to use — the terse, often bizarre error messages do not help.

There is also a lack of compatibility between different vendors. AT&T owns the 'official' Unix and licences it to individual manufacturers — who apply their own customization. Then there is Microsoft's Xenix, a separate product that looks like Unix and works like Unix but includes none of the Unix code. Xenix is 'friendlier' than Unix and was designed for microcomputers rather than minis; it now accounts for something like 75 per cent of all Unix-type applications.

The variations available have meant that software developers could not be sure of a large enough market to justify their investment; the result until recently has been a lack of off-the-shelf applications software, and most Unix systems have been purpose-designed. But things are now settling down. There is a good deal of standardization work being done on both Unix and Xenix — in particular, the X/OPEN group of eleven major suppliers (mostly European) has come up with a common version of Unix endorsed by America's IEEE standards body, and the principal suppliers of Xenix are also collaborating. Unix System V Release 3, for 80386-based computers, will bring together the currently separate strands of Unix and Xenix development; and the trade-name 'Xenix' will only be used thereafter for implementations on smaller systems.

The result of all this standardization work has been a growing library of Unix and Xenix packages. Importantly for the integration issue, the Unix approach is flexible enough for software developers to provide implementations of mainframe software and micro packages. So the same software and the same data formats can be used throughout the organization. Apart from the immediate benefits, this helps to protect the corporate investment in data, procedures and equipment.

□ The Pick operating system at one time looked like a serious rival to Unix, and it currently occupies something of a niche market where ease of use and ease of software development is crucial. Pick provides a multi-user environment that incorporates a powerful database system with excellent search and reporting facilities; the orientation towards handling files and records makes it well suited to many business applications, particularly as end-users can usually produce their own applications (there is also a built-in program generator, and the command language is commendably intelligible — it is even called ENGLISH).

□ MUMPS is another established multi-user operating system that probably deserves wider prominence (though it can claim 50 000 users worldwide). Again, it is intended for database-oriented applications — more so even than Pick, probably — and it too claims simplicity and friendliness for end-user operation. MUMPS also has the advantage that it runs on a very wide range of computers, either as a stand-alone system or in harness with an existing operating system.

□ BOS Software has versions of BOS to support multiple users on a network (BOS/LAN) and from a single machine (MBOS).

One of the key elements of the new technology in offices is the LAN, a 'local network' or 'local area network'.

The 'network' is basically a cable that connects two or more computing devices — which may be separate computers, or shared devices like large hard disks and printers, or access points of some kind that give network users the chance to call external services.

The 'local area' in question is usually a single building, or a departmental floor or office suite within a building, and the networked devices are usually connected by cabling. Some work has been done on other link methods, notably microwave radio and infrared, but a physical link using cables represents the cheapest, easiest and most flexible option for most applications.

Why LANs?

The principle of a local area network is that multiple users, each with their own system, can share resources which may be expensive (like hard disks) or of common value (like a centralized set of departmental records).

□ *Resource-sharing*. One key argument is essentially economic: more users can get more information-handling facilities for less cost. This is at the heart of most LAN decisions.

The obvious economy is in *hardware*. The individual user can be given a processor, memory and some local file storage, but it is not usually cost-justified for the workstation to include expensive components that might be desirable only on occasion — like large-capacity disks for the odd extended file, top-quality document printers that would be used only for 10 per cent of their availability, high-speed modems for occasional access to on-line databases.

This also applies to *information*, which can more easily be viewed as a corporate resource when held in a form that is accessible to individual users.

And there are implications as well for *software*, for multiple copies of the same package need not be acquired for separate users. Instead, a master copy is held centrally and utilized as required by workstations.

□ *Organization*. As well as cost savings, the LAN can provide the important requirement for standardization. With shared facilities and software, individual users are restrained from exercising personal preferences; users can access required information produced at other workstations, and those files will be in a usable format.

Systematic control is also feasible when the LAN provides a standardized procedure and centralized data store for backups.

□ *Integration*. Related to this is the matter of integration. With different users and different types of equipment able to communicate easily via the network, formerly disparate components of administration and management can sensibly be related to each other.

More generally, the structured flow and use of information introduces the desktop computer into a regulated environment. With consistency enforced, it is true that some of the gains in personal productivity claimed for desktop computing will be compromised or lost altogether — notably esoteric applications with no place in the corporate scheme. However, improved management control of information resources along with more comprehensive and more up-to-date information should help to improve the operation of the organization. In short, the LAN approach fits well with current management concepts that stress information and communication are the keys to productivity improvement; to some extent, the LAN can 'automate' the role of users, relating personal goals to those of the business.

For the future, the LAN also provides a common conduit that probably passes the desk of every key individual in a department. In theory, it should be capable of carrying any digitisable information — including voice and image as well as data. As well as the economic attractions of a single set of cables and a single interface point for each user, the integration of functions has important benefits for the quality of communication. In practice, many of today's LAN products cannot offer such scope.

In theory, a LAN can provide an individual user with access to:

□ *Local services:*
- — Electronic mail
- — Voice mail
- — Voice conferencing
- — Computer conferencing
- — Desktop publishing
- — File servers for shared data and programs
- — File transfer between workstations
- — Laser printers
- — Management of the network

... and the same system may also be used for:
- — Internal telephone calls
- — Video conferencing
- — Security systems
- — Building management systems

□ *External links:*
- — Electronic mail
- — Typesetting bureaux
- — Translation services
- — Voice mail
- — Voice conferencing
- — Computer conferencing
- — Facsimile
- — Telex
- — Mainframe computer
- — Information services
- — Other LANs

... and appropriate interfaces may also provide for:
- — External telephone calls
- — External video conferencing

Servers and users

Most networks distinguish between workstations and other devices attached to the LAN:

□ The *workstation* typically gets a 'network interface adapter' (NIA) or 'network interface card' (NIC) which fits inside the user's computer and handles most of the contact between the LAN and the workstation.

□ '*Servers*' provide the equivalent control for shared resources — file servers for disk stores, print servers for printers, comms servers for gateways and modems, and so on — by detecting incoming data transfers and performing the required operation.

In some LAN setups, a server (particularly a file server) will include a high-powered microprocessor to control the LAN; in such cases the file server will probably be a desktop computer that may be dedicated to the task, or it may be a computer that can also be used as a workstation.

Gateways and bridges

A comms server may just provide shared access to a modem line. If it does rather more, giving access to other networks (local, private or public) or to a mainframe, it may be described as a 'gateway' or 'bridge'.

A *bridge* is usually a quite simple interconnection that enables selective data transfer with no protocol conversion; a *gateway* usually involves massaging the transfer so that relatively incompatible networks can communicate.

Their precise nature depends on the nature of the link they are required to make, but the effect is to build up quite complex configurations of interlinked LANs and other networks.

How LANs differ

There are numerous practical differences at the detail level, but there are three broad areas of distinction and they are interrelated:

- ☐ *Topology*. The basic shape of the network. This affects its versatility and capability.
- ☐ *Bandwidth*. Determines the maximum possible speed of data transfer and the number of different types of service that one cable can carry.
- ☐ *Protocol*. Decides how data transfer is actually done — how one element in a LAN passes information to another.

Topology

Star. Rather like an internal telephone system, the 'star' network has a central controller and a number of devices connected directly to it. All transfers go through the central point.

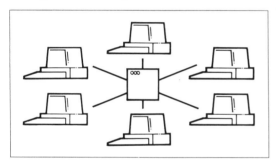

Ring. Rings are much more versatile, since they do not rely on the power and capability of a central controller. Instead messages circulate around the ring; a message intended for a particular device is spotted by the addressee as it 'passes' and is diverted to be read. In theory, messages continue circulating until they *are* read (the first time around, the destination may have been engaged in doing something else). Once the message has been delivered, an acknowledgment of some kind is circulated back to the sender.

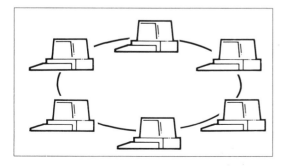

Bus. A bus is a single line with devices hanging off it. Buses are the most basic of the LAN configurations, and they are probably the most widely used now; it is cheaper to wire up, since the end does not have to return (as with the ring layout) and each device does not have to be connected to a central hub (as with stars). A message is put on to the LAN with an address; all devices check the line for messages addressed to them. The only drawback with this approach is that each component of the network has to monitor the line more or less constantly, detect messages for itself, check that the transmission is correct, and acknowledge receipt so that the sender can stop broadcasting. By comparison with other LAN topologies, this requires rather more intelligence in the network interface controller provided for each node.

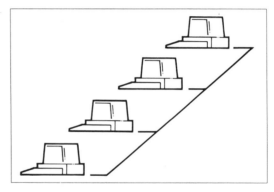

Protocols

In essence, the only commodity a LAN has to offer is time — to send a message, all the nodes have to compete for a chunk of time on the network. LAN protocols essentially decide how that time is allocated: which sender gets the user of the network and for how long.

If there is a central controller, as in a star layout, two fairly simple possibilities are interrupts and polling. In an *interrupt-driven* LAN, any station can initiate a request-to-send signal. If the network is free, the controller grants permission. If two stations request the network at the same time, a set of predetermined priorities comes into play.

The capability and speed of a LAN are partly a function of the bandwidth that can be supported on the cabling that links its components. Bandwidth is a measure of the range of frequencies that a transmission medium can carry; it is the difference between the lowest and the highest frequency. Bandwidth is measured in hertz, cycles per second. In practical terms and as far as LANs are concerned, the bandwidth indicates the number of different channels that can be supported for different functions and/or the speed of data transfer.

The key distinction for LANs is between 'baseband' and 'broadband'. *Baseband* LANs utilize a single channel, which means that only data can be transferred and the measure of bandwidth can be translated directly into 'bits per second'. Baseband networks can in theory go up to 30 MHz (30 Mbps — 30 million bits per second) but a more normal rating is between 1 and 10 MHz (one to ten million bits per second).

Most networks are baseband. *Broadband* networks can carry multiple channels of information on a single cable, each channel being reserved for a different function — in much the same way as radio or TV signals are carried, the different channels are selected for different purposes. For example, Wang's WangNET is a broadband LAN with a frequency range of 390 MHz. That is separated into six channels with different functions:

10.0 MHz 20.6 MHz	Interconnect Band for transfers at 9600bps or 64Kbps. In theory, any equipment that talks to other equipment in an office can simply be plugged on to the system.
29.1 MHz 44.1 MHz	Professional Computer Service Band — for ARCNET-compatible networking at 2.5Mbps.
49.6 MHz 81.6 MHz	Interconnect Band rated at 9600bps
93.5 MHz 149.4 MHz	Peripheral Attachment Band
174.0 MHz 216.0 MHz	Utility Band — intended especially for video conferencing
216.0 MHz 243.0 MHz	Wang Band, for a 12Mbps CSMA/CD network
243.0 MHz 400.0 MHz	Spare for future use

The drawback is that low-priority workstations might get too little access. Besides, a problem with the central controller halts operation of the whole LAN.

That also applies to a *polled* network, which has the central controller 'polling' each station in turn looking for an access request.

Most LANs do not use either of these relatively inefficient techniques. Instead, they employ either a *ring* or a *contention* method of control:

☐ *Contention*. This is a nice and simple approach. Any node can send — provided that there is no traffic currently on the LAN, which it checks first via a technique called CSMA (Carrier-Sense Multiple-Access). It then tries to send a message; if two nodes try to send at the same time, they both back off and try again a fraction of a second later. One of two techniques is used for that, CD (Collision Detect) or CA (Collision Avoidance) — for practical purposes they are identical.

Accordingly, contention LANs are often characterized as CSMA/CD or CSMA/CA. EtherNet is the most common example of a CSMA/CD network; the US standards body IEEE has formalized the EtherNet approach into a standard known as IEEE 802.3.

Contention networks are good for short bursts of transmission, for they can be idle or in collision and undergoing retries for around 80 per cent of the time. On the other hand, ring networks guarantee a minimum delay before a sender gains access to the network; the big advantage is that this is also the *maximum* delay.

☐ *Slotted ring* (or more usually *Cambridge ring*, after the best-known example). This works by dividing the network into preset 'packets' or time slots, and can be thought of as a collection of railway wagons connected in a loop and circulating rapidly around the ring. A node with something to send grabs an empty slot and dumps a message in it. The message includes an address, which is spotted by the intended receiver; the message is then read and that slot is marked as 'empty' for use by another sender.

This can provide fast transmission, as the slot does not have to come full circle before it is reused. It also allows several messages to circulate at the same time: no one sender hogs the network.

The downside is that a good deal of address and error-checking information has to be carried along with the actual message. It also needs a controller to handle the housekeeping — to generate the slots initially on start-up and to empty any undelivered messages addressed inadvertently to nonexistent nodes.

☐ *Token ring*. In fact this method is not restricted to ring configurations, but that is how it is most often used. This one is nice and simple, too: an electronic tag or 'token' is circulated around the network; any sender can grab the token and attach a message to it if the token is currently unused. That node gets the token for a preset period — when it has finished transmitting, or if its time runs out, the token is relinquished and passed around the network for another sender to use.

Unlike slotted rings, token-passing does not need a controller. It does, however, require more intelligence in the network interface unit. Otherwise it shares the advantage of minimum wasted time and fairness in allowing only a fixed time-slot for each user.

Token ring also has a formal standard, IEEE 802.5.

LANs versus multi-user systems

At first sight, there seems little practical difference between a LAN and a network of terminals attached to a minicomputer or mainframe. In practice, there are important distinctions.

LANs characterized

☐ A network of desktop computers allows a good deal of local autonomy for the individual user; there are no problems about access to the computer.
☐ Computers on a LAN can run applications software independent of that available on a central machine. There will also be a great deal more choice in packages.
☐ Desktop computers of different makes can still be used on the LAN.

Multi-user systems characterized

☐ All software is purpose-designed for multi-terminal access. This is not likely to be the case with packages that run on desktop computers.
☐ Extending a multi-terminal system is likely to be cheaper and easier.

There is a widely used argument to the effect that most LANs are more resilient to failures, because there is no central machine; when the mainframe or minicomputer fails, the whole system is down. In practice, this may be more a theoretical objection than a real consideration. Multi-terminal computers are quite resilient these days — certainly as resilient as the servers on a LAN. When a LAN's servers fail, the main benefits of LAN operation are wiped out.

Another argument centres on performance degradation: the multi-terminal system has one computer that has to do all the work for all users. So the more work they want to do, the slower the central machine will perform for them. In practice, most applications are not processor-dependent and a multi-user system will be festooned with independent I/O processors that take the load off the central processor.

Ultimately it should come down to a question of horses for courses. LANs allow a great deal of personal flexibility, some exercise of personal preference and the ability to work independently of a central computer — an extension, in fact, of the benefits for desktop computers in general. Multi-user systems are easier to control and are customized for specific applications requiring multiple access.

RS-232 cable. The simplest networks — zero-slot LANs — use standard multi-core RS-232 cable. This is the cheapest option, but it also the most limited in terms of data transfer rate and maximum distance between LAN components.

Twisted-pair. This is familiar from internal telephone lines and is widely used for LANs. It is bent easily and so laying the cable is no problem; it is also easy to add devices by cutting and splicing. The bandwidth is high enough at around 1MHz (a million bits per second) to permit a reasonable level of performance in data transferred, but twisted-pair cabling cannot be used for broadband LANs. It also has little protection from external interference — indeed, twisted-pair wires can be used as radio antennae to pick up RF signals. Adding a metal sheath gives what is called *twinax* (better shielding and better performance — up to 15MHz — but at a price) or *quadrax* (expensive and rare).

Co-ax. Co-axial cable is used in the home for TV aerials, and is the other widely-used connection method for LANs. Co-ax has a single wire running inside a metal sheath, which provides good protection from external interface and permits bandwidths of 300 MHz or more; bending it to go round awkward corners is not easy, though flat versions are available. Connection from co-ax is easy enough via what is called a T coupler. Co-ax (and the heavy-duty extra-shielded version *triax*) is suitable for baseband and broadband LANs, and is used in both.

Fibre-optic cable. These are bundles of fine, flexible glass filaments down which light can be pulsed. Since they do not use electricity, they are immune to interference and represent no fire hazard; and very high bandwidths are possible — 25 times better than co-ax (or more). For the security-conscious, it is also very difficult to tap into a fibre-optic cable. But special fittings and couplings are required, and the line may need 'repeaters' to boost the signal every so often. Still, despite the relatively high cost of cable, fibre-optics

represent the very best choice for broadband LANs and this method of connection is becoming the norm for such networks.

Infrared. The only other method of connection that may be considered is infrared light. This does away with the need for wires; each element in the network has a special transmitter/receiver unit to pick up signals. The bandwidth is good enough for broadband operation. The drawbacks are the relatively high cost and the need for line-of-sight links or at least a minimum of obstruction. At present, very few LAN suppliers offer infrared as an option to cabling.

Zero-slot LANs

The simplest LANs do not require a network interface controller. That usually comes in the form of a plug-in circuit card, so such networks are often called 'zero-slot' LANs since no expansion slots are taken up.

Accordingly, installation is relatively simple; RS-232 cabling is used, so the physical connection is simply a matter of plugging in to the standard RS-232 sockets on the computers and other devices. Instead of the network adapter card handling chores like formatting data for transmission over the network, all functions are handled by software.

That simplicity also contains the major drawbacks of such an approach:

□ The RS-232 cable is not designed to transfer data faster than 9600 bits per second. It is possible by unorthodox programming for a zero-slot LAN to increase this to as much as 115000 bits per second, but that is still considerably slower than most other cabling.
□ RS-232 data transmission involves a large number of parameters and variable factors; all devices on the zero-slot LAN have to be set up appropriately — and accurately. Installing such a system can require a greater degree of hardware skill than many alternative LANs.
□ The fact that the computer has to do so much of the work can greatly impede the efficiency and speed of the transfers, because it has less time to give to other work.
□ To provide maximum simplicity, some zero-slot LANs are extremely limited. The simplest systems are designed only to give a handful of workstations access to a shared hard disk data store, and with some of them that access is handled very crudely. All users get the ability to *read* from the disk, but only one at a. time can read and *write*; read/write status has to be set very deliberately by the user, which can mean another workstation having to relinquish read/write status quite specifically.

Zero-slot LANs can, however, provide a very economical approach to sharing printers and files, particularly for occasional access to files (where the speed of transfer will not clog up the network for too long) or for systematic end-of-day backing up (local files are transferred to an archive area on a shared hard disk).

LAN management

LANs can be complicated. They can also be susceptible to performance problems that negate the potential benefits of desktop computing in general: a sluggish LAN will provoke adverse reactions from frustrated users.

This puts some premium on a management function. Selection and implementation should be handled with considerable care, covering the culture and working style of the organization as well as its practical requirements; the needs of users should be balanced against the needs of the business; training and end-user support will be important.

The LAN will also have to be monitored and controlled to ensure that those needs and requirements are met. The nature of the LAN applications and the number and type of end-users will determine exactly how much management is required, but this could become an important function, particularly at the nitty-gritty level of fine-tuning (setting the rate of CSMA/CD retries, for example, or altering the time-slots for rings).

The LAN supplier should be able to provide tools for management. Such functions might include:

□ Fault-logging and evaluation of LAN performance quality
□ Analysis of usage by node and type of traffic
□ Passwords and access control

Trends in LANs

The LANscape is currently dominated by one of two combinations of the LAN technologies and protocols:

□ *EtherNet-type*. Baseband bus systems using twisted-pair wiring and CSMA/CD contention protocols. Good for shortish data-only transmissions at data rates around 10 Mbps.

□ *Token ring*. Baseband at high speeds, or broadband; normally using co-ax. Good for more complex networks with multiple users, quite long data transfers and the presence now or in the future of extra non-data services.

To make the most of the possibilities of LANs — in particular, to develop networking as a genuine corporate asset rather than as a pragmatic response to immediate resource-sharing needs — it is likely that broadband networks using the enormous bandwidth of optical fibre cables will become the norm. The token ring will probably be the dominant protocol, largely because IBM has espoused it; slotted rings may be preferred for technical reasons by some.

The OSI model

OSI is one of the key standards for information systems. It represents an attempt by the Geneva-based International Standards Organization to develop a comprehensive 'model' for interconnecting any and all devices — hence the name OSI, for 'open systems interconnection'.

The OSI model is not a product but a frame of reference — at best, a set of rules — to indicate what kind of functions should be represented in a working system. There are detailed specifications for some but not all of these seven 'levels' of connectivity; but in practice, OSI is already achieving its goal of forcing vendors to fit the standard.

In theory, OSI should allow information to be exchanged between devices irrespective of:

☐ Supplier
☐ Model
☐ Age
☐ Operating system

OSI covers interconnection from the ground up — specifically, from the plug-and-socket connection to the way an application program sends and receives data.

The seven levels or 'layers' of the ISO model are arranged in three groups. At the lowest level are those functions relating to the network on which data is transferred; the TRANSPORT layer provides the end-to-end control; the top three layers cover the way a particular application would send and receive information.

The ISO has defined the four lower levels, and there are a number of existing standards that fit — notably the CCITT X25 specification for connection to packet-switched networks like PSS; X25 meets the standards for layers 1 to 3. The X400 message-handling standard for electronic mail systems is a layer 7 standard (although the ISO has not formally specified the higher layers, the standard is relatively 'stable' — and in any case the X400 spec is likely to be adopted by ISO). Various manufacturers are offering partial or full implementations of OSI.

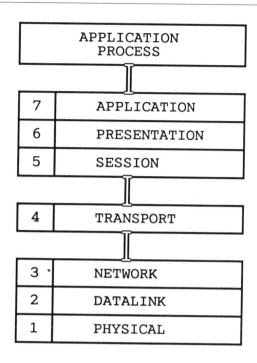

	APPLICATION PROCESS
7	APPLICATION
6	PRESENTATION
5	SESSION
4	TRANSPORT
3	NETWORK
2	DATALINK
1	PHYSICAL

Simplicity in connection

The network should be easy to install, preferably without much disruption to the existing layout of the office.

Simplicity in use

It should also demand a minimum of effort from end-users. Working with a LAN should be no more difficult than working with a desktop computer.

Flexibility

The LAN should be able to cope with rearrangements of office furniture; it should also be expandable enough to add new services, extra devices, and different *types* of devices.

Compatibility

The LAN should fit the existing hardware and software in the office, and any proposed additions to that. It should also meet current and future standards for information technology that have been set within the organization. Ideally it will meet any relevant external standards, including *de facto* standards and those set by formal bodies such as ISO and CCITT; this should ensure maximum longevity and flexibility.

Cable options

The type of cable will affect the speed of data transfer, the total length of the network and the maximum distance between individual elements of the LAN, and the bandwidth — which in turn affect the number and range of services that can be provided. Many LANs are limited to a specific cable type, which inevitably restricts the options.

Performance

The actual performance of the LAN in practice will depend on many factors — including speed and capability of workstations and network resources like disk drives and printers, the performance of the network controllers that handle them, the provision of hardware buffers and software facilities to smooth out resource access, and the amount of traffic the LAN has to carry. As a rule of thumb, the number of workstations may have less impact than the number of different services available; the network protocol is usually the main limiting factor. It is difficult to apply benchmark tests to a LAN; the best option is usually to go for the fastest claimed data transfer and the maximum number of network management tools to permit some fine-tuning.

Vendor support

The design and implementation of any LAN can be tricky; access to at least some kind of ongoing support from the supplier is usually essential. Since most LANs are sold by dealers rather than by the LAN manufacturer, this can put a premium on evaluating the supplier — look for previous experience and contact existing users if possible.

Services

All LANs provide file transfer to and from a shared disk; most also provide queued output for shared printers. The number and capability of file and print servers varies, however. Other services to look for include in-built bridges and gateways, inter-user electronic mail and — crucially — management facilities for the LAN.

Applications software

Not all software performs satisfactorily in a LAN environment, meaning multiple access to the master copy is not supported. Some software suppliers are finding it hard to cost their package for network use, where a single copy may be purchased for use by several workstations.

Access security

Users will want to retain private files; the network manager may have to impose varying levels of 'privilege' on access to individual files and services. Normally this is done with passwords, in which case there should be facilities for setting and subsequently changing both individual passwords and the access levels they imply. Some LANs include encryption facilities to restrict file usage further.

Data security

The LAN should include facilities for rigorous and structured backups of files.

Data integrity

In the simpler LANs, the first user to get access to a file locks out any other user to prevent any attempt at simultaneous updates. A more sophisticated system might apply this locking at the record level, so two or more workstations could be using the *file* simultaneously but are prevented from updating the same *record*.

There are several digital alternatives emerging to replace paper-based information storage systems and to make the most of the possibilities of digitization. The ideal requirements are:

- Fast *access* to information
- Storage of a variety of *different types* of digitized data (primarily text, though)
- High *capacity*
- A *compact* medium to simplify storage and distribution
- *Control* — consistent, accurate and cross-referenced filing of information with easy updating

Disks and tape streamers

Many applications can tolerate the rather slower performance available in proven form from one or other of the types of magnetic disk. Reliability and capacity is always improving; the physical dimensions of the disk drives are shrinking. Removable hard disk 'packs' and the so-called 'streaming' tape drives (the streamer is a simplified tape deck using reels or cartridges) provide a means of transporting data.

Disks are inherently sensitive, though, and that will always keep prices fairly high. Removable disks are particularly expensive, and tape backup media are slow. Still, for many applications today the magnetic disk is the best option for relatively low volumes of information storage.

Microform

Microfilm and fiche are probably the most immediate option for large-volume long-term record keeping; the space required is small, costs are reasonable, distribution of information on microform is cheap and easy, and the technology and the market are both well understood by suppliers.

Access speeds are not great, though, largely because it takes time for the user to locate

the correct fiche or film and then the correct page on it. Computer-assisted retrieval systems do help, but it can still take three seconds or more to find and extract filed documents. Capacities can be quite impressive; CAR systems exist with over two million documents on file.

Another drawback is that most microform systems are not rewritable. One or two do enable a user to add, annotate, erase or replace information, in the same way as a paper filing system; but they command a premium price.

Above all, microform is inherently non-electronic and non-digital. It cannot easily be linked to other office systems, and in operational terms it compares unfavourably with digital alternatives. The electronic media can be updated and referenced as required; microfilm must be updated and perhaps accessed when convenient.

Solid-state memories

All-electronic memory banks provide the most compact type of storage and the fastest access to information. Technologies available include the same kind of semiconductor memory chips used for a computer's RAM. Despite the falling costs of memory, this approach is generally too expensive for large volumes of information — except in applications where the high-speed access can justify the cost.

Video cassette backup

The Philips audio cassette found applications in home computing for a simplified, low-cost storage medium using a well-understood electromechanical technology. For the same reasons, a digital version of the domestic video cassette recorder may be attractive to system developers; an ordinary E180 VHS-format cassette stores over two gigabytes (that is two thousand megabytes) at a cost of around 0.25p per megabyte.

Information is transferred to the tape at about 120KB per second, but inevitably this is a pretty slow device when it comes to re-reading data — average search time is over two *minutes*. The obvious applications are in large-volume backups, for taking multiple successive copies of backups of smaller volumes without overwriting the previous one, or for archiving, and the controller for such a system will typically enable it to appear to the computer as a conventional streamer tape unit.

Interactive video via VCR

Another approach has been taken with the use of VCR tapes; interactive video combines sound with high-quality still and moving pictures and graphics and text produced by a computer. Output has to be to a TV-type monitor, but this and the VCR unit are controlled by a computer.

Because tape is a serial medium and relatively slow, interactive video is basically unsuitable for the kind of information storage where reference may be required to any point on the tape. But it has found ideal applications in demonstrations and training, where the user typically works through a programme from start to end. The system is controlled by software in the computer which starts and stops the VCR tape; the 'interaction' is provided by the software, which can invite the user to select options that may result in something from the tape being displayed.

Interactive videodisk

The first videodisks were basically an equivalent of video cassette tape, carrying information in analogue rather than digital form. They can be adapted to hold data as well as sound and pictures; the digital data has to be converted to analogue form first. This kind of setup is what Philips calls LV-ROM, for LaserVision read-only memory — LaserVision is the Philips product name for its videodisk.

The Domesday Project

The Domesday Project is a classic application for interactive video using laser videodisks.

It represents an attempt to update the original Domesday Book of 1086 to present a detailed picture of Britain and its people on two disks:

- The *National Disk* contains text, charts and pictures on the economy, culture, society and the environment. Sources include government statistics, the BBC's *Daily Life in the 1980s*, newspaper and magazine articles, *Hansard* and specially-commissioned essays. Access is via a simple keyword reference system.

- The *Community Disk* is based on Ordnance Survey maps (some 24 000 of them) with associated text (150 000 screen pages of it) and around 20 000 photographs. It is arranged as six different levels, allowing the user to home in on very specific features; the top level covers Britain as a whole, intermediate levels go down through successively greater detail (the individual countries, 40x30km regions, 4x3km local areas, street maps) and the bottom level provides individual features and floor plans of selected sites.

Despite the wealth of information, the Domesday Project system is remarkably easy to use. It requires a colour monitor, a specially-developed 'professional' version of the Philips LaserVision laser disk player, and a BBC Master or RML Nimbus microcomputer. The software provided handles the information access; it can also sort and select information, and present it in bar-chart or pie-chart format. As an interactive reference source for education, marketing, and local and national research, it is probably unrivalled.

There are a number of optical storage techniques — including 'smart cards' and tape — but the principal commercial option is the reflective disk.

All optical disks, or 'laser disks', work in the same way. Information is recorded on the disk by burning pits into the surface coating with a high-power high-precision laser. That information is read by scanning the revolving disk with a finely focused laser beam of lower precision, which is reflected by the surface on to a photoelectric sensor. The pattern of pits can be decoded into a signal representing either digital or analogue information.

Analogue vs digital. That represents one distinction between types of laser disk. An analogue laser disk — what is conventionally called a 'videodisk' — *can* hold digital data, but it has to be converted into an analogue form first. No conversion is necessary with digital laser disks, which makes them more suitable for computer-related applications.

Read-only vs write-once. At present, all laser disks are either *read-only* (as with audio compact disks, the information is put on by the supplier) or *write-once* (data can be put on to the disk by the end-user, but only once — thereafter the disk becomes read-only).

Rewritable laser disks. The missing option is a commercially-available *erasable* laser disk. This could be overwritten at will for new information to be recorded, just like the computer's magnetic disks. The problem is that the disk's surface is physically altered by burning in those pits; with a magnetic disk, there is no physical alteration. Research is proceeding on ways of smoothing out the pits or avoiding them altogether, however, and erasable rewritable laser disks should appear in the near future.

Such products will appeal as straight replacements for today's hard disks. The large capacity, removable media, low media cost and reasonable access times could well make them the natural choice when the technology is sorted out.

Applications. In the meantime, there are advantages to a non-alterable information storage medium. Broadly, the applications fall like this:

□ *Write-once* media (WORM or DRAW) will be used much as microfilm and fiches today — for archival records storage and small-scale distribution of information.

□ *Read-only* media will be used for new types of electronic publishing — particularly for reference information, training and education, and (in the case of CD-V) consumer products.

Advantages. In both cases the technology will appeal for a number of reasons:

□ *Random access*. The software control will take the user quickly to the required information, no matter where it is actually located on the disk (the contrast is with *serial* access as used by tape, where the read head has to pass over all the data preceding the searched-for item).

□ *High density*. A lot of information can be stored in a small package — the laser-burnt pits are typically only about one micrometre in diameter. A 12in WORM disk can hold around 2000MB, 5$\frac{1}{4}$in CD-ROM disks up to 600MB.

□ *Compact media*. Laser disks can be as large as 12in in diameter, but the 12cm (4.7in) standard for audio compact disks is nearer the norm. Increasingly there is a move towards the 5$\frac{1}{4}$in and 3$\frac{1}{2}$in diameters familiar from floppy disks.

□ *Compact drive*. Current products using the largest size of disk tend to be about 5in high, 19in wide (that fits a European standard for rack-mounting) and some 25in deep.

□ *Removability and portability*. These are key features. Even in a protective plastic cartridge, the disks will be sufficiently small and light for easy storage and distribution.

□ *Archival quality*. While magentic media start to decay relatively soon, optical storage offers a data life of around 30 years in current products.

□ *Machine-readable information*. Information on CD-ROM and WORM disks will be directly usable by a computer.

□ *High reliability*. The minimal use of mechanical components, the removal of many friction problems, and the clever positioning mechanisms employed all contribute to extremely low error rates and impressive claims for the unit's reliability.

CD-ROM

Audio compact disks already use digital recording for sound; and this is another technology that has adapted easily and effectively to storage of digital information. CD-ROM— 'compact disk, read-only memory' — is one of the digital laser disk technologies that looks most promising. A single-sided CD-ROM disk stores around 600MB (the equivalent of around 200 000 typed A4 pages) with an average access time that is acceptably low at two seconds or less.

CD-ROM is primarily a distribution medium, just like audio CD disks; it represents a new publishing medium, delivering large quantities of digital data for use at the desktop computer or workstation. Applications include detailed *maintenance information* for products, mixing graphics and text: *software distribution* is another possibility, with the package on the laser disk along with its manuals.

But the principal use will be for *reference* in a variety of fields. A variety of databases of various kinds are already available; index and selection techniques will enable users to locate required information and extract it for possible use in reports. Such databases would include anything currently available as an on-line information service; more generally, dictionaries, Roget's *Thesaurus* and encyclopaedias could be sold in CD-ROM form.

CD-ROM also has a good future for mass storage of digital data of all types — text, image and voice can be combined on the disk, which gives it considerable relevance to the mixed-application all-digital office systems as well as in training and information reference.

WORM disks

A WORM disk is another laser disk option. CD-ROMs come to the user already containing information; WORMs are blank. They provide 'write once, read many times' storage (sometimes the acronym DRAW is used, for 'digital read after

write); in other words, data can be written to a WORM disk by the user's computer — but that can be done only once. Thereafter the disk is effectively a CD-ROM in use, though it does not have the same replication facilities as the CD-ROM technology.

Clearly the main uses for WORM disks will be in archiving and backups, though they may also find applications in small-scale distribution of information produced in-house.

CD-I and CD-V

These two are laser disk technologies that are not related to computer use. CD-V is compact disk — video, effectively a combination of current VCR playback features (fast and slow-motion replay, freeze frame and the like — but not recording) and the music facilities of audio compact disk. It can be connected to a standard TV or hi-fi system; the pioneering Philips Combi model also plays existing audio-only CDs and video-only LaserVision disks.

CD-I (compact disk — interactive) will probably become a consumer-oriented item as well, aimed at education and entertainment. CD-I can mix text, sound, and video (CD-ROM cannot handle moving pictures) with interactive selection of options; a CD-I player is hooked on to a TV set just like a video cassette recorder and controlled via a joystick or a remote infrared keypad controller.

The immediate sales are likely to come from audio-visual equivalents of music LPs, much like video cassettes but with track selection facilities. The possibilities are illustrated by a recent example of a multi-media medical training course for nurses. This involved four 30-minute video cassettes, 465 pages of text and workbook exercises, and 165 35mm slides. Putting the whole lot on to CD-I would eliminate the need for constant cross-referencing between the different media; it could be presented in three other languages as an alternative to English; and it would still fill only 85 per cent of a single CD-I disk.

Laser disk

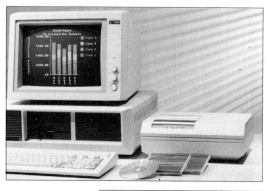

WORM drive attached to a PC

Laser disk standards

Philips and Sony, pioneers in laser disk technology, have together produced specifications for CD-ROM and CD-I (CD Audio, too, as it happens) in an attempt to avoid the multi-standard confusions around VCR formats. These *de facto* standards are widely accepted and will probably be made official, though in some respects they are a bit quirky — the 74-minute maximum capacity of a single-sided audio CD is said to correspond to the length of the Sony chairman's favourite symphony.

In general, though, these specifications cover only the physical aspects of CD. A number of other parties are working towards standards for other aspects of laser disk technology, notably the so-called 'High Sierra Group' of interested volunteers who aim to propose standards for the format of information on CDs. The goal is interchangeability; at present, a particular WORM disk will work only in a specific drive. (On the other hand, any CD-ROM disk produced to the High Sierra standard will run on the Philips drive.)

Smart cards

Credit cards store a limited amount of information on a dark magnetically encoded strip; 'smart cards' actually include their own microprocessor and memory embedded in the plastic.

Consumer applications are the immediate goal; smart cards can include stringent security checks on usage, for instance, which could prevent fraudulent use of existing chequebooks and bank cards. A single card could replace all one's credit and cash cards; it could also hold updated account information in greater detail and more privacy than a monthly statement.

Smart cards could also be used for health and security records, the volume and complexity of which bedevil the current system. In theory, all an individual's social records — including passport, employment history and the like — could be held on a single card.

Customer resistance will probably hold back the mass market for smart cards. Meanwhile there are obvious applications in business; a smart card, for instance, could provide a very high level of security access and be used to log movements.

Such a card can also have less obvious applications. Communicating data with the home base, especially while travelling abroad, can be difficult because of the need for lengthy dial-up and log-on procedures; it may also need a local subscription to connect to the various international data networks.

The Swiss company COMCO has arrangements with public and private telecom groups, including various national PTTs, for the use of smart cards to automate the whole messy business.

'Smart card' and reader

With its associated reader, the card can automatically connect the user through a local data network and IPSS to a predetermined system on the other end. The user does not need to translate the connection messages on the screen from the local language. Network addressing, any system routing and log-on procedures are all automated, and because the card carries a running balance of phone credits available (you pay for them *before* you use them) there is no local invoice. The card is available with various preloaded amounts and the credits can be renewed. This should provide a convenient, cost-effective method of accessing a mailbox from abroad for users who travel regularly.

Laser cards

Laser storage permits very high capacities in a very small area; because the information is stored *optically*, data is tolerant of dirt, dust, fingerprints and destructive magnetic fields. CD-ROM is the application attracting most attention at present, but other possibilities are emerging — including the optical memory card.

This credit card lookalike can store up to *two megabytes* at present, with manufacturers claiming that the technology could be pushed to double that capacity. It is intended for

data recording and storage, and the technology it uses resembles that of WORM disks and CD-ROM. A shimmery gold rectangle covers most of the front of the card; within this, you can make out thin parallel lines separating wider stripes. Digital data is laser-encoded in the stripes.

Optical storage is not intended to replace erasable magnetic disks in normal day-to-day work. Instead, they apply in archive applications — the kind of tasks that currently consume a lot of paper and a lot of space, or require the use of microfiches. Medical records are a candidate; laser cards have potential in health and medical systems, permitting individuals to carry their entire medical history in their pockets as they move from doctor to doctor and clinic to clinic. That would reduce the time needed at present to locate and forward medical records — and potentially it could save lives by reducing the chance of oversight, such as allergies to specific medication.

There are also markets in publishing (especially for reference works), record-keeping (banks need detailed historical records, for instance, and companies in Britain now have to keep VAT information for six years) and transaction systems (where all activity has to be logged).

SoftStrip

Another novel storage mechanism provides an update on bar-code reading. Bar-codes are simply strips of printing that can be decoded into information by a reader; SoftStrip Systems has developed this into a

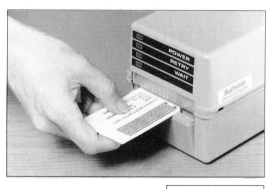
SoftStrip on card

SoftStrip on paper

data. That will fit easily on to something the size of a credit card — and because the signature is not visible, it provides a considerable degree of security. The SoftStrip reader decodes the digitized signature for comparison with a handwritten one when you sign for something.

general-purpose data storage technique for any digitized information, and with considerably greater density — its coding technique is claimed to store up to a hundred times more information than barcodes in the same space.

Because the reader works simply by detecting the difference between light and dark areas, the codes can be printed on virtually any material by standard print devices. The result is a low-cost method of producing computer-readable information. Three examples:

☐ Medical records can be stored as SoftStrips on paper. The storage space required for a patient's details can be minimized; direct output from the computer at a clinic can be used as input via a SoftStrip reader elsewhere. The technique ought to be cheap enough in capital terms to interest the NHS, media and system incompatibilities are minimized, and the savings on patient record storage would be considerable.

☐ Programs and data files could be output as SoftStrips on to plain paper. They could then be copied as required simply by running the paper through an ordinary office photocopier.

☐ A signature can be encoded on a credit card in about 1200 bytes of

For the multi-function workstation, the conventional layout of display screen and QWERTY keyboard will probably never be supplanted. In practice they are economical and their role in a system is well understood. The options are all relatively expensive, not least because the lack of demand means they are not mass-produced; and the physical and ergonomic interfaces are not well understood yet.

There are, however, a number of options to *supplement* the present setup.

□ *Graphics tablet*. An electric stylus is used to select functions listed in rectangles on the surface of a cable-connected pad. In a text editing application, for example, these might execute commands such as drawing boxes, changing typefaces, indenting, and adding or deleting characters, words or lines.

In practice the graphics tablet adds little to existing input facilities.

□ *Touch-sensitive screens*. The user actually presses the screen lightly to select an option displayed thereon. The faceplate may have a flexible layer containing an invisible mesh of fine wires that are brought into contact by light pressure of the finger. Alternatively the bezel will include miniature light sources and photoelectric sensors: moving the finger into the field breaks the beam and an X-Y co-ordinate signal results.

These have been around for some time, and typically produce smudged screens and rather slower operation.

□ The *'cat'* originated along with the mouse from Xerox's Palo Alto research centre in the seventies. It is a *tracker ball*, effectively an upsidedown mouse embedded in the keyboard that can be rolled with the fingertips to move the cursor quickly around the screen.

Mice seem more natural to use, and the buttons on the top mean that the user's fingers are nearer the keys which make selections.

□ *Writing tablets* or pads incorporating sensing equipment can be used for freehand written input. Writing paper is placed on the surface and the tablet senses either the pressure of the writing or the position of the pen, decoding this into shapes it attempts to recognize as characters.

Quite apart from the pattern recognition problems in software, none of the existing freehand input units can compete with a keyboard for speed of input. There has been a surprising amount of resistance to this kind of approach; people find it less than convenient, and there is a psychological resentment of the computer invading the personal privacy of handwriting.

□ *Voice annotation*. For casual annotation of existing documents a better solution might be the ability to add spoken comments via a microphone or telephone-like handset. The system records and plays back the digitized speech alongside the text.

To date this has suffered from the same problems as other uses of voice.

□ *Voice input*. Since speech is a natural and quite speedy communications method, it has received a lot of attention. Voice input, or automatic speech recognition, is relatively simple in theory — analogue-to-digital converters digitize the human voice, the speech pattern is compared to those stored in memory, and the computer takes some appropriate action as a result. Currently speech input is used primarily in 'hands busy' tasks such as data entry, machine control and inventory management.

Most of these systems are 'speaker-dependent' — they are trained to understand the voice of each and every operator. They also tend to be limited to discrete commands rather than continuous speech, vocabularies are restricted and a good deal of memory is required to store the speech patterns. Even more memory is needed for speaker-independent systems; these utilize programmed speech reference sets, and in theory can recognize any voice. The falling costs of memory and the increasing speed and capability of computers auger well for speech input, though.

□ *Voice output*. Digital-to-analogue conversion is a rather different and more complicated technology, though considerable advances are being made in speech synthesizer chips.

At present the amount of memory required limits the usefulness of voice output impractical for all but the simplest applications. In any case, it is a relatively slow method of communicating information. There are obvious applications though in language translation, warnings or alarms, where the eyes are being used for some other task, and if there is simply an overload of information. Voice output from database information to telephone callers is another promising area.

When IBM launched the PC back in 1981, everyone assumed that it would dominate the desktop computer market. The design was either conservative or out of date, depending on your viewpoint. But in many respects, it was immeasurably superior to anything else available at the time. Besides, IBM had the resources to guarantee market domination.

What has happened is that IBM is the largest single vendor in the field, but worldwide it has around a third of all desktop computer sales, not an outright majority. Instead it is the *specification* of its computers that dominates, rather than the computers themselves. If you want to buy a computer that does everything an IBM can do, you are better off not shopping at IBM.

What is so special about the IBM spec?

The IBM PC and AT introduced or popularized a number of key features for desktop computers:

- The *three-box layout* of screen, keyboard and 'system unit', with cables connecting them. This is a convenient arrangement if the computer is not going to moved around much; it gives a certain amount of flexibility in organizing the workspace, and internal access for repairs or adding options is quite simple.

- The *5¼in floppy disk* — compact and fairly robust by comparison with the possible alternatives (notably the 8in floppy disk).

- The MS-DOS *operating system* and the *Intel 8088/8086 microprocessor* family — neither of which were ideal then or now, but standardization was important.

That last point is the key one. A potential purchaser might see uses for a computer, and the IBM-type solution might be both appropriate and affordable. If there is no software to run real applications, no computer will appeal. Conversely, if there are no buyers, no software developer is going to waste time developing software.

The IBM 'standard' and the certainty that it would create a large market enabled software developers to get cracking on new types of product, secure in the knowledge that *someone* would buy it. That produced a variety of choices for just about every conceivable application. Because of this range, IBM-compatibility is a good choice for the user; the size of the IBM-compatible market has also guaranteed the availability of a good selection of support services, from books and training courses to maintenance companies and floppy disk suppliers.

IBM may have set the *de facto* standards, but it left lots of gaps both in marketing and technical terms.

- Unusually for IBM, nearly all the components for the PC were bought from outside suppliers. Other manufacturers can buy the same components. That particularly applies to the operating system (MS-DOS) and the microprocessor (the Intel 8088 chip). Only one aspect of the PC carried IBM's copyright — the BIOS, a bit of built-in software that links the operating system to the electronics — and in the event replicating this did not turn out to be a major problem.

- Equally out of character was IBM's willingness to publish the details of how it all plugged together.

- Since the components and the principles were available, and since IBM had not gone for the highest available technology by any means, it was not too difficult for manufacturers to improve on the original specification while still retaining IBM-compatibility. For instance, the faster 8086 chip was used by some — and an NEC alternative to Intel's product would run faster still. The PC keyboard was solid enough, but the arrangement of keys was easy to improve — as IBM acknowledged when it showed a superior keyboard with subsequent models. Similarly, the PC was a bit short on sensible connections to the outside world in terms of built-in sockets for printers, modems and the like; IBM-compatible manufacturers added them as standard. The original

IBM PC came with five expansion slots for extras; most IBM-compatibles have eight. Where the original IBM PC came with only 128K or 256K of memory, the standard clone today comes with the maximum possible of 640K.

What is an IBM-compatible?

Software. The IBM-compatible runs any and all software that is sold for the equivalent IBM machine. That means it has disk drives that can read IBM-format floppy disks and a BIOS that provides IBM-type control of the hardware elements — especially the display.

Expansion slots. The compatible has slots of the same size and with the same connections as the IBM — anything that you can plug into one will fit the other.

Memory and operating system. The compatible follows IBM's use of memory and the MS-DOS operating system, including the restriction to a maximum of 640K that is built into the simpler versions of MS-DOS.

Keyboard. The content and layout of the IBM keyboard is followed by the IBM-compatible, since software packages will make assumptions about the positioning and use of all the keys.

Options in compatibility

PC-compatibles

These will have at least one 360KB floppy disk drive, expansion slots that take IBM-format cards, and an MS-DOS/BIOS combination which should run any and all software designed for the PC and XT.

Many of these clones are still made with the 8088 processor that IBM originally used. That does help to guarantee complete compatibility, but by current standards its performance (a clock speed of 4.77MHz) is mediocre.

The immediate alternative is the NEC V20, an 8088 lookalike that is the subject of a long-running legal feud between Intel and the Japanese firm; it runs 10 to 15 per cent faster than the 8088. A better bet is the 8088-II, a version of the original chip from Intel with a dual-speed option (it runs at the original's 4.77MHz or at a speedier 8MHz). The best option is the Intel 8086-II, faster still (10MHz) and technically a more flexible member of the same family. NEC has another lookalike, the V30, which again improves the overall processing speed by up to 15 per cent.

All of these will run most PC/XT software — but faster. (The qualification 'most' is there because some software has in-built speed limitations and will not run at higher speeds.)

AT-compatibles

Here the requirement is as before — similar disk drives (at least one that will take 1.2MB floppy disks), expansion slots for new-format cards as well as XT type and an MS-DOS/BIOS combination which should run any software for the AT.

The AT uses Intel's 80286 processor, originally in a 6MHz version (which made it no faster than an 8086-based PC-compatible) and subsequently at 8MHz. This is now the norm for AT-compatibles, though some can go at 12 or even 16MHz.

In practice, clones using the 8086 or NEC V30 are perfectly serviceable low-end machines, but it is not worth paying anything more than a budget price for them because of the falling costs of the much faster 80286-based offerings. Computers built around the 80286 run all PC programs at between seven and ten times the speed of a PC; they should be the immediate choice for any workstation-oriented system.

As for the 80386, the immediate future is not in the workstation — except for specialized applications that can take advantage of the huge memory capacity and superfast speeds, such as CAD work. The 386 is not even necessary for OS/2; the operating system can run happily on an 80286.

Instead it seems likely that the bulk of sales for 80386-based computers will be in 'workgroup' environments, where the processor's capabilities can be shared between many users in a local network or multi-user system. Those capabilities do not stop at the thing's processing speed: the 80386 is organized internally in a quite deliberate fashion to support multiple users.

IBM PC family

IBM PC. The original IBM desktop computer. In its most recent incarnation it featured:

☐ IBM's mild customization of the MS-DOS version 3.2 operating system
☐ Intel 8088 microprocessor rated at 4.77MHz
☐ 640K memory at most
☐ Monochrome 640x200 display
☐ Original keyboard
☐ Two floppy disk drives with 360KB capacity on each
☐ Five 'full-size' expansion slots (one already occupied)
☐ 63.5W power supply

PC Convertible. Expensive and unexciting portable version of the standard PC with detachable screen and 720KB 3½in floppy disks.

IBM PC/XT. The hard-disk version:

☐ MS-DOS version 3.2 operating system
☐ Intel 8088 microprocessor rated at 4.77MHz
☐ 640K memory at most
☐ Monochrome 640x200 display
☐ Original keyboard
☐ One 20MB hard disk drive with 40ms access time
☐ One 5¼in floppy disk drive with 360KB capacity
☐ Five 'full-size' expansion slots (two already occupied)
☐ 130W power supply

IBM PC/XT286. Not a particularly serious product — a stopgap upgrade in advance of the AT's launch, it put most of the AT specification (notably the Intel 80286 chip and 1.2MB floppy disk) inside a PC case, but included the PC keyboard and several restrictions (slow hard disk, relatively low processor speed).

☐ MS-DOS version 3.2 operating system
☐ Intel 80286 microprocessor rated at 6MHz
☐ 640K memory standard
☐ Monochrome 640x200 display
☐ One 20MB hard disk drive with 85ms access time
☐ One 5¼in floppy disk drive with 1.2MB capacity
☐ Eight expansion slots (two already occupied; plus five 'full size' and one 'half size')
☐ 157W power supply
☐ Original keyboard

IBM PC/AT family

IBM PC/AT. Features an 80286 processor, 1.2MB floppy disk, hard disk as standard, and MS-DOS. This one is usually referred to simply as the AT:

☐ MS-DOS version 3.2 operating system
☐ Intel 80286 microprocessor rated at 6MHz
☐ 512K memory standard, 640K maximum
☐ Monochrome 640x200 display
☐ One 30MB hard disk drive with 40ms access time
☐ One 5¼in floppy disk drive with 1.2MB capacity
☐ Eight full-size expansion slots (two already occupied)
☐ 192 W power supply
☐ AT keyboard

IBM PC/ATE. The 'AT Extended' or 'AT Enhanced' with faster Intel 80286 microprocessor (rated at 8MHz, switchable to 4.77MHz), bigger power supply (200 W) and improved keyboard

IBM PS/2 family

IBM PS/2 Model 30. Features an 8086 processor with 720KB 3½in floppy disk and enhanced colour graphics, but is otherwise similar to the PC:

☐ MS-DOS version 3.3 operating system
☐ Intel 8086 microprocessor rated at 8MHz
☐ 640K memory maximum
☐ Monochrome 640x480 display, colour graphics 320x200 (256 colours)
☐ One 20MB hard disk drive with 80ms access time
☐ One 3½in floppy disk drive with 720KB capacity
☐ Three full-size expansion slots (all available)

IBM PS/2. Other models in the PS/2 line are totally different — 80286 processor in the smaller models, 80386 in the larger units; OS/2 or MS-DOS version 3.3 operating system; new colour graphics controller and a new design for expansion slots; 1.44MB 3½in floppy disk; 1MB memory or more as standard:

☐ MS-DOS version 3.2 or OS/2 operating system
☐ Intel 80286 microprocessor rated at 10MHz or 80386 at 16 or 20MHz
☐ 16MB (or more) memory as the theoretical maximum
☐ Monochrome 640x480 display, colour graphics 640x480 (16 colours) or 320x200 (256 colours)
☐ At least one hard disk, from 20MB (80ms access time) to 115MB (28ms)
☐ One 3½in floppy disk drive with 1.44MB capacity
☐ Three or seven MCA expansion slots (all available)

IBM standards: PC and AT

- ☐ **MS-DOS.** All PCs and ATs use a version of Microsoft's MS-DOS operating system, and virtually all IBM-compatible software assumes its presence. The customization done for IBM has not been too specific, and Microsoft sells MS-DOS freely to other parties.

- ☐ **BIOS.** The only significant part of the PC design to be copyrighted by IBM is the BIOS, which mates the operating system to the hardware components. After some legal squabbles, a number of IBM-compatible BIOSes are available to the clone-builder.

- ☐ **CGA.** IBM's Colour Graphics Adapter is a plug-in card that provides low-resolution colour graphics — up to four colours in 320x200 resolution — with crude text characters. The CGA standard is the minimum that any IBM-compatible might want to emulate; in practice most graphics suppliers will offer either Hercules-compatibility (see below) or EGA standards.

- ☐ **EGA.** IBM's Enhanced Graphics Adapter is another plug-in card that provides better resolution (640x350) and 16 colours for graphics. Many packages with the option for colour graphics output demand the presence of an EGA-compatible display controller and screen.

- ☐ **Hercules graphics.** IBM's MDA Monochrome Display Adapter is the simplest standard for text-only displays. IBM did not come out with any product that would allow graphic display in high resolution on a *monochrome* screen (the CGA supports monochrome graphics in 640x200 resolution only, and text displayed is rather coarser because fewer dots are used per character), so an independent manufacturer called Hercules stepped in, and its add-in card is now a *de facto* standard — so much so that other IBM-compatible suppliers are emulating Hercules graphics as well. Hercules provides a 720x348 resolution for graphics, and Hercules-compatibility has effectively replaced MDA as the standard for clone-makers to offer.

Emulating the PS/2

IBM's introduction of the PS/2 showed that the company was no longer prepared to assist the competition; there are a number of proprietary features that will prove difficult — though not impossible — to emulate. Leaving aside the entry-level Model 30, which is basically a re-engineered and updated IBM PC, the main features are:

- ☐ *Processor.* PS/2 uses Intel's 80286 or 80386, both of which are readily available — and capable of working faster than in IBM's design.

- ☐ *Memory.* OS/2 is a large operating system, and PS/2 is also intended for sophisticated applications that will demand a lot of memory. To get 1MB or more of memory into a smallish space, IBM uses high-capacity chips. These too are freely available.

- ☐ *Operating system.* OS/2 is a major advance on its predecessor, but it retains compatibility with MS-DOS so software written for MS-DOS can be run under OS/2. In any case, Microsoft sells OS/2 to any computer manufacturer.

- ☐ *Floppy disks.* For PS/2, IBM appears to have standardized on high-capacity 3½in floppy disks storing 1.44MB. These drives can read existing lower-capacity IBM-format disks. Such drives are again available to clone-makers.

Thus far, the PS/2 line is not hard to imitate. The crunch for the clone-makers comes in the novelties:

- ☐ *Micro-Channel Architecture.* In practice this translates into a new format for the connectors on expansion cards. So existing add-on products cannot be used with PS/2. What is more, this 'bus' is fundamental to the operation of PS/2; any PS/2-compatible computer will have to provide an exact equivalent. MCA represents a thorough (and thoroughly modern) approach to the way a computer's components communicate with each other; it embodies more than a hundred novel features and IBM holds patents on most of them.

□ *BIOS*. The BIOS on PS/2 is customized to make use of the features of OS/2 and MCA. It will not be easy to emulate, but presumably that is no harder than cloning the BIOSes from the PC and AT.

□ *Colour graphics*. PS/2 features good-quality text and superb colour graphics, produced via new standards (VGA) and new electronics — for the PS/2 IBM developed a proprietary graphics-producing chip. The Virtual Graphics Array controller (VGA) allows graphics to be built with up to 64 colours (from a total range of 262 144 possibilities!) in a resolution of 640x480; on monochrome displays, colour can be simulated with 64 shades of grey. VGA is compatible with both CGA and EGA, so existing programs that assume either standard can work with graphics colour on the PS/2.

The VGA electronics are on the main system board rather than a plug-in card. Since all PS/2 users will therefore have this as standard, they will not be a market for add-on cards to compete with VGA; that limits the scale of production for VGA emulations.

□ *MCGA*. This colour graphics controller can effectively be discounted — it is an improvement on the CGA standard (text mode 640x400, 256-colour mode at 320x200) but it is available only with the stopgap entry-level PS/2 Model 30.

The tasks that the workstation computer can perform for management directly will depend on precisely what software packages are available — and there is a huge range of possibilities. This section considers the principal candidates.

It is software that really makes a computer work for you. There are broadly five kinds of software:

- The *operating system* in practice decides how the hardware will work — how the different electronic and electromechanical components of the computer will actually operate when presented with the user and some programs to run.

- *Utility* programs provide extra facilities not built into the operating system — for taking hard-disk backups, formatting disks and the like.

- An *'applications environment'* or *'front-end'* uses windows, icons and pop-up menus to provide the user with a clear and simple method of selecting operating system functions and running programs. Many applications packages themselves also utilize this graphical approach in their operation.

- *Applications packages* are prewritten load-and-go programs that perform some task for you. They are usually supplied on floppy disk. Extra add-on *utilities* are also available for many applications to fill out their capabilities — adding a graphics-drawing capability to a file manager, type effects to a desktop publisher, etc.

How to buy packages

You should be clear about just what is covered by the cash you are paying for a package. Of course you will get a disk with some software on it, and there should be a manual or two.

But there should be more. *Help* is the main extra to look for:

- A decent 'how to' manual
- A tutorial (preferably an interactive self-teaching guide)

- Context-sensitive on-screen help available at the press of a key ('context-sensitive' means the advice that appears should be geared specifically to the point you have reached in the program)
- Personal assistance with setting up new software if it is complicated
- Formal training if that would be useful (some suppliers with packages that do normally need implementation support will throw in a couple of days' of training at your office; some dealers will provide a little free)
- 'hot-line' query-answering telephone service

Nearly all packages come with a return-to-vendor *software registration card* that identifies you as a licensed user (note that you are not actually buying the package, you're just buying a licence to use it). Returning the card gets you on to a sales promotion list for bumf mailshots. It is worth doing, however, because registration may also qualify you for some free help — for instance, some suppliers give registered users any product updates for a while at no charge (usually for 12 months). To use a 'hot-line' support service you will probably have to quote your licence number. You may also need to be registered to qualify for discounts on any major revamp of the product.

As for any guarantee of *performance* — you probably won't get any at all about speed and capacity. However, you may have a legal case if there are claims in advertising and the package's documentation that are clearly misleading.

If there are specific *faults*, most software suppliers these days will fix any errors at no cost to you. On the other hand, the package vendor may not share your view of what exactly constitutes an 'error'.

In general, there is safety in numbers. Buying a popular package means that:

There has always been a problem with computers — they just aren't natural. Even a typist well used to keyboards can feel intimidated by the computer. These days a good deal of effort is being put into making the computer 'friendlier' and more easy to use:

□ *Windows* are small displays that might appear superimposed on the screen's current contents. Generally the window will hold a selection of options, a panel of information or help, or another file (for 'cut-and-paste' operations, taking a block of material from one file for insertion into another). The window and its contents disappear once the user has finished with them.

Front-ends at work, using 'icons' — such as the dustbin (for deletions), index cards (files) and sheets of paper (files) — and 'windows' containing menus and other functions

□ *Icons* are small graphic symbols on the screen. Instead of using the keyboard to select a command or option, the cursor (generally an angled arrow) is placed on top of the relevant symbol or menu selection. The kind of icons that might appear are a wastepaper basket (for deleting something) or a filing cabinet (for saving your work on disk). Many people find this approach quite simple and very effective — it is easy to mistype something when you have to use the keyboard all the time. But as users become more familiar with the computer, it's likely that they will find the icon-pointing too slow and visually verbose.

□ A *mouse* is normally used with icons as an alternative to the arrow keys on a keyboard for moving the cursor. The mouse itself is a lump of plastic connected to the computer; on its base there is a rolling ball and as you sweep the mouse across a desk or a tabletop the cursor on the screen follows its movement. Buttons on the top of the mouse are used to select functions (rather like pressing the Enter key on the keyboard) or to cancel selections. Again, not everyone likes using a mouse: pressing the arrow keys is often easier.

A mouse is a handheld cursor-movement device connected by a lead to the computer. Moving the mouse across the surface of the desk or over a special pad will cause the cursor on the screen to move in the equivalent direction. The buttons on the top of the mouse are used to select or cancel selections. Mice are often used with graphical 'front-end' environments

- The supplier is likely to be well established, so it will not disappear overnight and product upgrades should appear regularly.
- The product is likely to be proven and largely free of bugs — more users means that software problems are found (and corrected) more quickly.
- The package is likely to be a reasonable piece of work, both in terms of the features it includes and the help and documentation users receive.
- Mass sales give the supplier enough margin to invest in the product's documentation, facilities and upgrades.
- A large user base means more shared knowledge of tips and tricks, and more third-party suppliers with add-on utilities, books and general expertise.
- A large user base can also kick up more of a fuss when the vendor does something that is not in the users' best interests.

Multi-function 'integrated' packages

The four applications most popular with individual users of personal computers are *word processing*, *data management* (that is, the processing of structured records), *spreadsheet* analysis, and *graphical display*, especially for presentations. A general-purpose *comms* facility may also be required: *'desktop'* utilities such as a simple address book, appointments diary and instant calculator may be useful.

Using separate packages is not the only choice. It may also be a poor option:

- The user has to get used to three or four different approaches and different sets of commands.
- It can be inconvenient to swap packages in and out when a particular task requires the use of more than one function.
- Standardization is more difficult, with different users exercising different personal preferences.

- It is likely to be very difficult to pass information among the different packages.

The alternative is an 'integrated' package, which aims to provide two or more of the four types of processing in a single, consistent environment and meets all the points above. If you need the span of functions and if the simplicity appeals of multiple functions provided from one program, an integrated packages may well fit the bill. However, there may be problems with this approach too.

Functions

Integrated packages vary widely in the range of functions they provide and in the capabilities they offer within each of the functions. Most have a distinct bias towards one function and provide a reduced level of capability in others.

For people who need just one type of package, there are unlikely to be any advantages in buying an integrated package on the 'just in case' principle. Single-function packages do often include extras that may be adequate — several file management packages provide good personalized letter functions, for instance, which may obviate the need for a word processor.

The user may also require more than the integrated package can provide. The integrated facilities may be inadequate for high-grade full-colour presentation graphics, for instance; a purpose-built word processor is likely to provide more capability, more and easier ways of handling text, than the WP functions in integrated packages.

The sensible approach, then, is to decide on the most important requirement and seek a package (integrated or not) which is strongest in that area.

User image

Integrated packages have a major advantage in the standardized way in which the software appears to the user. The instructions used to operate integrated packages are generally as similar as possible in all parts of the package; for example, the same pair of function keys may be used to move the cursor forward and back a word when editing a document, forward and back a cell when analysing data in a spreadsheet, and forward and back a field when processing structured records. 'Help' information is usually accessed through a single key throughout. In menu-driven systems, a task which occurs on menus in several parts of the system should always be activated by the same key throughout (for example, the exit command in *every* menu might be 'X').

This contrasts strongly with the markedly different approaches taken by individual packages, which can be very confusing for people who use more than one such package.

Processing links

Where several different packages are used, the user normally has to invoke each separately from the operating system (unless the operating system provides concurrent, or multi-tasking, working). In an integrated package, by contrast, it is usually possible to run the various parts of the package from a common menu or by issuing internal commands — without returning to the operating system first.

Sharing of information

This may be the most significant aspect of integration, allowing data created within one function (sales information in the file manager, say) to be projected into another (such as a spreadsheet). Output from spreadsheets may have to be incorporated into a word-processed report, perhaps after graphic transformation, and so on.

Advantages

- A greater degree of similarity in approach and method of use than with separate products
- A single source of support for all software (an advantage only if the support is good ...)
- Possibly simplified procedures — only one or two disks to load, only one set of data files, no hunting around for the disk containing the next function to run
- Standardization

Disadvantages

- Integrated packages may lack functionality compared with individual, specialized packages — they may not provide as many features.
- There can be considerable variation in the level of functionality between different aspects of the package.
- Packages with such a range of applications may be difficult to use or verbose in taking the user through option menus to a particular task.
- Generally there is a more restricted choice of hardware configuration. Many of these products run only on the IBM PC and very close compatibles; the choice for Unix/Xenix-based machines and for Apple is limited, for other machines there may be no choice at all.
- They often require more memory and more disk space than an individual package.
- As with any multi-purpose package taking a catch-all approach, the software will probably be larded with facilities and functions that are irrelevant to a user's own work.
- Standardization and control may be easier, but it can result in a package solution that does not fit the needs of all users. This is true of any attempt at a rational policy for using packages, but will be amplified by the smaller range of choice in integrated packages and the wider contrasts between capabilities.

Checklist: comparing packages

Find out what you need

Look at your general office work now: analyse what goes on, so that you will be able to compare the computerized solution offered with your existing procedures. Make sure that all the contenders do what you need, and make sure they can fit quite closely to your ways of doing things.

Try to anticipate what else you might want on the computer. You don't have to buy all the programs at once, but it might prejudice you in favour of packages that can be expanded and added to in the future.

Look into the future for significant changes of operation, too. And ask the awkward questions: what happens if your contacts file doubles in size? What happens if the volume of transactions to be entered increases?

Talk to existing users

By getting in touch with present users of existing systems it soon becomes obvious how reliable and effective the system is when used in anger. More important, you can also find out how the supplier performs in terms of help and advice.

If you are going to be a guinea-pig for a new piece of software, make sure that it will be financially worth while and that you can continue to run existing systems while the new software gets bedded in.

Don't get too carried away. New packages and new computer systems can be very good: apart from anything else, they will reflect any recent legislation. They will also exhibit new facilities and new functions (based possibly on the shortcomings of their predecessors).

Otherwise, go for safety in numbers.

Try before you buy

It goes without saying that you should try the package. Pay special attention to what it is like in operation. Is it easy to use? You should be led through the process by instructions and lists of options (called 'menus') displayed on the screen. On the other hand, the programs should get you where you need to be as quickly as possible: commands to perform common tasks should be straightforward, and should not require awkward combinations of keys. They should also be easy to learn and remember.

Check out the reports and documents produced by the system. A computer can generate prodigious amounts of paper, but quantity does not count. Does the printed output tell you things you really want to know, laid out in a way you can understand?

What about operator errors? Mistakes will be made; how does the system react to them?

Read the manuals

You will need manuals to explain the facilities that the computer and its packages provide, how they can be used and how they should be operated. A good manual should be clear and unambiguous, comprehensive as well as comprehensible. It should have a decent index, and it should include 'how-to' guides that show exactly what you have to do for common required tasks.

Be flexible

Most packages work in general terms, are of general applicability and in general are as good as any others. Low-cost solutions demand some flexibility on the part of users as well as of the packages themselves. You may have to decide what you cannot change and what you can adapt to fit the package.

Free software

Some of the best software available for your computer will probably be virtually free; it is 'in the public domain'. This means that someone has written the program for their own use (or amusement) and made it generally available, typically through a users' group.

There are well over 3000 programs in the public domain. Most are games or useful utilities tools, but they do include full-scale word processors, file managers, spelling checkers and spreadsheets.

The literal definition of 'public domain' is 'the condition of being free from copyright and patent'. Most public domain programs include a statement something like this: 'You are welcome to copy and use this software provided (a) you do not remove any of the notices, documentation files, or author's credits; and (b) it is not done for profit'.

In other words, once you have bought the software you can do what you like with it — so long as you do not sell it. User groups and others who *do* charge for public domain disks are only covering their costs: the disk itself, the copying, the postage, maybe the admin expenses involved in processing orders.

You cannot expect too much from such programs. Some just do not work, others are not worth using anyway. Some have illiterate documentation that actually prevents you using them; others are not documented at all. Some have special requirements in terms of hardware or additional software that are not mentioned. Many are US-specific.

But many are excellent. Besides, there are few more economical ways of adding to your software library.

There is also a related style of package available from the same sources — user groups, some magazines, bulletin boards — that *does* take a professional approach.

These are called 'shareware' packages. The authors may simply rely on your good nature — if you think the package is a Good Thing, you mail them a contribution.

Some vendors take a less amateur approach, and use shareware as a method of cutting their promotional costs; the package you acquire from a user group will be fully featured and it will be perfectly usable as it stands — but there will not be any documentation that indicates how to make the most of it. Alternatively, it may be an appetite-whetter for a more advanced successor.

Either way you are invited to register with the supplier and pay a cost more like commercial package prices (which is still likely to be under £100) to receive the full manual and/or the upgraded version.

The shareware business applies primarily to packages for MS-DOS computers. Under its umbrella are some excellent pieces of work — notably for communications (the likes of PROCOMM and TELIX), for file management (PC-FILE III is a true database management system for microcomputers), for word processors and spreadsheets, even for expert system shells and 'outline processors'.

Software can sell computers as well as any salesman; it is the *software* that fits what the user wants to do. That is especially true of a package called VisiCalc, which probably sold more Apple II computers than Apple Computer.

VisiCalc was the pioneer spreadsheeter. The so-called 'spreadsheet' packages have been so successful because they fulfil two of the prime criteria for ready-to-use software on small computers — they do something genuinely useful and they are genuinely quite easy to use.

A spreadsheet package (or a spreadsheet facility within a package) will set out a grid on the screen akin to the spreadsheet layouts used by bookkeepers and accountants: you can fill the grid with numbers and textual headings, and the package will perform calculations on them.

Spreadsheet by hand

In fact an electronic spreadsheet (or 'worksheet') is exactly analogous to the way most business planning and other repetitive calculation is done. You could rule several columns down a sheet of paper and give them headings — one per time period, say. The rows *across* would also have headings for the variables, such as cost items. Figures entered in the appropriate 'cells' of the grid could be used in calculations that produce results along the bottom (totals for each

month, perhaps) and in a right-hand column (totals for each item).

To do an alternative set of calculations with the headings and columns, a different set of figures could be entered and the same calculations repeated.

The computerized spreadsheet calculator provides exactly that — with greater speed, more flexibility, more completeness, probably better precision, and considerably more complexity, if that is required.

Classic uses for spreadsheet packages:

☐ Financial forecasting and business planning, with alternative scenarios being considered
☐ Detailed costing of business propositions
☐ Rate-of-return calculations
☐ Assessment of breakeven points
☐ Alternative pricing strategies
☐ Manpower assignment and other resource scheduling
☐ Calculating depreciation and loan write-off periods
☐ Profit-and-loss statements and balance sheets
☐ Preparation of budgets and comparison of actual performance against budgets

---

Building the worksheet

Into a cell of the worksheet on screen you can put:

☐ *Text* — titles, headings, notes (and you can define a 'format' for one cell or a group of cells such that the text is left- or right-justified, or centered; you can adjust the width of any row or column of cells to suit what you are entering)

☐ *Figures* (again, for one or more cells you can specify a variety of different formats — depending on the package your options could include integers only, decimals to a specified number of places, negative figures in brackets or with a minus sign, percentage signs, a preceding dollar or pound sign, and so on)

☐ *Formulas* that indicate how the value to go into that cell should be calculated (normally you will not see the formula itself on screen; as soon as you enter data, though, the results calculated by the formula will appear in the cell which has the formula attached to it)

	A	B	C	D	E
1					
2					
3	-----------	-----------	-----------	-----------	-----------
4	Units sold [000s]	70	75	80	85
5	Unit price	£125.00	£125.00	£125.00	£125.00
6					
7	Production cost	£27.00	£25.65	£24.37	£23.15
8	Sales cost	£62.00	£58.90	£55.96	£53.16
9					
10	Gross margin	£36.00	£40.45	£44.68	£48.69
11					
12	Sales value [000s]	£8,750.00	£9,375.00	£10,000.00	£10,625.00
13	Gross margin [000s]	£2,520.00	£3,033.75	£3,574.20	£4,138.96
14	Return on sales	28.80%	32.36%	35.74%	38.95%

Spreadsheet by computer

The most important attribute of the spreadsheet calculator is the way it can be set up *independently* of the entries you put into it. That applies to the size of cells, the heading text and — crucially — to the formulas that will automatically calculate the contents of a specific cell on the basis of data entered elsewhere in the worksheet.

A crude example: one such formula for a particular cell might be 'sum the numbers in a column and enter the result here'.

This means the data on the sheet is easily altered, replaced or deleted; and all the affected values are recalculated automatically using the same rules and formulas that you had applied to a previous set of calculations, but with different sets of information — in particular to answer 'what if' questions.

To illustrate this, take the simple spreadsheet in the examples which investigates some of the effects on profitability of reducing costs and increasing sales. It includes a number of formulas:

□ *Units sold (000s)*. Cell C4 automatically adds 5000 units to whatever is entered in B4, and this effect is repeated for D4 and E4.
□ *Unit price* does not change, but the value in B5 is automatically repeated for C5 to E5.
□ *Production cost* progressively reduces by 5 per cent from the value in B7.
□ *Sales cost* similarly reduces by 5 per cent from B8.
□ *Gross margin*. The value in B10 is calculated as B5 minus B7 and B8, and this is repeated for C10 to E10.
□ *Sales value (000s)* is calculated by multiplying the unit price by units sold.

□ *Gross margin (000s)* is gross margin per unit multiplied by units sold.
□ *Return on sales* is gross margin divided by sales value and expressed as a percentage.

Once this spreadsheet is set up, you only have to enter four figures — for B4, B5, B7 and B8 — for the 'what if' calculation to be done.

Presentation

The simplest output options are to print the worksheet without the row and column numbering, which makes it more legible for presentation purposes, and to save the worksheet on disk rather than printing it, which means it could subsequently be read as a straight text file for formatting or inclusion in some other document by using a word processor or desktop publisher. Most spreadsheet packages also have a variety of output options that convert the worksheet into a coded format which can be read by other packages — so the data can be entered automatically into a file manager, an accounts package or a graphics formatter.

Nearly all spreadsheet packages have a limited graphics capability built in, typically an option to replace actual numbers with a bar of asterisks at specified points in the spreadsheets to give a crude means of instant comparison. Several examples of the current crop of packages can produce more sophisticated graphs — pie charts, histograms, line graphs, and the like. There is a genre of graphics package which run separately, taking spreadsheet data and producing presentation-quality graphics; more about this in the chapter following.

Formula functions

Functions vary from one package to another, but this selection indicates the range of possibilities.

ARITHMETIC

INT	integer value of reference given
ABS	absolute value
EXP	exponent to the base e
LN	natural log
SQRT	square root

STATISTICS

AVERAGE	mean average of range given
COUNT	number of entries in range given
SUM	sum of values in range given
MAX	maximum value in range given
MIN	minimum value in range given
STD	standard deviation in range given
VAR	variance in range given

TRIGONOMETRY

COS	cosine of value given
SIN	sine
TAN	tangent
ACOS	arc cosine
ASIN	arc sine
ATAN	arc tangent (2 quadrants)
ATAN2	arc tangent (4 quadrants)
PI	pi to 11 decimal places

CALENDAR

TODAY	enters today's date
DAY	day value of specified date (1-31)
WDAY	weekday value of specified date (1-7)
MONTH	month value of specified date (1-12)
YEAR	year of specified date (in four digits)

FINANCIAL

ANRATE	annuity rate for specified start value over given term
ANTERM	annuity term
PMT	annuity payments
PV	present annuity value
BALANCE	remaining annuity balance
KINT	annuity interest in period
KPRIN	annuity principal in period
PAIDINT	total interest paid in period
CTERM	time to reach specified future value of investment at given rate
COMPBAL	compound balance of investment
RATE	periodic interest rate for investments
FV	future value of investment
IRR	internal rate of return
NPV	net present value
TERM	period to achieve specified future value
SLN	straight-line depreciation
DDB	double declining balance over specified period

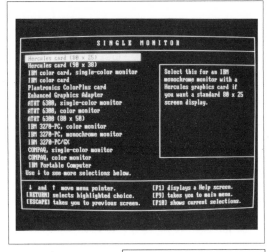

Market leader: Lotus 1-2-3

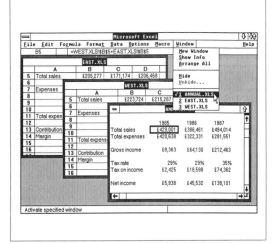

Windows on Microsoft's Excel

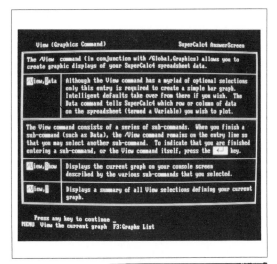

Output options in SuperCalc 4

Safer spreadsheets

Spreadsheets illustrate the computer's ability to get more work done faster and in a cleverer fashion. The wide use of spreadsheets among business executives highlights the corollary: the computer also creates the opportunity to make more mistakes and to multiply them more rapidly.

Spreadsheets also illustrate one of the key problems with personal computing — the fact that it *is* personal often means that no-one else can understand how a spreadsheet works (and often the spreadsheet user cannot understand his or her own work of a few weeks ago).

Informal sharing of spreadsheet 'templates' and ill-conceived adaptations exemplify the lack of standardization and control. Errors can creep into calculations; adapting someone else's template propagates the errors.

Any serious use of spreadsheets should be subject to sensible control procedures.

Management

Plan ahead. As with many desktop computer applications, there's a tendency to jump straight in — switch on the computer, load the spreadsheet package, start entering data, add the formulas and headings later. Immediacy is one advantage of microcomputers over larger machines; and that also applies to spreadsheeting by comparison with 'true' financial modelling. But it still makes sense to think ahead, to map out at least the row and column headings and the calculations before you start entering data. At the very least, this will save you having to insert or move too much information later — those changes can really mess up formula calculations.

Match existing practice as closely as possible. Provided the existing forms and report layouts are adequate, your computerized version should follow them as closely as the spreadsheet will allow. This will help with data entry, and the printed end-results will be more immediately comprehensible to the recipients. At the very least you should utilize the same headings (expanded if necessary) and the same general order in which information is presented.

Audit critical spreadsheets. Check the data sources, the formulas and the results. At the very least, this means adequate (more is better than less) explanation and comment for all cells containing any formula whose function and operation are not immediately obvious. Any key spreadsheet should be accompanied by an annotated printout of cell contents — with Lotus 1-2-3's /Print Options Other Cell-formulas command, for example, or SuperCalc's /Output Contents option. It also makes sense to use one of the purpose-designed spreadsheet auditing packages; these can highlight inconsistencies and possible errors.

Identification

Identify the spreadsheet. In cell A1 you should always have a line of text stating as clearly as possible what the model actually is.

Identify the responsible parties. All spreadsheets should carry a text note saying who actually produced it; and there might also be a note of who has amended it subsequently.

Date the spreadsheet. That means including the original date of creation, the dates for any amendment, and probably the date of the last recalculation; date functions in most decent spreadsheets allow you to do this automatically. It makes sense to combine dates and names in an 'amendment record' somewhere in a spare corner of the worksheet.

Identify the spreadsheet's users. If the spreadsheet is passed on to someone else for consolidation, indicate the destination and the date.

Explanation

Annotate the spreadsheet. Sensible use of titles and headings will help the author and anyone else understand exactly what is going on, but unless there is absolutely no room left it also makes sense to include notes about what a particular formula means and how it is assembled — spreadsheet formulas can look pretty cryptic to the uninitiated, and while it may have been clear to you at the time you might well have forgotten precisely how you had decided the spreadsheet should arrive at that particular figure. Comments like this can often be 'hidden' or placed well out of the way so that they would not be printed when the figures are produced in hardcopy form.

Standardize on spreadsheet layout. For instance, you might always reserve the top 20 rows for identification and amendment records; column A, set to a decent width, could always contain explanatory narrative for the formulas in particular cells.

Spreadsheeting

Do not SUM from first to last. If you want to add up the entries in cells D6 to D9, the obvious method is SUM(D6:D9). However, subsequently adding a row at D6 means the SUM will not now be accurate — the formula will have changed to SUM(D7:D10) after the /Insert Row command. The solution is to include something like a repeating rule above and below the values to be added:

```
            |   D   |
   4          SALES
   5        ---------
   6         12663.55
   7          1039.60
   8         37173.11
   9           450.00
  10        ---------
```

Now D11 can contain the formula SUM(D5:D10), and the result will still be an accurate adding-up of the values — text like repeating dashes is not counted in the SUM. You will be able to add subsequent rows anywhere within the rules, and the SUM will accommodate the new entries.

This also applies to SUMming rows. Put a delimiter mark of some kind in the cells on either side of the values, and have your SUM adding up everything inside the marked area — including the marker text. Then you can safely add extra columns within the SUM range.

The same procedure can be used for several other functions, including COUNT and AVERAGE.

Write the formulas before entering data. That way you can test the worksheet with dummy data to check formulas before you commit yourself to entering any values. To pick a simple example, you can test a row or column SUM by entering '1' in each cell; if you have 10 cells, obviously the SUM should produce '10'.

Use column widths to verify results. In some cases, you can set a column width to provide an instant check. For example, if the largest number you should get from a calculation is 999.99, set that column's width to seven characters and make sure it is formatted for no more than two decimal places. With most spreadsheet packages, any number larger than 999.99 will appear as a row of asterisks or less-than signs in that cell when you recalculate. You might have to do some dummy runs to find out the maximum column width for a particular number with decimal places, percentage signs, commas, currency symbols and the like.

Cross-check formulas. As a general rule it makes sense to provide cross-foot totalling whenever you can. It may be the case that you SUM a series of rows and then calculate a Grand Total by adding up the SUMs in that column. If you also SUM each of the data columns, you can cross-check by adding up the row containing the crossfoot totals.

Use manual recalculation. It is much quicker than having the spreadsheet recalculate automatically after each amendment. Include a note at the top of the spreadsheet warning other users that manual recalculation is required when any alteration is done; or reset the spreadsheet to automatic recalculation before you save it and distribute it.

Use names for key data and formulas. Most up-to-date spreadsheets allow this; it reduces the risk of your inadvertently referencing the wrong cell. Specify 'absolute' cell references for key data, too; a form like SuperCalc's G11, for instance, means you will not get any unwanted 'adjustment' of cell G11 when you use /Copy or /Replicate.

Last words

Buy more memory. If you are keeping your spreadsheets short and cryptic to fit them into 256KB, consider shelling out on an upgrade. You'll be able to run larger spreadsheets and you'll have more space for explanatory text.

Buy an updated version of the spreadsheet package. If the spreadsheet software was a free gift from a kind friend in 1983, consider an upgrade. You'll get more functions, a better manual, and — most important — more ways to validate the work.

Consider a formal statement of procedures. A number of firms have introduced standards for documentation and operation that detail and enforce rules like these.

Checklist: spreadsheets

Size of the worksheet

A business forecast can take a lot of rows and columns. Avoid spreadsheet packages with restricted worksheet sizes; 256 square is the least you should consider.

Speed

On the other hand, the larger your spreadsheet the slower it will take to 'recalculate' when data is altered (even if only a single figure has been changed — most packages seem to check *every* block to see whether it needs to be recalculated). Time the recalculation speed; check the speed of moving and copying groups of entries, too, and the speed with which the cursor can be moved around the worksheet.

Commands

Most spreadsheets offer the same basic 20 or so commands. Some have many more options: potentially useful are 'cut-and-paste' moves (of a specified rectangular area rather than a single row or column), presentation options (like currency signs, commas in numbers, negatives in brackets), a search-and-replace facility and calendar functions that automatically calculate and enter dates and time periods. More sophisticated extras would include risk analysis (showing the critical elements of a business plan) and goal-seeking (how inputs have to alter to produce a given result).

Lotus-compatibility

Lotus 1-2-3 is by no means the last word in spreadsheet packages, but it still dominates the market in IBM-compatible spreadsheets. Because of this, there is a wide range of facilities available as add-on packages (for auditing, graphics, extended calculation, even word processing), there are numerous courses and books that teach 1-2-3 in basic and advanced forms, results output from 1-2-3 are the norm for input to business graphics packages, and the scale of the package's market penetration makes it likely that any

template you are invited to use has been produced by 1-2-3. This does not mean that only 1-2-3 should be considered, but any spreadsheet for use on IBM-compatibles should have a degree of compatibility with the procedures of 1-2-3 and should be able to load and use spreadsheets produced by 1-2-3.

Linking spreadsheets and 'consolidation'

Most people prefer to work with multiple spreadsheets that are related by some common data, rather than have to create a single large spreadsheet. Can the package link worksheets in this way?

Macros

Most spreadsheets include some macro-writing capability that allows the user to set up a sequence of commands and subsequently execute them by one or two keystrokes; the contents of the macro duplicate the effect of typing individual commands one by one. There is wide variation in how easy it is to create macros and the extent of programming-like facilities that may be included (GOTO commands to switch execution to another part of the macro, for example).

Links to other packages

Can the spreadsheet take information easily from other packages such as file managers? Can the results be passed to a word processor for incorporation into reports, proposals, and the like? Can they be passed on to a graphics package to produce figures and graphs for presentation purposes?

Printing

How easy is it to set up printout options — suppressing row and column identifiers, adding headers and other titling, automatically putting overruns on to a second sheet, etc.? How much control does the package have over the different functions provided on particular printers? Will your printer be able to work with the spreadsheet software?

If there is a key to effective management, it is the availability and use of relevant, timely information. As one manager expressed it, 'A surfeit of *data*, but a lack of *information* — that is the paradox of many management information systems'. The cliché about a picture being worth a thousand words may be overoptimistic, but anyone who has been invited to 'glance over this spreadsheet' to identify the principal conclusions will know the value of a summary in graphic form.

Such facilities may be provided within a problem-oriented package; modern spreadsheets like Logistix or SuperCalc 4 have the ability to take figures from a worksheet and present them in a variety of ways. Similarly, the 'integrated' packages will provide a means of moving data simply from another application into the 'graphics' component.

The transformation of data into graphic form can require some clever software, however, and added cleverness usually translates into more program code and possible inefficiencies in operation. Besides, not all users will need any or all of the graphics capabilities. So the variety and capability of such in-built facilities is likely to be restricted.

The market for presentation graphics has grown with the spread of personal computers and the availability of appropriate output devices. A new genre of special-purpose graphics packages has grown up in the last few years; these can read in data produced by another package and transform it into a visual message.

This 'stand-alone' solution is generally more elegant. The graphics presentation package does not have to fit into memory with a spreadsheet or anything else, so it can be as large and as clever as it needs to be. Because the software writers have only the one function in mind, their package can be customized for its role and fine-tuned for performance.

What happens

With most presentation graphics packages you can enter data directly from the keyboard. More likely, you will read in data already produced by other packages. Some have a ready-to-go graphics format which will need little extra work, such as Lotus 1-2-3 files with a .PIC suffix. Others have an 'export' format which does not include much graphics layout but which a graphics package will be able to read and convert into its own internal format — the CSV, DIF and SYLK options are quite widely offered by data-producing software.

Once you have the data, you can manipulate it. The basic aim is simply to improve the overall appearance. If it is raw data — lists of numbers — you will want to produce a graphic equivalent. The basic options are:

- *Line graphs*. Conventional enough, with a line moving through different points on an X-Y axis with, say, 'months' along the foot and something like 'units sold' up the side.

- *Bar graphs (histograms)*. Solid bars reaching up from the bottom — useful for comparing more than one entity on the same chart, such as sales per month in different regions.

- *Stacked-bar*. Similar, except that the different entities are shown in due proportion on the same bar.

- *Pie chart*. An excellent way of showing quickly how the different proportions of a total are made up. For emphasis, one or more slices of the pie can usually be 'exploded' — separated from the circle.

- *Hi-lo graphs*. Summarize different values on a single line. Typically these are used for share price movements; the X axis shows prices, the Y axis has dates, and the line charted includes points for opening, closing, high and low prices.

- *Flowcharts*. Indicate procedure sequences with options.

To these you will be able to add text in a variety of styles for titles and explanatory notes. More important, you will be able to add extra graphic effects:

- □ *Contrast*. You can select different shading or line styles to identify the separate elements of the figure.

- □ *Colours*. You can usually specify several dozen colours, both solid and in graduated tones. Usually they match the colour range of a particular video controller which may or may not be provided inside your computer (the IBM EGA or Olivetti EGC, for instance) and the colour capabilities of a specific output device (the Polaroid Palette can handle around 72). The result is a true what-you-see-is-what-you-get display on the screen ... provided you have the necessary hardware, the colour graphics controller and a suitable monitor.

- □ *Three-dimensional images* for pie charts and histograms, probably with shading on inside surfaces and maybe even with perspective.

- □ *Increased resolution* beyond that of the computer's own display, so that output will appear more precise if it is produced photographically.

- □ *Slideshows*. Some packages allow the user to build a sequence of displays mixing text and graphics with options for the viewer. That is especially useful for training applications, but it could also apply, for example, to sales presentations — a multiple-product sales pitch could quite easily be structured for an individual customer's requirements by the presenter on the spot.

Output

With some graphic packages the results can be filed on disk for use actually on the computer — typically as part of a demonstration or tutorial.

It is more likely, however, that the output will be required in some presentation format — in a paper document or as visual aids for a presentation.

The quality of output devices is a restricting factor. If you want text and graphics on the same page, as part of a report, for instance, a *daisywheel printer* will not be much use to you — preformed characters on the printwheel are fine for the words, but graphics would have to be built up crudely using punctuation marks.

Matrix printers build shapes by assembling a pattern of dots, and these days most such printers can produce both near-letter-quality text and dot-by-dot graphics. Because they produce dots, however, curves and circles inevitably appear to be notchy; they are not capable of sufficient resolution (the number of dots per inch that they can print) to give the illusion of a continuous curved line. The pins in the print head cannot strike the ribbon against the paper hard enough to produce a really dense image, and the dottiness plus the lightweight impact mean that solid areas in a graphic generally look pale and patchy at best.

At least you can now buy matrix printers with a colour option. Solids will still be less than perfect: you are limited to four or six colours with most such units: and shades of a colour are not possible.

Laser printers produce good-quality text, but as yet very few can produce colour: and they too use printing-by-dots, so curves will still appear rather notchy — at 300 dots per inch the image resolution is better than other matrix printers, but it is still not good enough. At least you can mix good-looking text and graphics on the same page, if your software can handle that. Most laser printers can also print on to acetate for overhead transparencies.

Plotters use pens to draw continuous lines, so the shapes produced are much better — nearly all plotters move the pen only in two planes (up/down, left/right) but the movements can be very fine and precise. Again, there is a problem with solid areas: drawing parallel and/or cross-hatched lines very close together does not really deliver an even, solid surface. Shades of a colour are out, of course. You're also restricted to the number of pens provided (typically between three and ten); and swapping pens to get more colours can be tedious. Plotters are usually very slow, and are not very good at mixing text with graphics.

The best compromise at present is probably the laser printer for monochrome reports mixing text and graphics: a colour matrix printer for acceptable print quality on text plus colour graphics: and a colour plotter for producing overhead transparencies.

The only real option beyond that is the photographic *image processor*. Most of the packages that produce graphics in addition to their main function will assume that you'll be working with the best possible resolution produced by your computer's display, and they translate this into the best possible resolution that your chosen output device can handle.

The purpose-designed presentation graphics software increases the theoretical resolution of the image you want to print: the screen will not be capable of showing them, but in fact the end result will include many more dots than you can see.

That is because the best quality for presentation graphics comes from photography, and such packages assume that you'll be producing 35mm slides as the end result. Typically these will be done on a plug-in image processor unit that can take output from the computer, process it via a camera mechanism, and produce 35mm slides or OHP transparencies. The best-known such device is probably the Polaroid Palette image recorder, a pricey cable-connected box which in essence includes a camera that photographs the assembled image and gives you a roll of film from which colour positives can be processed and printed for mounting as slides.

The results are of course excellent, with all the precision and colour options available in a camera and a resolution many times greater than anything the conventional computer-industry output devices can manage.

There are drawbacks, though:

☐ *Cost*. The image processors themselves are not cheap (though prices are falling as the market expands) and the consumables involved can be expensive (especially as a number of retries may be needed before the results meet expectations).

☐ *Production time*. If the processor includes a photo developer, you might expect half a dozen completed slides per hour. Otherwise you'll get a developed reel of 35mm for processing and printing by a photo lab — which could add hours or days to the production timescales.

☐ *Duplication*. A 35mm slide may not convert easily into a text equivalent for incorporation into any accompanying paper documentation.

There are, however, a number of specialist slide-processing bureaux in major metropolitan areas that can offer fast turnaround on small orders.

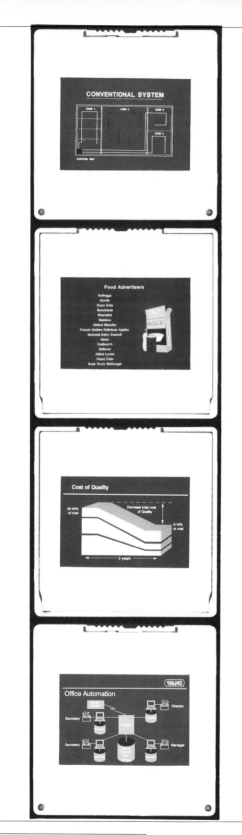

Slides from computer output

Simplicity

No special design ability should be required to assemble a presentation screen; look for pop-up menus to select existing images and components, text, colours and 'icons' (predrawn graphic symbols).

Capability

Will the presentation package be able to handle everything you want to say on a particular picture — enough different values on one graph line, for example, and enough different lines on the graph? Will it handle 'best fit' curves as well as straight line? Can the package be used with simple text to produce point-by-point summary lists for presentation slides or overheads?

Presentation options

Look for a good range of picture options — not only different types of graph, but also different effects that can be applied to the images to make them more meaningful. (Be wary though of the Parkinson effect — just because the facilities are there does not mean you *have* to use them each and every time. As with word processing and desktop publishing, the legibility and impact of a picture decreases in direct proportion to the number of presentation facilities used in it.)

Input

Will existing packages be able to work with the graphics software — preferably passing over data that will not require too much extra work?

Output

What options are available? Can you justify the cost? Will existing equipment be able to work with the graphics software?

Resolution

Does the package improve the resolution of the output beyond what you would normally get from your computer's display? Some IBM-compatible packages produce slides with the standard 640x400 resolution of the screen, which could mean that the slides produced are not good enough for top-quality presentation.

Spreadsheet calculators can be quite sophisticated. But they are restricted by their capacity and by the 'what you see is what you get' approach; many business problems cannot adequately be expressed within a spreadsheet.

Spreadsheets are appropriate when some or all of the following criteria are met:

- Rapidly changing data has to be processed.
- Immediate results are required (with a financial modelling package the process of creating a model, executing it and preparing formatted output can be time-consuming and laborious).
- Limited amounts of data are involved.
- Non-technical users have to create and use the model.
- Relatively small problems have to be processed.
- The problems involve relationships between individual cells rather than whole rows or lines.

A 'modelling' package is capable of what its vendors would like to characterize as 'true' financial planning. The essential feature of such packages is the way you have to define what you want to do before you can do it. With a spreadsheet you can just put the working grid on the screen and start using it; a modelling package is much more like a programming language — you have to start with some thinking and then give the computer a series of commands which tell it what is going to happen. You do not have to 'run' the 'program' right away, but when you do initiate it that is the point at which data is entered.

Instead of filling boxes on the display, you may well not get a visible worksheet at all: the model may work in terms of rows and columns, but to put something into them you'll probably just be entering figures in response to the questions the program is asking you — those questions having been previously determined by you in the 'programming' process.

Financial modelling packages score in these circumstances:

- Large amounts of data are involved, particularly for consolidation of separate business results (using 'consolidation' here as an accountancy term).
- Complex models are required, with more than one programmer having to understand the logic.
- Regularly-used applications in a standardized format are called for.
- Sophisticated functions are required, where the number and type of operations you want to perform on that data goes beyond the capabilities provided in a spreadsheet package (contemporary spreadsheets can, however, match most of the in-built capabilities of modelling packages, albeit in a usually more laborious manner).
- The end user is not expected to create the model.
- Different end users have to use the model.
- Problems involve relationships between larger blocks of data than individual cells.
- Control and standardization can be applied to the procedures of creating models.
- A degree of control and standardization is required from the results of modelling.

Creating models

All the work goes into the design and creation phase. Once the model is created, it can be used by anyone — typically, when the model is 'run', the user will merely be invited to enter data into specific boxes on the screen: the program will then execute the model on the basis on that input and produce the results.

Most modelling packages work with a grid-like matrix set up with rows and columns, just like a spreadsheet; but you can usually refer to the rows and columns by names you have assigned to them — 'UK sales' for a row, for instance, and '1988' for a column. So an individual 'cell' entry for UK sales in that year could be identified in the 'programming' phase as UK SALES, 1988.

```
             PROFIT PROJECTION
         assuming 15% sales increase

                        1986          1987

  PRICE               150.00        150.00
  UNITS             1,000.00      1,150.00
  SALES           150,000.00    172,500.00
  COST PER UNIT        93.00         93.00
  COST OF SALES    93,000.00    106,950.00
  GROSS MARGIN     57,000.00     65,550.00
```

This simple report could have been produced either by a spreadsheet or by a modelling package. This might have been the spreadsheet template:

```
Cell    Content

A1      PROFIT PROJECTION
A2      assuming 15% sales increase
A3      (blank)
A4      (blank)
A5      PRICE
A6      UNITS
A7      SALES
A8      COST PER UNIT
A9      COST OF SALES
A10     GROSS MARGIN

B1      (blank)
B2      (blank)
B3      (blank)
B4      1986
B5      150
B6      1000
B7      B5*B6
B8      93
B9      B6*B8
B10     B7-B9

C1      (blank)
C2      (blank)
C3      (blank)
C4      1987
C5      +B5
C6      B6*1.15
C7      C5*C6
C8      +B8
C9      C6*C8
C10     C7-C9
```

The equivalent from a modeller could look something like this:

```
\ PROFIT PROJECTION
\ assuming 15% sales increase
columns 1986 thru 1987
PRICE = 150
UNITS = 1,000, previous * 1.15
SALES = PRICE * UNITS
COST PER UNIT = 93
COST OF SALES = COST PER UNIT * UNITS
GROSS MARGIN = SALES — COST OF SALES
```

From the user's viewpoint, the key difference between spreadsheets and financial modellers is the way the logic of the model is set up *outside* the worksheet. In other words, modelling packages store data *separately* from formulas; the spreadsheet keeps its data *and* its formulas *within* the model.

This means that the modelling package can produce larger and more complex models — it is limited in capacity only by the size of the available disk space. It is also more comprehensible, an important advantage with complicated models.

Commands

To some extent the principles will be familiar to the spreadsheet user. The basics of 'programming' will also be recognizable; individual entries might take the form of PROFIT = ROW1-ROW2, which is not dissimilar to a spreadsheet formula.

The modeller's command language will have its own syntax, which means the user has to learn a few more rules than for spreadsheets about how things are expressed, and the language will include a variety of special-purpose commands and functions that a programmer would recognize (loops, IF/THEN/ELSE expressions, conditional jumps, maybe even line numbers) as well as others familiar to financial management.

On the other hand, the commands and most of the syntax rules will be familiar to non-computerate users too. Most of them will be in plain English, some are in business terminology (such as INTEREST, DCF, PAYBACK, TAX), others will be instantly recognizable for what they do — GRAPH, TITLE, HEADINGS, for instance.

The commands allow you to define the three key aspects of the model — *data entry* (how it is entered, where it comes from, in what format it should be used), *calculation* (with a very wide range of formulas and functions that you can apply to the data) and *output* (with most modelling packages fully half the commands refer to how the results should be produced).

Data input

The basic data can often be taken from a variety of sources apart from the keyboard — including files created by other packages like word processors, accounts systems, databases, spreadsheets and indeed other models.

The command language will allow you to define menus for data entry along with prompts, both helping to guide and simplify the task. Thus you could set up a model for use by clerical staff as well as management. Verification checks can be done on anything entered to ensure that it fits what the model expects to receive.

Calculation

The model will allow multiple sets of data to be filed for use with a single 'program' of commands, so many different 'cases' can be set up, tested and stored for future use.

The actual calculation facilities will include:

☐ *Consolidation* of figures for a hierarchy of departments and subsidiaries, often with automatic currency translation for multinational operations and proportional consolidation for part-owned activities.

This is one of the key features of true modelling packages, where their capabilities will greatly exceed anything even remotely similar in plain-vanilla spreadsheets.

☐ *Conditional processing* and *control over the order of evaluation*. Modellers can include program 'loops' and conditional 'go to' commands that decide precisely what will be done; spreadsheets provide only a very limited range of 'IF/THEN' facilities.

☐ *Risk analysis* (or 'sensitivity analysis') is another key feature that few spreadsheets can provide, measuring changes in results from different combinations of variations in the input data to highlight crucial factors.

☐ *Goal-seeking* (sometimes called 'reverse calculation') is the other facility omitted from most spreadsheets, indicating what input data will be required in getting to an optimal solution.

The *capacity* of the model will be substantially larger than the spreadsheet, since it does not all have to be in memory or on the screen at the same time: the largest spreadsheets tend to be restricted to something just over 65 000 cells at maximum; most modelling packages can do double that.

Output

The results of a modelling exercise can generally be presented in a variety of graph, text or spreadsheet-grid styles. Reports are automatic on command, since you use the 'programming language' to predefine what you want — and indeed to define what options you may want.

Most contemporary modelling packages can also output in a file format that a presentation graphics package or a word processor can use.

At its most basic, a file manager is a program (or a facility within a package) that allows a user to set up a format for records in an individual file — and to set up different formats for different files.

Information can then be entered into those blank record formats. Subsequently the user can pick out selected records or selected items from records, including summaries of all or part of the file. The file manager will also include facilities that determine just how such reports and summaries are to be presented on the page.

One of the attractions of the filing packages is that the principles involved are so familiar. Everyone knows what a 'file' is: it's a collection of related information. Files consist of 'records', which are fairly obviously individual items of a like nature that will be complete in themselves — holding all the relevant information in a form that allows comparison with the same kind of information held in other records in the same file.

Computerized files are not quite analogous to the office filing cabinet, though. In one of those folders or suspension files can be placed any kind of information that you regard as relevant to the name on the file — documents, correspondence, photographs, bills, newspaper cuttings. The computerized system requires you to set up a much more rigid format for records, and in practice each of the file entries therefore has to look much the same.

A better analogy is with a card index, where the file consists of a bunch of individual cards each containing information in more or less the same layout — but with the scope to add information that does not fit the rigid headings that have been laid down.

Types of filing system

The nature of the information to be stored and the way it is used will largely determine the type of file manager that is appropriate:

□ *'Flat-file' systems.* The simplest kind of file manager contains records that have the same form and content. A crude example is the kind of 'address book' facility provided on many desktop computers; all records will have entries for name, address, phone number and other information. More sophisticated but still economical approaches, where the user designs the record format, are called 'flat-file' systems. These are the closest analogy to card index filing.

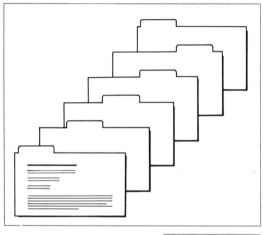

Flat-file system

□ *Master/slave systems* — sometimes called *transaction* filing systems — provide for 'one-to-many' relationships, where the number of items of information per record is less easy to predict. A 'master' record can be linked to one or more subsidiary 'slave' records. An example: a marketing information system might have Master records for individual countries that represent export targets. Linked to that are a number of subsidiary records for national statistics, competitors' activities and sales promotions there.

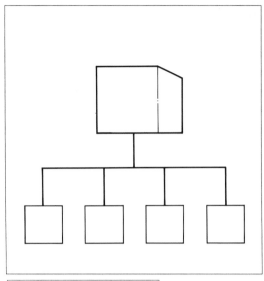

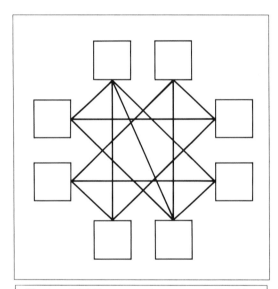

The true DBMS — many-to-many relationships

□ *Database management systems*. A full-scale DBMS represents the top level of capability, allowing any record to be linked to any other. Different types of information are set up in different types of file and record format, and each record will have an associated index of some kind that links it to other records in other files. Each record in the 'database' — which for practical purposes can be defined as a group

of files — may have links *to* any other record, and it may be used *by* one or more records. Such complex systems are said to provide for 'many-to-many relationships', and clearly require a systematic and probably highly technical approach to their design.

Filing system pros and cons

In short, filing packages are very flexible ways of handling the kind of information that you can keep in files. They do impose some strictures, of course — particularly at their most limiting, in 'flat-file' cardbox-type approaches:

□ There is normally a restriction on the number of headings ('fields') that a record format can have (*files* consist of *records*, *records* consist of *fields*).

□ There will probably be a limit on the amount of information that can be entered in each field.

□ Most flat-file packages have a maximum number of records per file (though in many cases it is limited only by disk capacity and with some a file can spread across more than one disk).

□ Many packages also put a limit on the amount of information that can be held in any one record.

□ For user-designed records, there is some stress on getting the record format correct right from the start; you generally have to specify the format in considerable detail — how many characters per field, which fields may be used for 'sort and select' tasks, etc. Once you start entering the information it is often very difficult or impossible to change the layout.

□ There may be a restriction on the number of fields per record that can be used for sorting and selection (these are often called 'key' or 'index' fields).

Setting up records

For a start, the package will enable the user to set up records, probably in a self-designed format. (A key side-effect of this somewhat obvious point is the way the computerized system will impose order on record-keeping.)

Some of the data entry may be automated if the package provides appropriate facilities — *today's date* is often inserted without having to type it, the content of the same field in the last record entered may be *duplicated* to save on typing (creating an address book of similar contacts might involve a lot of names in the same town, for instance), field entries can be *calculated automatically* from information elsewhere ('date of next sales call' could be today's date plus 30 days).

A sorting sequence may be predefined. Irrespective of the order in which records are entered, the file will automatically be arranged to the user's specification of a key field — alphabetically, by date, in ascending or descending order for a filing reference field, and so on.

Most file managers require that all records are identical in format and of the same length. Those packages more properly called 'database management systems' may allow you more than one type of record in your files, however.

Maintaining files

New records can be added as they arise: when information changes, existing records can be amended simply, quickly, accurately and *rigorously*.

Searching

To select a particular record for display or printing, the package will allow a user to search through a file on the basis of the contents of one or more fields. Most packages require the user to nominate these key or index fields during setup; some allow searching on any field.

Such searches can usually be 'conditional' — the user can select the record by specifying that a field must be the same as the search 'criteria', not equal to the criteria, or less than or greater than the criteria. Multiple conditions may be possible, for instance permitting a selection like 'find all records for sales of thermocouples to the Middle East later than 1 January 1985 that came from the Brighouse facility and were not shipped by air'.

Sorting

The records might be stored alphabetically by name: for particular uses, you might want them sorted into another sequence on the basis of a key field. Sorting can obviously be combined with selection to pick specified records.

Report formats

When one or more records have been located, the package will probably let you view it on screen, print it or save it as a disk file. Alternative formats or 'templates' may be specified for these; the original layout need not necessarily be the way the record is normally seen.

Browsing

Once a record has been located, the user may be able to skip on to the next or go back to the previous one. 'Next' might mean the next record originally entered, the next record selected after a search, the next record in the predefined sequence or the next record that appears after the user has told the package to re-sort all or part of the file.

Stored 'macro' routines

Some combinations of search criteria and arithmetic processes may be used frequently. Many packages allow you to predefine these and store them separately, usually by mimicking the keystrokes that would otherwise be employed but often as quite complex miniprograms that might also cover the whole data entry or output procedure.

Links to word processing

A number of filing packages have a simple word processing facility built in, typically another option now being encountered more frequently. A couple of packages have this built in, with all the facilities you would expect from a word processing package — plus the ability automatically to insert into your text selected parts of the records in a particular file. Most packages can also output in a format that can be read directly by popular examples of word processors and DTP packages, presentation graphics facilities and spreadsheets.

Checklist: file management packages

How much information?

Can the package cope with all the information you want it to hold? What limit is there on the number of records and the size of each record? Will it all fit on to your disks? How many different fields per record? Is there a limitation on the number of characters you can have in one field?

How complex?

'Flat-file' card indexes are the simplest kind of file, but sometimes you will need cross-referencing between different files — a stock control system, for instance, could involve links between a stock item file and a separate supplier file. Do you need this? If yes, can the package handle it?

What kind of searching and sorting?

Typically you will want to find a particular record by referencing the main subject on it, the supplier's name, for example. But you might want to pick it out by using some kind of subsidiary information which does not happen to be at the top of the record layout. Do you need to be able to select particular records on the basis of what is on different lines or fields? Can you have multiple search conditions and multiple fields in one search?

Sorting

If records are stored alphabetically by name, can you re-sort them — say into a 'date of last order' sequence, or by postcode, or whatever?

Calculation

If you have numbers in your record format, you might want to perform arithmetic calculations when you produce reports — to get a total stock valuation of an inventory file, for instance (it is possible to use many filing packages to set up business accounting systems rather than buy a ready-to-use package). Some packages do not even provide basic four-function arithmetic. Can dates be calculated? Can you apply formulas like percentages, exponentiation and other fancy maths on specific fields?

Stored routines

Some combinations of search criteria and arithmetic processes may be used frequently. Can you predefine these and store them, so that you can call up the sorting parameters simply and quickly or insert a standard formula easily into records or reports whenever it is needed? Is this done simply by mirroring keystrokes or is there a more powerful 'command language'? In the latter case, how easy is the language to understand and use?

Output

Can different output formats or templates be set up for different purposes? Most packages will have some options already provided — a label format for name-and-address lists, for instance. The layout of such output formats should be quite independent of the way the records themselves look, and not all of the information in the records need be included.

Links to other packages

Can you sort and select records and then output them in an appropriate format for direct use by other packages?

'Word processing' is about using a computer to create, store, revise and print text. In practice there are four elements to this, and they can be treated as separate operations:

☐ *Origination* — creating or retrieving a document
☐ *Amendment* and correction ('text editing'
☐ *Printing* and delivery
☐ *Filing* of copies on disk or in paper form

A document of some kind is typed at the computer or retrieved from an existing disk file; subsequently it is revised with new material added, mistakes corrected, some sections shifted around.

Before printing, the text will be fitted into a particular format (tabs, indents and the like) — which can normally be predefined quite separately from the text itself and called up for use with specified documents. Other formatting considerations would include the use of underlining, bold-face and other 'attributes'.

One of the important operational aspects of WP — particularly by comparison with typewriting — is the separation of editing, media handling and printing. This should result in more productivity, simply because the job no longer has to be done in the sequence and at the time dictated by the constraints of the machine.

Since users do not have to commit themselves to a final version for printing until they are satisfied, the quality of the document should be improved. There will be less temptation to compromise and leave in ugly phrases or minor errors.

The facilities provided in WP systems tend to be similar. But their implementation can vary considerably. Modern word processors utilize windows, single-key commands and drop-down option menus to good effect; a mouse may also be available, though for most WP operations (apart perhaps from pre-print text formatting) the keyboard is preferred.

A major difference, however, comes in their approach to the screen. From that viewpoint, word processors fall broadly into two categories:

☐ *WYSIWYG* — pronounced 'wizziwig' and meaning 'what you see is what you get'. The display approximates as closely as possible to the printed output. In particular, line endings and page breaks will be seen on the screen. Headers and footers, pagination and page-numbering will also be there.
☐ *Format-on-print*. While text is being edited, it bears no relation to how it will appear. Text appears with no breaks corresponding to the end of one printed page and the start of another; the display area fills with text across the available line width until the Return key is pressed.

WYSIWYG obviously shows the user more or less how the printed output will look (though few displays can show font changes, proportional spacing and the like) and how long it will be. It is also better suited to those used to rigidly-formatted documents — typists, for instance, tend to view their task in terms of the finished sheet.

Separating the editing from printing makes better sense for authors who do not have the same background in formatted documents — report-writers, for example, do not normally think in terms of how the output will look until the editing is complete.

WYSIWYG can actually be confusing and intimidating for such tasks. That also applies when the printing options are considerably more sophisticated than anything that the screen can display; laser printers can produce rules, boxed and shaded areas, variations in typestyles and sizes.

The format-on-print approach certainly appears preferable when the print formatting is actually being handled by another package like a desktop publisher.

Spelling checkers

Spelling checkers can be useful on large documents, when the author is a poor speller or when standardization for 'house style' requires a choice from alternative spellings.

Some word processors come with a built-in spelling checker or there are add-on packages to do the same job. They do not actually check spelling; they just compare a piece of text against a word-list. Words they do not recognize are picked out. These might be misspellings, or they could be valid terms not in the lexicon:

☐ Technical or esoteric terms
☐ Proper nouns such as names of people or towns
☐ Terms specific to an individual business
☐ Idiomatic words that are acceptable
☐ English spellings (many packages from the States retain a US bias)
☐ Plurals or participles the software authors did not bother to include

When a possible misspelling is detected, the user can normally change the errant word or elect to add a correct term to the main 'dictionary'. Alternatively, there will probably be options to add it to one or more supplementary dictionaries specific to a particular usage — such that the word will not subsequently be highlighted again if it is being used in an appropriate working context.

The more advanced spelling checkers will also look for duplicated words, a common typing error for authors who 'think at the keyboard'.

Text editing functions

Insertion may be done by the word processor splitting the displayed text at the cursor position and closing it back after the new characters have been added. Alternatively, the shape of the cursor will change and any characters typed will be inserted so as to push the rest of the text on the line towards the right-hand edge.

Block insertion for a chunk of text can be done by moving the text from elsewhere in the document and placing it at the cursor position (this is sometimes called 'copy' or 'hold' and 'unhold', both of which are commendably self-explanatory). Or information can be read into the text from an existing disk file. Either way, it is useful to have a window facility to pick up exactly the right amount of text.

Deletion can be done in several ways — by using a single key to delete characters under the cursor or immediately to its left (text on the other side shuffles leftwards to close up the gap), by using control key combinations or function keys to delete whole lines, or by similar keystrokes to delete whole words, sentences or paragraphs at a time.

Block deletion commands allow you to erase a chunk of text by indicating the start and finish point for the deletion.

Search and replace functions will locate every occurrence of a specified string of characters to be replaced automatically with another (or possibly to be deleted). Word processors vary in just how literal the specification has to be — in particular, for case-sensitivity.

Abbreviations and standard paragraphs provide for frequently used phrases, forms and longer pieces of text to be stored for subsequent insertion into a document when an appropriate marker code is used — useful for the classic personalized mailshot (called 'mail-merge') or to avoid repetitive typing. This is sometimes called a 'glossary' facility. 'Boilerplating' or 'document creation' is the related capability of creating entire documents from standard text modules stored on disk.

Automatic pagination and page numbering is available with most word processors. The document is divided into pages of a user-specified length, with each one numbered; automatic renumbering will be done as necessary following any amendments.

Automatic insertion of headers and footers on pages can be done by most WP systems.

Automatic placement of footnotes is more rare, but clearly when footnotes are used it is important that they do appear at the bottom of the relevant page.

Proportional spacing gives different widths for different letters (provided the printer can handle that); for example, an 'm' takes more space than an 'i'. It makes long sections of text much easier to read, but virtually no screen is able to display text proportionally spaced.

Justification means a suitable printer can make all lines the same length by adjusting the gaps between words or between letters. Best used with proportional spacing for really good presentation, it is generally unnecessary for normal correspondence.

Forms with different layouts can be created, stored and called up as required. With some systems this also includes a fill-in-the-blanks field-to-field movement: completing one entry and pressing return automatically moves the cursor to the start of the next field.

Predefined formats (or 'document templates', 'style sheets' or something similar) for subsequent use with particular documents are normally set up via a question-and-answer approach. Format information will include a pattern of tab stops, margin settings and line widths, print styles (pitch and inter-line spacing), etc.

Arithmetic facilities may be provided — either as an instant-access additional function for *ad hoc* calculation or actually for figures entered in the text. Basic four-function arithmetic is the norm, but more sophisticated systems can hold subtotals and totals in memory for columnar work and do percentage calculations.

Decimal tab functions enable the user to align figures in columns around a decimal point to improve the presentation and legibility.

Column functions permit more than one column to be used, with text inserted, deleted and moved correctly within columns.

Index generation may be automatic — words that the author wants in the index to a long document are marked somehow in the text, and during printing the word processor adds them to a special alphabetically organized index file (complete with the correct page numbers) for subsequent output.

Table of contents may be produced automatically in a similar fashion, with designated chapter-heading text being added automatically to another file for subsequent printing. Again, page numbers may be assigned correctly.

Macros and *'learn' mode* can simplify and speed up word processing, enabling the effects of several keystrokes and commands to be 'learned' by the system and subsequently reproduced by just one or two keypresses.

Spelling checks provide for a degree of 'house style' standardization as well as correcting typing errors.

Information processing features (also called 'list processing' or 'file processing') enable a simple filing system to be set up for the word processor. This may cover creation of record formats, multiple selection criteria to pick out information, and the automatic merging of this with other text. The number of selection criteria is usually limited, however, and in any case most word processors can more effectively utilize information retrieved from a purpose-designed file management package.

How clean is the display?

Many of the formatting features in word processors have to be indicated by special codes on the screen, since they do not correspond to printable characters. How meaningful is the display? How legible is the text on the screen? Can the package indicate text that is both underlined and bold?

How many keystrokes?

One of the cardinal sins of any word processor is to slow down or disrupt the train of thought. Look for the minimum of interruption. Are multiple keystrokes and complicated command sequences required for the principal operations? Is there an 'UNDO' or 'OOPS' facility to correct an inadvertent deletion?

How fast? How big?

Does the package allow you to move quickly around text? How quick are block moves and inserts? Is there a restriction on the largest size of document you can have in memory at once? If yes, is this likely to affect you?

Standard paragraphs

You should be able to store frequently used phrases, forms and paragraphs for recall and insertion into a different piece of text; and you ought to be able to create whole new documents from standard text modules stored on disk. But how easy is it?

Mail-merge

This facility personalizes form letters with variable inserts automatically merged into a standard text. How easy is it? Can the variable matter come from other packages or must it be in the word processor's own format?

Handling numbers and tables

If you want to include numbers in text, look for the ability to insert, delete and move columns within text. Does the package allow a 'decimal tab' which automatically aligns figures around the decimal point? Do you get the option to do arithmetic within columns on the screen?

Tabs and rulers

A 'ruler' is the formatting information that in particular specifies tab (and indent) positions. How many can you store and call up? Can you automatically associate a particular ruler with a particular document? Can you use 'outline' tabs (indent the first line of a paragraph) and 'reverse indent' (indents all but the first line)?

Print facilities

Output formatting may be restricted, particularly by comparison with DTP packages. For example, very few word processors cater for 'widows' or 'orphan' lines, or prevent paragraphs or tables breaking over a page end.

Background printing

Does the package permit 'background' printing of one document while another is being edited or formatted on the screen?

Printer support

Different printers may have different capabilities and different ways of controlling them. Can the word processor handle the printer you want to use — and vice versa? Can you continue working on one document while something else is being printed?

'Undo'

A facility to cancel the most recent deletion or block copying can be very valuable.

Backing up

What kind of safety features are included? Most word processors do not delete the original if a document is saved with the same name; instead the first version is retained with a special 'backup' name. But is the user warned that the names are the same? And is there an *automatic* backup copy taken every so often of the text currently on the screen?

The cynic might be forgiven for dismissing desktop publishing as a typical West Coast hype — probably one designed to prove that the admittedly superb graphics of the Apple Macintosh, for which the desktop publishing genre was virtually created, must be good for *something* after the initial techno-gilt has worn off the gingerbread.

But while a good dose of cynicism is probably a healthy attitude in today's computer business, it is true that desktop publishing might be a real eye-opener as far as the end-user is concerned.

What is desktop publishing?

Desktop publishing basically means using a smallish computer to produce documents with an appearance and a print quality which approaches that of traditionally produced material that has been typeset and pasted on to camera-ready masters.

By comparison with the traditional approach, this is done in-house. The user pays no professional fees and does not have to wait for a print shop or typesetting bureau to schedule the work.

By contrast with the conventional approach of producing documents with a word processor on a daisywheel or matrix printer, DTP will produce a much higher quality with a greatly improved appearance.

DTP would not be feasible were it not for the enormous improvement in print quality made possible by relatively inexpensive laser printers.

Desktop publishing packages

There is a considerable range among programs that describe themselves as 'DTP systems'. Most are just print formatters that take material produced by word processors and let you manipulate it into the form you want; many cannot handle the typesetting-style facilities of a true desktop publishing system.

Since the essence of desktop publishing software lies in print formatting rather than text manipulation, a case exists for treating DTP simply as the treatment of words previously created by word processors.

This does put a lot of stress on the quality of the software involved, however: you need to

---

Some classic jobs for desktop publishing

There are many applications ripe for desktop publishing. The obvious jobs for a DTP system are those where the documents would benefit considerably from improved presentation:

- *User reference handbooks*, where clarity and comprehensibility are greatly improved by putting some effort into the presentation. Incorporating graphics, tabular summaries, checklists, etc., also helps.

- *Technical reference documents* may have to be terse and fact-packed, but still need to be usable. Quality design and formatting should benefit them and graphics and tables will probably be required.

- *Technical bulletins* will have similar requirements. They may also be used as sales material, so presentation will be important.

- *Price lists* will usually need order forms, quick-reference devices and a mixture of descriptive text with easy-to-find item references.

- *Management reports* — to the Board, to shareholders, to employees, to investors — obviously demand an image-conscious presentation quality.

- *Newsletters* for customers, staff, suppliers, the Church Restoration Fund — all will benefit from attention to formatting and multiple typefaces. (More and more commercially available newsletters and even newspapers are also being produced by DTP systems.)

Advantages for DTP

Appearance. This is the obvious one: the end result looks good, which may be important for the corporate image. It should also be more readable, so information will be imparted more effectively.

The look of a DTP document comes not only from the print quality that is possible; it may also incorporate several design and formatting elements like rules, borders, boxes, panels and shading for emphasis. Text and graphics can be mixed on the same page. Text can utilize italics, boldface, underscoring, reversed print and combinations of them — in more than one typeface. Pages could be paginated automatically and justified both horizontally (so that the lines in each column are the same length) and vertically (so that each pageful of text occupies exactly the same area).

Speed. With many more formatting and presentation options to play with, it is most unlikely that desktop publishing will be quicker than the conventional WP-plus-printer setup. It shouldn't take too much longer; and in general it is much faster to produce a good-looking document on a desktop publishing system than by using outside services. It is also quick and easy to produce amendments, corrections and updates to a document.

Cost. Even if the computer is already available, installing a decent DTP system from scratch will probably cost at least £6000 or so — and probably much more, taking into account the laser printer, software, and some personnel time for familiarization and training. On the cost-for-quality basis, desktop publishing is definitely competitive with typesetting; more generally, though, DTP systems should be seen in terms of added-value rather than gross savings.

Control. The whole document production operation can stay in-house, with the possible exception of documents requiring a long print run — laser printers are not economical or very convenient for multiple copies of a multi-page document. The output quality is, however, good enough for laser printing to be used as masters for litho printing. At the very least, DTP will give more control over the look and content of documents.

New possibilities? Document-production jobs that were formerly infeasible or uneconomic become practical with DTP. The improved quality of presentation could benefit price lists, customer newsletters, even day-to-day correspondence (no need for a separate letterhead, because the document can automatically include a logo in the printing?) and compliment slips.

Desktop publishing in practice — the most likely material for DTP as reported by over 300 UK users:

Promotional brochures	73%
Reports	65%
Newsletters	62%
Training material	60%
Technical reports	58%
User documentation	58%
Forms	57%

[Source: Electronic Publishing in the Corporate Marketplace, Online Publications, 1987]

Desirable facilities in DTP

- *Multi-page handling*, with a common format applied as text runs on to the next page
- *Multiple columns* per page and *different column widths* per page
- *'Flow around'* to allow photographs and other graphics to be inserted such that they encroach on the text area
- Insertion of *graphics generated by other software* — anything from pie charts to 'clip art'
- On-screen *display of fonts and attributes* (bold, italic, etc.)
- *WYSIWYG page make-up* and test runs
- *Control of 'widows' and 'orphans'* — improving the appearance by automatically carrying text forward on to the next page or column or back to the previous one
- *Horizontal (line) justification*, altering inter-character spacing
- *Vertical justification* ('variable leading') for single and multiple pages — adjusting inter-line spacing minutely over the whole of each page so that text fits evenly
- *Boxes, borders, panels* and *rules* (with different line thicknesses); tables and panels should be accommodated such that they do not have to break at the foot of a page and carry over to the next
- The ability to set up and store *different print formats* and call them automatically; ready-to-use *templates* or 'style sheets' for common applications to aid the novice designer
- *Automatic pagination and page-numbering*, with distinctions between left- and right-hand pages
- Automatic control and insertion of *page headers* and *footer text*
- Automatic control of *footnotes*, inserting them at the correct place
- *Special characters* — foreign accents, Greek symbols, other scientific and technical characters
- Automatic *indexing* and generation of *table of contents*

be able to do quite a lot of the detailed things that come as standard on a phototypesetter for improving the appearance of text.

Relevant functions from typesetting include these:

- *Kerning* to adjust the space between characters
- *Vertical justification* to adjust the space between lines such that text fits a given area
- *Horizontal and vertical rules* automatically applied to boxes
- *Percentage shading* to emphasize headings and text
- *Bullets* and other symbols

DTP must be combined with word processing somehow. In practice, this means that the DTP package must incorporate text editing facilities, or it must be able to utilize text files produced with a specific WP package, including any formatting controls provided in the word processor.

DTP packages are already quite large and sophisticated, and most would like to be able to take text from a variety of different word processors, so most incorporate only quite primitive word processing functions, the kind of facilities that are intended only for amendments to imported text and not for document creation.

Page composition

As an alternative to conventional typesetting, the desktop publishing system should be quicker and cheaper — even if the results do not look quite as good. With DTP, you should also be able to do things the average typesetter cannot do.

The key plus here is 'page make-up', sometimes termed 'page composition' — deciding exactly what a printed page will look like. The laser printer can immediately produce something that looks like the finished page (even if some pasted-on material has to be added later, such as may be necessary with a simpler DTP package or one of the less capable laser printers).

Most photosetters produce 'galleys', long strips of text that bear no relationship to the finished page. The galleys have to be cut up and fitted into the space allowed for it: if the text is too short or too long, it is not easy to juggle it to fit without some clever but time-consuming work with a sharp scalpel — or a complete re-run of the original text.

So page make-up is simplified. Not only can the laser printer print complete pages, but you can also adjust anything and try it again — so if your text is running short you might tweak the line lengths and/or the inter-line spacing until it does fit.

WYSIWYG is probably a desirable attribute on the somewhat obvious grounds that it provides an indication of how the printed output will appear. But there are drawbacks:

□ Unless an extra-cost 'upright' screen corresponding more closely to the shape of A4 paper is used, the on-screen display may show only a portion of the printed text in readable format. Alternatively, it can be reduced to give a rough layout of the finished page; but then the actual text is lost.

□ In any case, the difference in resolution between display and printer is likely to mean that WYSIWYG only *approximates* to the printed version — fonts differ and so does spacing between letters and words.

□ WYSIWYG does not function too well when the page includes material (especially graphics) from a variety of different sources.

In short, WYSIWYG page composition systems may not be the best answer for every application. In particular, multi-page documents with a standardized format and few additional graphics (like this book) may gain nothing from the WYSIWYG approach.

DTP has created a market for add-on packages that enhance the printed output. Above is one example for applying graphic effects to text; below is a sample of 'clip art', ready-to-use illustrations and graphics that can be called into documents.

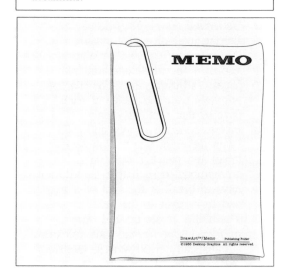

Laser printers versus typesetters

A phototypesetter (or 'photosetter', or 'imagesetter') is a device that produces the original from which lithographic printing can be done. The output is in the form of photographic film suitable for the printing process, but in operation, phototypesetters resemble laser printers. The key difference is the considerable improvement in resolution — 1200 dots per inch is normal for the smaller typesetters, 2500 or more is common.

This font is Helvetica (more or less):

ABCDEFGHIJKLMNOPQRST
IT'S GOOD FOR HEADLINES

This is a smaller version
good for second-level headlings

This font is traditional Times Roman (more or less):
ABCDEFGHIJKLMNOPQRSTUVWXYZ
IT'S GOOD FOR THE MAIN BODY OF TEXT
usually of course in Upper and Lower Case

From a Canon laser printer

This font is Helvetica (more or less):

ABCDEFGHIJKLMNOPQRST
IT'S GOOD FOR HEADLINES

This is a smaller version
good for second-level headlines

This font is traditional Times Roman (more or less):
ABCDEFGHIJKLMNOPQRSTUVWXYZ
IT'S GOOD FOR THE MAIN BODY OF TEXT
usually of course in Upper and Lower Case

From a phototypesetter

Quite apart from the facilities you'll get in the software (or not), the current generation of laser printers cannot compete with phototypesetters for top-quality work. Both create characters by building up patterns of dots: the average typesetter is capable of printing a thousand dots or more to the inch, most of the cheaper laser printers produce 300 dots an inch. Obviously, smaller dots and more dense packing make a cleaner, crisper print impression.

The difference is particularly marked on the larger characters, but a side-by-side comparison on the normal text also shows a definite notchiness.

Furthermore, laser printers are not good enough for printing detailed graphics. Tables and other images using horizontal and vertical lines are fine, and the laser printer can apply a (somewhat dotty) shading for emphasis, but curves and circles are less than perfect and no low-cost laser printer I know of can manage the density and range of dot positions required to reproduce a photograph with fidelity.

In theory that should be no problem: it is possible to digitize *any* image, to convert it into a binary pattern that represents the variety of shading you get in a black and white photo. But a 300-dots-per-inch printer simply cannot translate that information with sufficient precision.

Neither can a phototypesetter, of course, which is why the art room of a publishing house will use a special camera called a PMT machine. This photographs the photograph and comes up with a dot-by-dot image of it — only the dots are so fine that (a) the dot pattern can reproduce the variety of shade required and (b) you cannot usually see them, except in newspaper photographs.

The PMT picture is pasted on to the page, perhaps with typeset text around it, and the whole lot (which is now termed 'camera-ready artwork' or 'CRC' — 'camera-ready copy') is photographed again on a different machine. That produces 'masters', usually in the form of negative film, which can be put on to the printing press: the press uses the CRC to decide where to put ink on to the paper.

In other words, today's laser printer is not a substitute for typesetting in books, magazines and other applications where quality is at a premium.

But if you need to produce a lot of copies of something, and you are going to use a litho printer, it is equally clear that the production of printable material can be much easier, faster and maybe even better if you use a desktop publishing system with a laser printer.

It will be easier and quicker because it involves many fewer processes (and probably fewer people). As well as text,

the laser printer can print quite a lot of the rules and graphics that would otherwise have to be done separately and added to the CRC by the hand of a paste-up artist; the end result may be neater and cleaner too.

As an alternative to conventional typesetting, the desktop publishing system should be quicker and cheaper — even if the results do not look quite as good. This does put a lot of stress on the quality of the software involved, however: you need to be able to do quite a lot of the detailed things that come as standard on a phototypesetter for improving the appearance of text — like tweaking the inter-character spacing as well as the space between words and lines.

Laser printer practicalities

- Always have two extra toner cartridges ready in case one of the replacements is faulty.
- Avoid running out of toner during a print run; new cartridges tend to take some time before they reach full printing density — which can be as many as 200 copies into the run.
- If the image gets fainter during a print run, remove the toner cartridge and shake it to distribute the toner evenly. This will normally cure the problem for a while.
- Paper quality *does* matter. Some photocopier Bond papers are chalky and can result in black streaks down the page, and with some papers there is a tendency for the toner to cause one page to stick to the next, especially when finished pages are put on top of the laser printer or some other warm place.
- Insert the paper carefully; in particular, make sure the paper is settled and straight in the tray. Otherwise paper jams may result, or the page may be printed too high, too low or at an angle.
- If an additional character set is downloaded to the printer, make sure that is only done *once*. The printer will add all characters sent to its internal memory without replacing anything already there, so at some stage its memory will fill up and printing may halt.

DTP and typesetters — the simple option

There are, however, alternatives to a straight choice. The simplest by-passes the laser printer altogether. Text is produced as a straight file of ASCII characters in the simplest possible word-processed form; to it are added special control commands and symbols that specify font, typesize, line width and the like.

This is then passed to a typesetting bureau — either on disk or transmitted via a modem. The bureau has a photosetter with a microcomputer for operator control; the text is read in, run through a conversion program that replaces the user's commands with those recognized by the photosetter and the result is passed on to the photosetter.

The output should be returned within 24 hours, usually in galley form but sometimes as complete made-up pages ready to go to the printer.

Desktop publishing usually means having powerful software and a laser printer. With the bureau option, *any* computer user with a word processor can have professional-quality typesetting.

The results represent a considerable improvement in quality over laser output. By comparison with a conventional typesetting job — with a 'marked-up' typescript being re-keyed — the process is faster, cheaper and less prone to error.

There are three significant drawbacks, however:

□ The user has to insert the typesetting codes. Typography is a skilled craft with its own specialized vocabulary, and a degree of typographic design is inevitably required to utilize the options available.

□ Typesetting in this way is not WYSIWYG. What you see on your screen has very little resemblance to what will appear on the bromides that arrive the next morning. Unless a trial run can be done first on a laser printer, it can be difficult to anticipate the results precisely (forgetting to switch off a king-size bold font for a headline can be very wasteful if it is followed by a thousand words of copy).

□ The number and range of codes that can be entered by an amateur is strictly limited and so is the range of effects that can be produced. Such typesetting is restricted to relatively simple jobs like fixed-format magazines and price lists.

The bureaux that specialize in such services will generally be helpful to the newcomer, for instance including examples in their manuals along with short lessons in basic typography. There may also be a trial offer of some free typesetting.

DTP and typesetters — direct input

Alternatively, a typesetter can interpret the page description language commands sent by some DTP packages. Since desktop publishing via PDLs and laser printers is so akin to the way phototypesetters operate, a number of photosetter manufacturers have produced 'interfaces' of one kind or another that can take DTP documents direct.

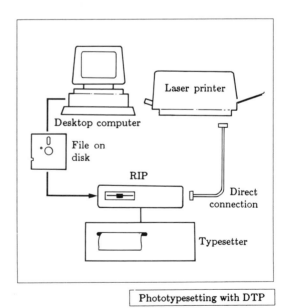

Laser printer

Desktop computer

File on disk

RIP

Direct connection

Typesetter

Phototypesetting with DTP

Usually the interface comprises a black box facility called a raster image processor. The

RIP is simply a converter; it changes the PDL commands (most work with POSTSCRIPT codes) into the controls the typesetter recognizes. An image destined for laser output at 300 dots per inch is progressively refined to suit the typesetter's resolution.

The smaller organization might utilize this by taking disks to a bureau with a suitable RIP facility and photosetter, or by transferring the data via a modem (which is less safe because of the increased likelihood of data corruption on the line).

A large organization with a heavy print load could justify the kind of setup shown in the panel. Either way, local laser printers would probably be used for trial runs and for short-run work that is not destined for litho printing.

New Century Schoolbook Bold
New Century Schoolbook Bold Italic

6

Optima®
Optima Oblique
Optima Bold
Optima Bold Oblique

7

ITC Souvenir® Light
ITC Souvenir Light Italic
ITC Souvenir Demi
ITC Souvenir Demi Italic

8

ITC Lubalin Graph® Book
ITC Lubalin Graph Book Oblique
ITC Lubalin Graph Demi
ITC Lubalin Graph Demi Oblique

9

ITC Garamond® Light
ITC Garamond Light Italic
ITC Garamond Bold
ITC Garamond Bold Italic

10

ITC American Typewriter® Medium
ITC American Typewriter Bold
ITC MACHINE®

15

Trump Mediæval®
Trump Mediæval Italic
Trump Mediæval Bold
Trump Mediæval Bold Italic

16

Melior®
Melior Italic
Melior Bold
Melior Bold Italic

17

ITC Galliard® Roman
ITC Galliard Italic
ITC Galliard Bold
ITC Galliard Bold Italic

18

ITC New Baskerville® Roman
ITC New Baskerville Italic
ITC New Baskerville Bold
ITC New Baskerville Bold Italic

19

ITC Korinna® Regular
ITC Korinna Kursiv Regular
ITC Korinna Bold
ITC Korinna Kursiv Bold

Some of the fonts available with POSTSCRIPT

Optical character recognition is not new; as a method of data entry via digitized images, OCR has been around for some time. But when OCR devices first appeared, they could distinguish only text — and then it had to be text in a specially designed typeface, normally the stylized OCR-A or OCR-B fonts. They were not cheap, either.

Desktop publishing gave OCR technology a new lease of life. To set up dot-by-dot images is possible though time-consuming and skillful work, but something like that was needed to get an exact image into DTP-processed documents — either for bulk input of typed or printed paper, or to utilize existing graphics like logos or drawings.

A new generation of economical 'page scanners' has appeared for this function. Put crudely, you feed a piece of paper into the scanner; within minutes, an image of the document appears on the screen.

Page scanners work rather differently for text and graphics, however — for characters, the technology comes from OCR. For graphics, it is more akin to facsimile transmission. Most scanners are biased towards one or the other.

Graphics scanning. The scanner works by shining a light source on to the original document and detecting the presence or absence of black areas. The light-sensitive receptors which pick this up are arranged in a matrix the size of the page, and a digital representation of the condition of each such cell provides a digitized page image.

Resolution. Obviously the more receptor cells, the better. Most low-cost page scanners match the 300 dots per inch resolution of the average laser printer, more expensive models have 480dpi, some text-oriented scanners manage only 200. Since scanners can work much faster at lower resolutions, most come with a switch-selectable choice that can drop down to 100dpi or less. This speeds things up, but clearly degrades the image.

Photographs. Because they work basically in black and white, the cheapest scanners are not very good at digitizing any image containing shades of grey as well — 'half-tones' — such as photographs. Some do have a half-tone mode that will handle a few shades of grey (32 is normal) as varying percentages or densities of black.

Memory. A dot-by-dot representation of an image can take a lot of the computer's memory, typically about a megabyte for a full A4 page scanned at 300dpi — more if a half-tone mode is available. Not all images will fill a whole page, however, and some scanners use the same data compression technique employed by fax machines to cut down on the memory requirement.

Text. Scanning characters has to be done in a rather different fashion if the text is to be manipulated inside the computer. The characters could be treated simply as an image to be input, but then the computer (and its word processor and DTP text editor) would not be able to treat the bit image as text — rewriting, deletion, insertion and reformatting would be impossible.

To input ASCII codes for text, the scanner has to use the OCR technique of matching characters it finds with a table of correspondences built into the software supplied with it; it is simply a comparison of shapes. When the scanner finds a shape it cannot recognize, a mark of some kind will appear in the text that arrives at the computer.

Typefaces. Different typefaces are the main problem; most scanners are limited in what they can recognize as identifiable character shapes — common typewriter faces are usually covered, along with OCR-B, but that's all (italic versions of a recognizable typeface probably will not make it, for instance). Proportionally-spaced typescript, which varies the space between characters, may be a problem. Text attributes like underlining can also confuse the scanner.

Mixing text and graphics. Most scanners cannot pick up text and graphics in one run — the user has to select one mode, pass the sheet through and then switch to the other mode for a second pass.

A systematic approach to the planning and control of projects — deciding what needs to be done and when, and then monitoring progress — has long been used in civil and industrial engineering.

There will also be applications in many areas of business — particularly those complex projects where time is a crucial factor, when the project depends on some tasks being completed before others begin.

The usual approach uses 'critical path analysis' (CPA) or 'PERT' (for 'project [or program] review and evaluation technique'), proven and effective techniques that essentially formalize a commonsense approach and which are not difficult to learn.

Principles

Critical path analysis is quite easy to grasp. Any project, whether it is planning an office move or designing a housing estate, can sensibly be broken down into separate tasks.

Clearly some of them can proceed in parallel; if you are planning a new product introduction, you can have market research going on at the same time as preliminary design. Other tasks must wait for one or more to be completed first — the final design specification would clearly have to await the work from R&D and market information.

The man-in-the-street approach is to do things in a logical sequence: boil the water, take a cup from the cupboard, put in the teabag, pour in the water. The project planner looks at things in a different way, considering the overall project in terms of a network of separate activities that start linking into paths that themselves join up eventually at the end of the project.

The key dimension is *time*, and by identifying how long each separate activity will take the project planner can locate the 'path' of linked tasks that will take the longest to complete. This is the *critical* path, for any delay in the activities along that one will have the most profound effect on the project's overall completion date.

Locating the critical path and having the time-critical tasks highlighted is clearly an aid to any project control. It shows which activities have to be watched most closely.

It is also possible to work back along all the not-so-critical paths to identify the amount of time that activities there could slip without affecting the overall completion date — this is called the 'float' or 'slack' on a task. It is just as important to watch them, because the slack can easily be taken up; an over-schedule activity could have a knock-on effect which turns *that* path into the critical one.

All this is called 'time analysis' in CPA/PERT jargon; it is the job project planning systems were originally designed to do. While the theory might be easy enough to grasp, the practice on any but the smallest project can be inordinately complicated; it takes time and effort to map out the relationships and paths between tasks, and while the calculation required is pretty trivial the sheer volume can easily lead to mistakes — assuming it does not deter the would-be project planner altogether.

This is precisely the kind of repetitive calculating work that computers do efficiently, accurately and quickly.

Functions

The computerized system can also control other key aspects of a project. With most project control systems, time analysis remains the key function. Additional facilities may include:

☐ Identifying and summing *resources* required for activities and stages and producing 'resource analyses' showing how non-consumable resources should and/or will be used throughout the project

- *Costing* the project — and costing individual activities, activity paths and overall checkpoints too

- *Allocating* costs and resources to tasks

- Performing *what-if* assessments, for instance on the costs of extra overtime against the penalties for late completion, and actually running *budget controls* against actual performance

- Locating appropriate *milestones* for assessment of progress

Modern project planning packages for desktop computers may be no less capable than mainframe implementations. However, packages aimed at business use do not normally require the capabilities and capacity of the engineering equivalent; the number of tasks and variables they accommodate will probably be limited. Instead such packages major on comprehensibility, ease of use and presentation options. They generally have 'fill-in-the-blanks' forms, provide option menus, employ English-like commands, use function keys for single-keystroke entries.

They also lose little capability; most business applications do not have the same complexity as engineering projects. The overall size of the networks that can be analysed can still involve several hundred activities (some packages will top 10 000).

Similarly, there will probably be restrictions on the functions that can be performed. But few packages omit the key calculations, like resource and cost aggregation, and most offer a variety of standard and user-definable reports.

Output

The results of project planning can usually be provided in a variety of forms:

- A *critical path chart* for a project's 'network' of paths and associated information
- Time-based *Gantt charts* showing start and completion dates for each task
- Project *diaries* or *calendars* highlighting key dates

- Lists and tables for *resources and costs*
- *Barcharts* showing *planned schedules and costs against actual performance*

Most planning packages for desktop computers will permit results to be 'exported' for massaging by other packages — for incorporation into a word-processed report, for instance, or for presentation treatment by a business graphics package.

There will be some graphics capability with the package itself, of course — those results should be viewable on-screen as charts and diagrams rather than mere incomprehensible text. To see a network laid out clearly demands a screen with relatively high resolution; colour will help show interrelationships and highlight critical points.

To produce the project chart in hardcopy form, a high-resolution printer or plotter (ideally with colour) will obviously be required. Printing may in any case demand a wide-carriage printer and/or an option to print 'sideways' — conventionally, time is shown along the horizontal and subtasks down the vertical side of the display. This can mean that the resulting chart is wider than it is deep, so you might need a print option for turning the whole thing on its side.

To include project planning charts in a presentation, the package might usefully include options for output in OHP or slide form.

Checklist: project planners

Features

As well as the basics of project planning — identifying subprojects, indicating critical paths, highlighting conflicts — can the package handle both time *and* resources? Can it do automatic 'resource levelling' to resolve conflicts? And can that be done across several unrelated projects? Can fixed and variable costs be broken down and tracked across subprojects? Can it produce work diaries and calendars? Is there an instant 'what-if' facility to see the potential effect of changes? Can the package handle 'backwards' calculation, producing a start date when you set a completion date?

Capacities

How many resources per activity? Per project? How many diaries and calendars per project? How many projects can be linked for analysis?

Configuration

How many activities can practically be run in the memory of your computer? Will the package print on your printer? Can the 8087 numeric processor option be used to speed up operation?

Ease of use

A major problem with most project planners is the sheer number of alternatives. The best approach is probably an omnipresent Lotus-like main menu, with 'pull-down' submenus for each selection that finally guide you to what you want; but there should also be a 'quick' option for the experienced user. 'Macros' can automate repeated tasks; is that facility provided?

Help

No project planner can be as quick or as intuitive to learn as, say, a spreadsheet package. Expect some kind of interactive tutorial, instantly available 'context-sensitive' help displays, and a quick-reference 'route-map' card. Look for sympathetic support from error messages — instead of 'overflow at location 0768H' the package should indicate what it cannot do for you and suggest some remedial action.

Performance

Project planners are large programs that necessarily have to do a lot of calculating and recalculating; speed in operation is essential. The results may also generate a lot of data, so check how compact the files will be.

Graphics

Good-quality on-screen graphics are *de rigeur*. Colour is highly desirable, but the program should also be able to perform effectively on monochrome displays.

Output

Are the results clear? Is there a 'sideways' option for printing long charts vertically? How well are colour displays reproduced on monochrome screens and printers?

Links to other packages

Can the package produce results in a form that can be used by other software? Word processors and graphics packages are the usual requirement. Can they take input data produced by a spreadsheet, for instance?

'Artificial intelligence' and 'expert systems' have been much bandied about in the computer and business press. In fact, they promise a good deal for the business executive with access to a desktop computer. On the other hand, there is no wide agreement on how the terms should be defined. What follows is more a pragmatic introduction than the last word.

Expert systems

A human expert is someone who knows a great deal about a specific subject. To provide a working example, a business consultant has access to a large store of generalized information (both in terms of experience, and on file) from which he or she can select information relevant to a particular case. The consultant is able to take in additional data — the present status of the company, current problems, future goals and the like — and synthesize all that information into concrete advice.

If the expert was able to break down that knowledge into simple discrete pieces, all the facts and rules used to come to a decision could be formalized. Since computers are essentially fast rule-following machines, this is clearly a case for automation — a computer program which could apply all of these facts and rules should be able to replace the expert. A program of this type is described as an expert system.

Expert systems request information from the user, apply knowledge and reasoning to that, draw conclusions and explain them, and communicate those conclusions to the user. Expert systems cannot replace the full potential of human judgement. In most applications, expert systems function best as a kind of 'assistant' to an individual or team, speeding up analysis and indicating options for decision-making.

Producing expert systems

Clearly, the great difficulty with expert systems is not the production of the final program. Rather it lies in extracting the expert's information and formalizing it into a workable set of facts and rules.

Computerized expertise: advantages ...

☐ *Availability*. Expert systems provide expertise at any hour of the day or night, in any geographical location, and any non-expert user should be able to utilize such a system to make decisions of expert quality.

☐ *Consistency*. Human experts can have good days and bad days, and they can exercise intermittent and/or irrational prejudices.

☐ *Accuracy*. People can make mistakes. A badly-written program can also do most of those things, but at least that variable is known, predictable, and alterable.

☐ *Speed*. It is not necessarily the case, but an expert system is likely to produce decision-aiding information more quickly than a human.

☐ *Efficiency*. Expert systems can free human experts from the mundane and repetitive parts of their work, leaving them available for new and probably more satisfying challenges.

... and limitations

☐ *Comprehensiveness*. The major problem in producing expert systems is the need to cater for *all* the data, *all* the rules and *all* the possible conditions.

☐ *Flexibility*. Expert systems are restricted to rigorously-defined situations — applications that are amenable to the use of strict rules and where the nature (and usually the quantity) of input data is known.

☐ *Relevance*. Such systems cannot normally determine the relevance of information and the weight it should carry in particular situations.

☐ *Selective rule-breaking*. All rules have exceptions. A computerized expert cannot usually spot one-off situations where the rules should not apply.

Expert systems at work

- Probably the most widely-used expert system in use in Britain covers employment law for dismissals. Endorsed by the Institute of Chartered Accountants, it included over 1100 'rules' clarifying this labyrinthine area.

- ExperTAX is an advisory system developed by Coopers and Lybrand to help its accountants audit US tax returns.

- In mid 1987, IBM said it was actively using some 22 different expert systems in both management and technical areas, with another 75 under development.

- MindReader is a word processing extra that tries to guess what you want to say next — it learns from the way you habitually use words. Give it *Henry IV Part II* and it could probably write a Shakespearean history; more usefully, it can remember and automatically insert phrases.

- Unisys's MAPPER is an intelligent program development system with which end-users rather than DP staff can develop applications for themselves.

- This one may be apocryphal, but the Senate Committee on the Iran-Contras affair reportedly used an expert system to sort out the mass of evidence it collected.

This is partly because of the complexity of a true expert's 'data base', partly because humans are good at being experts and poor at explaining exactly how they reach a decision — experts often have little idea of the cognitive path that they follow to reach a decision.

Ask a racing driver, for example, why he will elect to start braking at a particular point on the approach to a corner: you may well get the reply 'because it is the correct place' or something equally unhelpful like 'any later would be too late'. In fact the driver is taking in a mass of data about speed, heat of brakes (in turn estimated by experience), condition of road surface, wind speed, wind direction and so on. This in turn is processed — and the braking is begun at the correct place.

Artificial intelligence

Expert systems almost always evidence artificial intelligence. AI is more difficult to define precisely, but a few generalizations can be made:

- AI concerns computational methods of providing examples of behaviour that are characteristic of human intelligence. To put this less formally, a program that behaves more or less as a human would is exhibiting AI.

- AI often involves the use of heuristics, computational methods which may not finally solve a particular problem but will probably help towards a solution. In practice this often translates into 'trial and error'. For example, any program written to play chess cannot guarantee a win since it cannot know in advance how the opponent will play. It *can*, however, suggest moves which are likely to produce an advantageous position from which a win can be achieved.

- The computer must be able to 'learn' any information it is given. AI systems often have the capacity to learn from experience as well, to remember situations they have met before and the way in which the situations were resolved.

- AI systems often have very large databases.

The dividing line between 'expert systems' and 'artificial intelligence' is not impossible to draw, though it is true that they will often go together. In medical diagnosis, for instance, an expert system could accurately deduce a condition by considering symptoms; it asks for the results of a large number of tests and produces the most likely diagnosis. But such a system is by no means *intelligent*.

Conversely, it is possible to have AI without expertise — you could envisage a program which imitated a human very closely but was not actually particularly good at anything. In practice, of course, any system designed to display intelligence will also contain at least one expert system (and possibly *many* of them).

The fundamental difference is that expert systems are invariably built with specific applications in mind. Artificial intelligence is a more general attribute whose use will not necessarily be specific. In practice terms, expert systems are task-oriented programs; artificial intelligence is a methodology or technique.

Much of the development work in expert systems is still coming from the States. Basic R&D was done there in the seventies, advanced development has attracted considerable funding, and Fortune 500 companies are actively espousing the advantages — by all estimates, there were well over a thousand expert system applications in US corporations by mid 1987.

By comparison, Europe lags well behind. There is very little basic research — the EEC-funded ESPRIT project concentrates on precompetitive development and allowed only four per cent of the second-round budget for fundamental research; the UK's Alvey Programme has included basic research, but funds are drying up. The vendors of developed commercial systems are unwilling to invest in large-scale marketing or unable to raise the money. Partly because of the lack of promotion but also as a result of innate conservatism, prospective purchasers in Europe seem unconvinced of the merits of expert systems.

Expert systems can be written in a purpose-designed programming language such as PROLOG or LISP, or they can be constructed using an expert system generator like ESP ADVISOR or KEE. The results may be similar, but the methodology is rather different.

Programming AI

Most of the features of artificial intelligence and expert systems can be produced in conventional programming languages. In practice this would be very difficult, because such languages were not designed for those features — for example, they include no commands that will easily enable a program to learn from experience. The result would in any case be over-large, unwieldy and consequently very slow in operation.

A language designed specifically for AI can incorporate purpose-built features (like learning) and the whole programming procedure can fit the specialized tasks required of the language.

The majority of conventional programming languages can be described as *procedural*: the programmer writes out a detailed set of instructions which describe exactly which steps must be followed in order to solve the current problem. As one author puts it, 'the flow of control through the program statements is expressed explicitly by the programmer'.

By contrast, languages like PROLOG — available at low cost and one of the simplest AI languages to use — are *declarative*. Instead of specifying the way in which the problem is solved, the programmer enters a set of facts and rules (collectively known as 'clauses') which describe both the problem and the information which will be required to solve it. The *language* then solves the problem. The actual way in which this is done, that is 'the flow of control through the program statements', remains under the control of the language; the programmer is largely freed from concerns of exactly how the program needs to be structured.

The Turing test

The British computer pioneer Alan Turing proposed a well-known test to determine when a computer might be considered to be 'thinking'. A person is installed in a room with two identical lines of communication (the actual means of communication are unimportant, but for the sake of comprehensibility each line could be connected to a terminal). At the end of one line is a woman, at the other is a man. You can communicate with both. Each tries to convince you that they are the woman; you try to decide which is which.

Now, if the individual in the middle is replaced by a computer, would it be better able to distinguish between the two? If yes, the computer is 'thinking'. And if it is thinking, it certainly is displaying artificial intelligence.

In general, the programmer works by providing basic data and information about how those facts are related. Once those rules are provided, a language like PROLOG can be used to recall both explicit and implied facts. These rules are often written in a form reminiscent of the logic commonly used by people, though the actual statements in the program may not look particularly English-like.

The strength of such languages lies in the way rules can be built up from rules such that the whole structure rapidly becomes very complex — leaving the programmer to consider only fairly simple concepts.

In short, the purpose-designed languages can produce programs displaying the four given characteristics more easily than a conventional language:

☐ *Behaviour characteristic of human intelligence.* 'Intelligent' behaviour can more easily be programmed because of the very complex responses which can be produced. This complexity is based on the ability to write rules which depend on rules which depend on rules ....

☐ *Heuristics.* Again, this is feasible because of the sophistication and complexity that a program can include.

☐ *Learning.* The AI programmer can write rules which, in specific circumstances, will themselves add facts and rules into the program itself. Thus the program can grow and evolve with time, gradually acquiring 'experience'.

☐ *Large databases.* By their very nature, most AI programs are themselves large databases — the program is a collection of facts and rules that make up a database. With this type of language, in fact, the distinction between program and database is difficult to make.

Expert system generators

The alternative is to use a program generator to produce an expert system. Such 'expert system shells' often work with a kind of fill-in-the-form approach that elicits from the programmer a structure for the resulting

program, the rules that apply and any base data involved. When the program has finished assembling this into a usable system, it will give you the option of testing and amending it. Finally you are normally able to produce a 'run-time' version, the expert system itself.

Unfortunately, many of the so-called expert system generators are too restricted to merit the term — they may be useful as 'outline processors' or 'thought organizers', or maybe even as 'file managers', but they cannot accommodate enough rules in sufficient complexity to produce a true expert system.

Decision support systems

'Decision support' is one style of expert system with immediate application in business. Such systems aim to:

☐ Assist the decision-making process for semi-structured management tasks
☐ Support (and not replace) managerial judgement
☐ Improve the effectiveness (rather than the efficiency) of decision

In short, they should improve the quality of information and detail on options available to decision-makers.

There is nothing magic about the use of the computer; most such systems elicit the views of an individual or team, allow the relative importance of different criteria to be established by them and summarize the results in a mathematically accurate but comprehensible form to indicate the best practical priorities and policies.

As an illustration, take the Priority Decision System marketed by Work Science Associates. It is arguable that PDS is not a true 'decision support system' as the phrase might be defined by an academic — it is based on an algorithm rather than a 'knowledge base' — but this product (and its close relatives) do represent practical and genuine 'decision support'.

The meat of the PDS, as for most decision support systems, is the priority scaling method it employs. In essence the procedure is as follows:

- State the issue (in plain English)
- Enter the options
- For team decisions, note who is involved and indicate their relative importance (as a percentage of 100)

At this stage, PDS could work out individual priorities and produce a team decision on the basis of the weightings. A similar approach can be taken to criteria, with weightings applied to each of the relevant considerations; the result would be an evaluation of the relative importance of the criteria. Subsequently those policies could be combined with the priorities for a 'policy in practice' report.

The user can be an individual manager; the PDS is probably more effective, however, when used by a team — it can propose a consensus of consistent views, and it does not necessarily need all members of the team to be present in person.

Work Science Associates has two other products that also illustrate applications. WPS is its Work Priority System — the user lists ongoing projects, rates their importance and indicates the time constraints. The WPS can produce a report on what can or should be done in the time available, what could be postponed, and what resources will be required. This can subsequently be used to monitor the progress of individual projects against actual performance. Similarly, the BPS Budget Priority System evaluates input (priorities, costings, expenditure to date, resources) to produce a budget plan (how best to distribute available money) and an operations plan (how much to supply of what).

It is unlikely that the fast-track executive will need to get too involved in the accounting function.

Keeping accounts involves a lot of record-keeping, much transfer of information from one file to another and a good deal of producing reports. All those attributes make accounting a natural case for computerization — especially as accuracy and attention to detail are vital (computers are very accurate and very picky) and timeliness is desirable (computers are very quick).

Sales and purchase ledgers

Computerizing a sales ledger ('accounts receivable') in theory should reduce losses from bad debts and mean faster collection of debts, with more and better information on your customers and their accounts.

The purchase ledger ('accounts payable') is usually a mirror-image of the sales ledger that keeps track of cash requirements and pays suppliers when required.

The nominal ledger

The nominal (or 'general') ledger is rarely the first accounting system to be computerized, but it is one of the most powerful business tools that can be applied to the financial management of a company.

Its purpose is to take all the operating information in your company and summarize it in two basic reports — the profit and loss account and the balance sheet. From these you should be able to determine the current financial status of your company and establish proper controls for direction.

Invoicing and order processing

For many companies, this has turned out to be the most valuable function of the computer. Taking orders and dispatching the goods is right at the sharp end of most businesses: a computer operates quickly and accurately, and that makes for satisfied customers — and it allows you to get invoices and statements out more quickly.

'Integrated' accounting packages

Some accounts packages come as a single disk holding all the software to do all your accounting; the 'integrated' part means that a transaction posted to one ledger will automatically update any other ledgers that should be affected. In a non-integrated system all those postings might have to be individual jobs for the user to do separately.

Checklist: accounts packages

Functions

Just because all businesses produce accounts does not mean they produce the same kind of accounts in the same way. Make sure that any package fits your business, your way of doing things: be firm about where you will and will not accept compromises.

Size

Will the accounts package accommodate your immediate requirements plus a bit extra for growth? Can transaction journals and other files exceed the capacity of one disk? Just how much disk swapping will be needed?

Reports

All packages can produce quite a lot of paper — but are you getting all the reports you (or your accountant) need? And are they laid out in the format you'd like?

Coding

Unique codes are required to identify many items in accounting packages — supplier and customer accounts, your invoices, stock items. A package may not allow you to use your existing codes and some will impose a system you may not like (numbers only, for instance, when you'd prefer a code that mixes numbers and letters).

Future development

You may start with invoicing plus sales, purchase and nominal ledgers. But can you add extra facilities? What happens when size of your files expands? Or the number of transactions? Or the number of cost centres in your nominal analysis?

Payments

Do you get the option for open-item and balance-forward accounting? 'Open item' means that payments are allocated to specific invoices rather than just to the total outstanding balance.

Links to other packages

Once you have accumulated the information needed to account for your business, you might find ways of utilizing it for other functions. A full list of customers would have names and addresses that could be used for a sales mailshot — provided there's a way of linking that information to your word processor. If you want to do some business forecasting on the basic data, that may be included in a nominal ledger. If it is not, look for ways of extracting the information for use in something like a spreadsheet package.

Audit trails

All accounts packages produce audit trails that record all transactions, and this provides a degree of checking for input errors and fraud. The amount of information on the audit trail varies greatly: ask your accountant to list what you require and then compare what the packages produce.

Programming is the process of setting up commands for the computer to follow. Like other languages, a programming 'language' has its own vocabulary, its own 'nouns', 'verbs' and 'conjunctives', a grammar and a syntax. It is a bit like learning French or German, in fact, except that most programming languages are a lot simpler. They are just designed to tell a *computer* rather than a foreigner to do something.

Exactly what constitutes 'programming' is a subject open to debate. Formerly programming was the inviolable bailliwick of professional and (theoretically) expert programmers, but the arrival of 'personal' computing and quite sophisticated packages has opened a wide range of possible choices to the non-programming end-user. Those options can be made available to the end-user in a variety of ways, many of which effectively involve 'programming'.

Conventional programming

Assembler

This is the form of programming that is nearest to the nitty-gritty of the computer's operation. It employs a detailed and somewhat arcane structure with command mnemonics that are largely incomprehensible to the average user. It is possible (but unlikely, and usually unnecessary) for a non-expert non-enthusiast user to pick up enough information to write small assembler programs, usually for very low-level functions like presenting an option menu on start-up.

'High-level' languages

It is also unlikely that the end-user will get involved with these, the conventional computer programming languages used by professionals — 'high-level' languages work in much the same way on different computers, assembler is specific to one machine or one group of computers. Common examples include:

☐ *BASIC*. The programming language most widely used on microcomputers. The reasons for that owe little to an objective assessment of the language's technical merits. Even in its most clever implementations, BASIC is relatively clumsy as a programming tool; it is biased towards a numeric rather than a text-oriented approach and it is difficult to write the kind of programs that can easily be understood and amended by programmers without taking up a lot of memory. BASIC is still widely used because it happened to be in the right place at the right time — microcomputers needed a decent programming language in the late seventies and nothing else was available. It does have some merits, too, not least the fact that it was originally designed for use by beginners (the acronym stands for Beginners' All-purpose Symbolic Instruction Code). Inertia counts for a lot, however: many microcomputer programmers started by learning BASIC, so BASIC is provided for newcomers to learn.

☐ *Pascal* (and especially Borland Software's Turbo Pascal) has made an impact on BASIC's predominance for programming on the small scale. Pascal is technically superior, largely because the language itself encourages a more disciplined approach to programming that in theory produces programs that are easier to understand and subsequently amend.

☐ *COBOL* is a programming language oriented towards commercial data processing applications on large computers. It is comparatively verbose, heavy on memory and relatively difficult to learn, but it produces programs that can handle business computing jobs more effectively than many of the alternatives, particularly large tasks with a lot of file-handling. Its technical merits do not account for its (somewhat fading) popularity; the appeal of COBOL lies in the way it has been very largely standardized and in the availability of a large number of professional programmers who are skilled in its use.

- *FORTRAN* is another language implemented originally on mainframes but now available for machines of all sizes. It has much the same attraction as COBOL for scientific and technical programs, but is not particularly appropriate for anything else.

- *C* is currently the professionals' favourite for general-purpose programming, not least because it combines many of the nitty-gritty capabilities of Assembler with the multiple-machine portability of other high-level languages. It also fits well with Unix and Xenix, the operating systems that are becoming predominant at the departmental level of workstation computing. Programmers like it, perhaps in part because its complexity and incomprehensible structure reinforces their status.

End-user programming

There are circumstances in which the end-user could be said to be 'programming', however, and the principles of any program development apply equally here.

- *Expert systems* emulate and/or complement the reasoning that a human expert might put into a task, setting up a 'model' of different hypotheses in advance and then picking its way through them to more or less reasonable conclusions. Expert systems may in some cases be produced by end-users, though for anything but the simplest applications they are best left to professionals.

- *Command languages* enable an end-user of a filing package to write mini-programs to handle data entry, manipulation and output. Some of these facilities are as sophisticated as anything a conventional programming language provides, and there are professionals who specialize in programming file managers for specific applications (notably using the command language in Ashton-Tate's dBASE).

- *Program generators* are programs that write programs, inviting the user to specify the nature and operation of an application and using that information to produce a working program in a conventional programming language. As such, they provide a degree of hand-holding for the programming process while minimizing the amount the user has to know about the programming language itself. An expert system 'shell' is one example; there are also program generators which produce programs in BASIC, COBOL, the dBASE command language and others.

Fourth-generation languages

4GLS promise easier and faster development of applications. Broadly, they cut down the number of lines of program code required and they provide a simplified approach to the design of programs, such that (in theory) the end-user is able to do the programming work for a particular task he or she requires.

There are several hundred products on the market that can claim to be 4GLS. The term can cover program generators, command languages in file managers and spreadsheets, expert system shells — virtually anything that encourages an end-user to produce applications without resorting to conventional programming languages.

4GLS have not, however, had the acceptance that the promotional hype would seem to warrant.

- They cater for the production of new applications; they do nothing for 'maintenance' programming — amending existing software to remove bugs or add functions — which is the bulk of programming work.

- Most DP departments and information centres spend a good deal of their resources on running systems for users, but 4GLS do nothing for the operations area.

- 4GLs exemplify the software equation that more capability demands more of a computer. 4GLs need a fast computer and a lot of memory.

- Programs written in 4GLs cannot mate well with existing software.

- There are no universally agreed standards and little real-world experience.

- 4GLs may be relatively easy to learn, but the basic principles of good programming still apply. The end-user may not have the training or the professional background to follow them — error-testing, maintainability so that someone else can take on the task of future amendment, documentation so that others can use the program. That all takes skill; it can also take a good deal of time.

- The availability of 4GLs has encouraged end-users to utilize them in developing relatively trivial applications rather than the more sophisticated tasks for which they were intended. 4GLs can produce large, clumsy programs for such small jobs.

Individual software packages provide some local functions. The potential provided by computer communications greatly expands the options available to management, by providing access to information and a variety of means for distributing it.

Communication is concerned with the transfer of information from one place to another. In the case of comms on the computer, typically we are interested in transferring a message of some kind from one computer to another or in using one computer to interrogate another. Under that umbrella you might include:

□ *Local file transfer.* Exchanging information with other computers in your office without having to walk around with a floppy disk — e.g. to get hold of some data from files for use in some work you are doing.

□ *Electronic mail.* Send and receive messages, internally or with a distant contact. When you dial up the service, you are told whether there are any messages waiting for you and you are given the option of reading them or waiting for a while. You can send messages to anyone whose mailbox 'address' you know: you can send them at whatever time of day you want, knowing that they'll be in the recipient's mailbox within minutes: and you can send them without having to speak to the recipient in person — though you can ask to be notified automatically (via your own mailbox) when they have read your message.

□ *Telex.* Sending and receiving Telexes from a computer cuts down costs (no special-purpose Telex terminal, no ancillary charges) and eases the bottleneck in the Telex room. Most electronic mail services provide commercial Telex bureau facilities: you e-mail the message rather than speak on the phone. Or you can use a special Telex adaptor (a specialized modem, in fact) which connects your computer directly to the Telex network and allows it to be used just as an ordinary Telex terminal.

□ *Facsimile transmission.* Similarly, it is possible to send and receive faxes from a desktop computer. Again, there are bureau facilities on e-mail services — though obviously you are limited to very simple text-only images. Special fax adaptors are, however, becoming available to permit transmission and reception of anything that the computer is capable of displaying. A fax number and line are used just as with a conventional facsimile terminal.

□ *On-line information services.* Around the world there are several computerized databases, giant repositories of information on every conceivable subject which subscribers can call up via their computer. Many of them are academic or technical; more generalized services provide, for instance, company information, data on geographical and vertical markets, and press cuttings. Charges generally reflect the detail and complexity of the information stored and the sophistication of the search/sort/select procedures that subscribers can use to sift through it. Access can be direct or, for occasional use, via a 'gateway' provided in other services — most e-mail suppliers have extra-cost gateways to a number of information services.

□ *Prestel.* A desktop computer can be used as a Prestel terminal to access the consumer and business information on the viewdata service (though you may not get the colour). Prestel also has an electronic mail facility.

□ *Mainframe communications.* Talking to a central computer to pass on information or pull some out of the centralized organization files it holds is normal practice in organizations. Special software and additional hardware may be required to make a desktop computer appear to the mainframe as one of its own terminals.

□ *Money transfer.* BACS is the Bankers' Automated Clearing Scheme, a kind of on-line direct-debit facility for transferring money from your account into someone else's. Individual clearing banks are also starting to offer on-line access to account information by computer (usually via Prestel). In both cases you will need special software.

Telecommuting

Telecommuting aims 'to transport ideas and information instead of people', as one pioneer puts it. The principle is that employees use computers at home or in local offices rather than attending a conventional centralized office.

The technology is already in place — personal computers, modems, comms packages and dial-up access — and of course there is already of good deal of 'taking the computer home' going on. Predicted benefits include cost savings on offices, improved job performance and employee satisfaction, and energy and environmental savings. There are, however, some prerequisites if decentralized working is going to be a significant part of the organization's system:

Organization

- □ *Personnel selection*. Some people may not work more effectively in the decentralized environment. A formal means of assessing and selecting the likely candidates may be required.

- □ *Task selection*. Not all work can usefully be done independently — personal interaction is critical for many management roles. Routine work and tasks that require personal 'thinking time' are obvious candidates.

- □ *Equipment and services*. Many of the potential problems, including dissatisfaction with telecommuting tools (modems too slow, personal interaction required, access to a company's centralized files too awkward) can be alleviated by sensible selection policies. Conferencing, for instance, may replace the need for *ad hoc* meetings; voice and electronic mail can provide messaging; access to data from on-line information services from the quiet and privacy of your own home can actually improve the quality of sales and marketing decisions.

- □ *Strategic design*. If it is to become a normal mode of working, telecommuting requires design and probably some training. Tactics might include self-managed work teams and problem-solving groups away from the office, information sessions, relatively rigid monitoring and reporting

procedures, and decentralized local offices with some conventional facilities.

Personal issues

- □ *Isolation*. Face-to-face contact may be time-consuming and relatively inefficient, but personal relationships are crucial to virtually every organization. The key to effective interactions is quality, not quantity.

- □ *Motivation*. Telecommuting is probably not for everyone — goal-direction, independence and the ability to take personal satisfaction from tasks accomplished are required.

- □ *Non-productivity*. Given the distractions available and the ingrained habit of regarding home as the place where you *don't* work, a degree of discipline and organization is vital.

- □ *Burnout*. On the other hand, it is equally important to separate personal and professional life.

The growth of comms

The major increase in data communications will come from organizations with fewer than 20 employees. EURODATA 86 was a study by the PA Consultancy Group for the 18 European telecomms authorities; it predicts that by 1995, those smaller organizations will account for some 63 per cent of the total user base for non-voice services. Over 10 per cent of the working population will use such services, compared with just over 1.7 per cent in 1985.

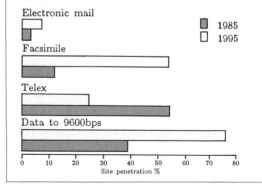

To talk to another computer you obviously need some sort of connection to whatever is at the other end of the link. At its simplest the physical connection could be a cable, probably plugged into a socket at the back of your computer. The other end would then go into a similar socket on the other computer. If the computers are part of a local network, of course, the link is already there.

That kind of computer-to-computer connection is usually described as 'local', meaning the two machines are in close proximity. The type of comms is generally 'file transfer', the movement of files — which could be documents, programs or anything else — from one to the other.

If you want to use electronic mail or a dial-up information service, however, in practice you'll be talking to a *remote* computer. For that you will almost invariably need a telephone line, a box called a modem and some software to drive them. Let's consider the first of those prerequisites.

The dial-up phone network

Using phone lines is not, of course, the only way of having your computer talk to another system, but there are practical drawbacks to all the alternatives. The telephone system covers the world quite effectively, it is in place and well understood, and the practical restrictions are easy enough to get round. Or rather, both the suppliers of modems and communications software have put a great deal of effort into getting around those restrictions, which simplifies your life.

The nature of the services provided by the telecomms authorities and other 'common carriers' inevitably impacts the shape and content of office automation.

For a start, while the phone system relies on old-style exchanges and outdated cabling you will still need a modem to convert between digital and analogue signals.

On the present analogue network, reliable data transmission at high speeds is simply not possible. There is too much extraneous electrical 'noise' that cannot be shielded out, there is too much signal distortion resulting from the physical properties of the cable and the present exchange equipment cannot screen the transmission sufficiently to

guarantee that a message arrives in ungarbled form.

Even at lower speeds, the software and the modem will have to do quite a lot of work to detect all the incoming signals and sort out which blips and squeaks actually represent a message rather than garbage.

In Britain, this means that data transmission over the normal phone system — the Public Switched Telephone Network (PSTN) as used for voice — is restricted to 2400 baud ('baud' is a technical measure that corresponds more or less to 'bits per second').

Public data-only phone networks

For faster data transmission, there are some possibilities even within the present setup. In particular, the telecommunications supplier can provide a special high-quality line between two points; modems will still be required, and the cost will be high, but a special data-only link like these can be optimized for high-speed traffic — with additional shielding, special signal repeaters to boost the transmission and the selection of routes that take it through the more modern exchange equipment.

Most Western European countries also have a special data-only network as a public service, again utilizing more modern equipment and selected routes. In Britain this is operated under the name PSS (Packet Switched Service); effectively the PSS network duplicates the PSTN in part, providing a set of purpose-designed links between particular telephone exchanges.

Packet-switching allows efficient and economical use of the network, so it suits the telecomms supplier, and it provides a high degree of error-checking, so the user can feel pretty confident that the transmission will be correct. Importantly, it also insulates the user effectively from most of the characteristics of the network; different types of computer and terminals working at different speeds can communicate with each other in a flexible yet reliable manner.

PSS is an alternative to the PSTN. It requires a separate payment and it requires that both ends of the link are subscribers — which is of course the case with the PSTN too, but you can usually assume that any contact will have a phone; you cannot assume PSS registration (British Telecom does publish a directory of subscribers for PSS, and this is also available on-line for reference when you call PSS).

In most cases, PSS will not let you send and receive any more quickly and it will not do away with the need for a modem. To get at PSS in the first place you still have to use the PSTN to dial the number of one of the PSS 'nodes' in the exchanges — in other words, you have to connect to it via a voice-grade link.

PSS access points

Aberdeen	Belfast
Birmingham	Brighton
Bristol	Cambridge
Cardiff	Edinburgh
Glasgow	Ipswich
Leeds	Liverpool
London (seven)	Luton
Maidstone	Manchester
Newcastle	Nottingham
Portsmouth	Reading
Sheffield	Slough

International PSS

Some 90 data carriers in 63 countries operate public-access packet switching networks similar in concept to PSS and linked by a 48Kbps international network which in Britain is called IPSS. Connection to PSS, therefore, enables you to communicate with almost anywhere in the world relatively economically.

Australia	AUSPAC
	MIDAS
Austria	RADIO AUSTRIA
Belgium	DCS
Brazil	INTERDATA
Canada	DATAPAC
	GLOBEDAT
	INFOSWITCH
Denmark	DATAPAK
Eire	EIRPAC
Finland	FINNPAC
France	TRANSPAC
French Guayana	DOMPAC
French Polynesia	TOMPAC
Gabon	GABONPAC
Greece	HELPAC
Guadeloupe	DOMPAC
Hong Kong	INTELPAK
	DATAPAK
Indonesia	SKDP
Israel	ISRANET
Italy	ITAPAC
Ivory Coast	SYNTRANPAC
Japan	DDX-P
	VENUS-P
Korea	DNS
Luxembourg	LUXPAC
Malaysia	MAYPAC
Martinique	DOMPAC
Mexico	TELEPAC
Netherlands	DABAS
	DATANET 1
New Zealand	PACNET
Norway	DATAPAK
Portugal	TELEPAC
Reunion	DOMPAC
Singapore	TELEPAC
South Africa	SAPONET
Spain	IBERPAC
	TIDA
Sweden	DATAPAK
Switzerland	TELEPAC
Taiwan	PACNET
USA	AUTONET
	COMPUSERVE
	FTCC
	ITT/UDTS
	RCA/LSDS
	TELENET
	TRT-DATAPAK
	TYMNET
	UNINET
	WUI-DBS
	WUTCO
West Germany	DATEX-P

In Britain there are fewer than 100 000 modem users among a computer population ten times that. Why?

One reason is the slow take-off for computer communications in general. Britain's outdated telephone network is partly to blame; British Telecom promises a fully digitized network by the end of the century, which will certainly improve the speed, capacity and reliability of all telephone connections.

Another problem has been the approval process that British Telecom imposes by law on anything connected to the phone system. While a modem does not have to be particularly clever to pass the tests, the protracted procedures involved have in the past militated against product and marketing planning. The bottlenecks appear to be easing, however.

Then there's the all too common mismatch between software and hardware, between the communications program and the modem itself — not all comms software will work with all modems, and *vice versa*. The absence of widely followed formal or *de facto* standards is to blame; modem-makers do not know how the software is intended to work; the software writers do not know precisely what functions and facilities the modem is designed to offer. Hayes-compatibility is the nearest we have to an operational standard, but that is by no means followed unanimously.

The all-purpose all-digital network

The future lies with all-digital networks, what in Britain is referred to as ISDN — the Integrated Services Digital Network. Digital transmission greatly simplifies the operation of the network while permitting higher capacities (more transmissions per cable) and faster communications.

The 'integrated' bit broadly means that all digitizable transmission is carried on the same medium. British Telecom picked on 64 000 bps as the basic subscriber bandwidth for its System X exchanges and the ISDN because that gives good reproduction of the human voice. When the network goes digital, however, *any* subscriber will be able to send and receive *anything* — data, voice, fax images — at 64 000 bps; compare the present top speed for PSTN data transmission of 2400 bps. And 64Kbps will be possible from *any* phone line in the country, simply by dialling.

X400 and the future

Improving the speed and quality of the phone system is not the only requirement, though. The main drawback to getting the most from the technical possibilities of computer communications has been the incompatibility between different services and different equipment. They all utilize different protocols and different data formats; they may all use digital data, but that is about the extent of their similarity.

Fortunately, the future here looks good. The other key development for the late eighties in comms is X400. This series of standards is actually a collection of 'recommendations' from a Geneva-based body called CCITT — *Comité Consultatif International Téléphonique et Télégraphie*, a committee of the International Telecommunications Union which includes most of the world's telecomms authorities and key suppliers. CCITT recommendations have the force of Holy Writ in most of the telecomms world.

X400 was developed as a set of standards to enable the interconnection of different electronic mail services — one of the major drawbacks of electronic mail at present is the fact that a subscriber on one system cannot normally pass messages to a user of a different system. X400 defines precisely the rules, or 'protocols', that should be used; there are basically three key protocols involved:

□ *P1* defines how a message should be encased in an 'envelope' of parameters that function much like a real envelope in the postal system — the parameters include sender's and receiver's addresses, time and date of despatch, priority and requests for notification of delivery.

- ☐ *P2* covers the format of the message itself. As well as more envelope information, which will typically be in the format already used by the service, P2 specifies types of content — what X400 calls 'body parts'. These 'body parts' comprise the actual message and can be simple text, images (fax), Teletex-format text, and even digitized voice.

- ☐ *P3* provides for an additional type of contact between users and a 'message-transfer agent' (the messaging service or a comms network that relays messages). Ordinarily, X400 is expected to connect users directly to each other; P3 allows for subsidiary connections such as public electronic mail services, and covers the format of messaging between the service itself and the user's terminal.

As with most protocols, of course, all this is totally transparent to the user. The X400 formatting will be done by a service to which the user subscribes or by the comms software that provides a direct connection.

In theory, X400 will enable users to replace all their existing services, mailbox numbers and separate single-function equipment; in theory, users do not even have to know what kind of equipment will be receiving their transmission. If the manufacturers and service suppliers adopt the X400 standards, it will be possible for *all* types of electronic message service and *all* types of digital hardware to interchange messages.

Currently there are several private X400 systems and services from the likes of Hewlett-Packard, Nixdorf, Olivetti, IBM and DEC, permitting a variety of different equipment to run on local networks. More important, a user on a 'private' system like this will be able to pass information through a 'public' network based on X400 — and in 1987 the world's first such public service was launched in Britain.

It is still early days. P3 in particular has proved troublesome and full of potential problems; CCITT has come up with a revised version called P3+, but the European Computer Manufacturers' Association is promoting an alternative called P7. Other areas untouched by the CCITT work include security provisions and the specification of a directory service — it is obviously important to find out the receiver's address, but not everyone wants this published.

There are also several practical problems to be worked out, of course — how does a Telex machine receive a fax transmission? How much retraining of office staff will be required? And, crucially, will the comms industry put the required effort into user-awareness promotion — given the kind of inertia evidenced by Teletext and the like?

Still, a developed version of X400 is expected to be the preferred protocol for all information transfer by the end of the decade. Meanwhile, the immediate benefit might simply be the promise of inter-system compatibility for text messages — enabling a user on one electronic mail service to send to a subscriber of another electronic mail service. That depends on the willingness of the service suppliers to fall into line on X400, but in Europe at least this does seem to be imminent.

Satellite receivers

Domestic receiver dishes are becoming available for subscribers of satellite-based independent TV stations; adaptors and complete systems for personal computers are also starting to appear. Typically they comprise a plug-in circuit-board controller for IBM-compatibles that is cable-connected to a receiver dish, and in theory they can receive (but not send) any and all satellite-delivered information, including all audio, video and data signals. The result means elimination of modems and control hardware for receiving broadcast data. In practice applications are currently limited; the present crop of domestic TV signals is irrelevant to most computer users, so specialized public or private comms services will have to develop for broadcasting business-related information.

To communicate via a computer, you will almost certainly need some specialized software to set up the link to the outside world. It may come as a separate package, or comms functions may be provided within another application. The software controls a *modem*, a device that converts the signals used by the computer into a form that the telephone line can handle.

□ The computer has to be told what is going on. It normally expects to receive data from the keyboard or to read it from disk; it expects to output data by directing it to the screen, maybe to a printer, and by saving on disk.

□ You have to tell it what format the data will take. A modem is not a computer; even the fanciest examples will blithely try to shift information back and forth regardless of what it looks like. Your system must be configured appropriately — it must assemble data in a form that is compatible with whatever system you are trying to contact.

□ You want easy-to-use facilities for calling up different comms services, for logging everything that is happening (to receive messages, for instance) and for switching comms on and off.

In short, the comms software — like most packages — will act as an intermediary and organizer, fitting between the user, a computer and the modem. It tells the modem what to do without a user having to resort to a programming language or a series of operating system commands; it tells the computer how to manage the despatch and receipt of messages and data.

Hayes-compatibility

Hayes Microcomputer Systems of Georgia was one of the earliest US manufacturers to develop modems which are distinguished by their ability to be controlled by *software* as opposed to mechanical intervention by the operator.

These days, most modem makers have products that can be controlled by commands sent from a software package. However, their modems can usually be controlled by Hayes-type commands as well, for software authors found it easy to adopt the controls that Hayes produced. Since those commands are now widely featured in comms packages, many modem manufacturers have also adopted the *de facto* Hayes standards — though many of them additionally offer the software writers their own commands.

Those commands can be entered by hand at the keyboard, but more likely they will be passed to the modem by a comms package. The comms software can then give you comprehensible prompts like 'Enter the phone number', take your input, assemble it into a Hayes-style command and feed it to the modem.

The full Hayes command set provides considerably more than autodialling, of course — automatic answering, line speed selection, a choice of different telephone system standards and a host of other features designed to keep you from ever lifting a telephone receiver again.

Not everyone needs Hayes-compatibility. It is pointless having a modem that recognizes the Hayes command set if the comms package does not send Hayes-type commands. There are variations in interpretation of the Hayes standard among modem-makers, though most European-produced comms software accommodates a range of modems including several popular models that are not 100 per cent Hayes-compatible.

However, many packages (especially those derived from the States) will not work automatically (or at all) unless the modem *does* follow the Hayes command formats.

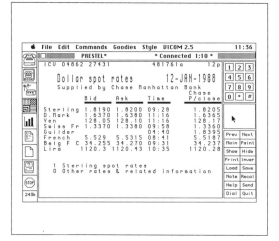

On-line with VICOM

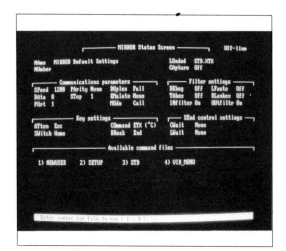

Call log maintained by CONTACT

Status display from MIRROR

Automatic access

To log on to the Telecom Gold electronic mail service manually will normally involve these steps:

- ☐ Set up communication parameters — line speed, data format, etc.
- ☐ Dial the appropriate number.
- ☐ Wait for a 'carrier tone' to indicate that connection has been established.
- ☐ Wait for the PAD> prompt from Telecom Gold, then enter the appropriate CALL message.
- ☐ wait for the ID> prompt from Telecom Gold, then enter your identification codes — your User Number and Password. Once they are accepted, you can use the system as you will.

All this can be automated if the software includes Directory and 'script file' facilities. This example comes from the shareware package PROCOMM, with the following Directory:

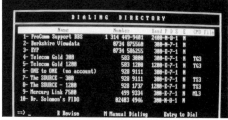

Directory entry 4 has been set up for access at 300 bps to the appropriate Telecom Gold number (01-583 3000) with the relevant parameter settings (E-7-1). A script file called TG3 has been associated with it.

When this entry is selected, the parameters will be used to set up the modem; the number will be dialled automatically; and the 'command' file will be used to log on automatically to Telecom Gold. In part, that file contains these commands:

```
WAITFOR "PAD>"
              [wait for prompt from the other end]
TRANSMIT "CALL 81"
TRANSMIT "^M"
              [send CALL 81 and a Return]
WAITFOR ">"
              [wait for the next prompt]
TRANSMIT "ID JET767 [password]"
TRANSMIT "^M"
              [send identification and another Return]
```

Checklist: comms software

Compatibility

The basic proviso with any such software is that it must be compatible with the computer, modem, printer (if one is used) and the facilities at the other end of the link. Crucially, the software and your modem may not get on — if the software does not use Hayes commands, you are likely to have some troubles in operating a Hayes-compatible modem. The software might also have problems with special character codes — the format used by Prestel, for instance, is rather special, and many comms packages cannot handle it.

Ease of use

Demand a minimum of delays in operation, a minimum of keystrokes in selecting functions, a minimum of background knowledge required before you can start using the package.

Assistance

Look for a decent reference manual, a short and simple 'how-to' guide, a route-map of some kind through the functions and facilities provided, and instantly available assistance both in the form of on-screen help and Hot Line telephone support when it is needed.

Dialling

Any comms package should be able to dial numbers through your modem, either automatically (working from a directory or some other sort of pre-stored input list) or from the keyboard (the modem dials the number as you type the digits). You should also expect simple facilities to terminate and/or abort a call. A useful extra would be unattended retry, to keep calling automatically until you are connected — particularly useful for numbers that get busy at peak times.

Directory

This is the ability to hold a list of regularly used numbers and for the modem to call them automatically. When you select the number — by entering a corresponding code or by moving the cursor through a list to highlight a selection — all the comms parameters associated with that service should also be loaded automatically before the package starts dialling. Options should include manual or automatic dialling and an easy way to amend, delete and add numbers to the directory.

Automatic log-on

Many comms packages allow you to include 'script files'; these may provide you (or another user) with some explanatory or advisory text before you actually start communicating. More usually, they enable the software to send the required 'log-on' information — password identifiers and so on. Auto log-on is usually provided by storing your password and/or ID number in the program's directory or some other callable text file; the package checks for the ID requests coming down the phone line and will automatically respond with the information for the bulletin board or mailbox on connection.

Setting parameters

Both ends of a link have to agree on the transmission format, and this means there must be some quick and easy way to set comms parameters — you do not have to understand *why* they are set, just find out what is expected by the system to which you wish to connect and configure your end of things in exactly the same way. So the comms package's 'configuration' information should be easy to access and easy to alter.

Downloading and uploading

It is usually important to be able to 'download' and 'upload' files — respectively, in order to capture on disk everything that is arriving down the phone line and to send pre-prepared text or other files from disk rather than inputting them laboriously at the keyboard. At its most basic, downloading should be available to capture a record of the session. That way you do not have to read everything as it appears on your screen — you can minimize connect and access charges by downloading it willy-nilly and studying the disk file later at your leisure. The software should enable the user to do this simply — and safely; for instance, when you nominate the name of a 'log' file to capture an incoming message, the package should first check that a file of the same name does not already exist on disk. You should be able to trust your software.

A modem converts *digital* signals (as used by the computer) into an *analogue* form — tones of sound, in fact — which can be transmitted over a telephone line; at the other end of the connection another modem will convert it back again. (When the phone network goes digital, in theory that digital-to-analogue conversion will not be needed and modems will be unnecessary; in practice that may not be the case for some years yet.) The word 'modem' is short for MOdulator/DEModulator; the digital-to-analogue conversion is called modulation — hence the acronym.

At the other end of the link, another modem converts the sounds back into electrical signals for the computer there.

The modem may be connected directly into the telephone system via special cabling and sockets. More usually, it will have a phone lead terminating in a standard BT connector that can simply plug into any telephone socket.

The modem may be an externally connected box, in which case it will probably have a power lead; a third lead goes to the RS-232 serial transmission port of a computer. For a few machines (IBM-compatibles, mostly) you can get a modem on a plug-in board for installation inside the computer.

A professional user might keep one phone line specifically for data transmission, but an external modem itself will probably have a telephone jack socket as well, so you can plug your phone into the modem if you want. You will then be able to use the phone normally when the modem is not taking the line.

Now there are two ways of actually dialling. Your phone is still usable, even when the modem itself is not being used. So with the simpler modems, you can switch on the modem and dial the number; when you get the carrier tone, you set the modem to 'on-line' or 'data' or whatever switch position the manual says. You can now replace the handset and the connection will not be cut because the modem has the line.

The alternative does away with the phone altogether: it is called 'autodialling', and requires that the modem itself is capable of sending the relevant dialling signals. This can be done by you typing the number at the keyboard in a format the modem likes, which again will be specified in the manual, or you may be able to select a number from a phone directory you have stored in the computer.

Autodialling is provided by most comms packages; the problem is that the autodialling software must match the autodialling modem.

Data rates

The technical term 'baud' corresponds to 'bits per second' (abbreviated to 'bps'). A 300 baud modem will send and receive characters at the rate of 300 bps, and since there are usually eight bits in a character that approximates to 37 or so characters a second. Some of the bits being sent and received will be non-printable control and error-checking bits used to oversee the actual transmission; as a rule of thumb it is safer to divide the baud rate by ten rather than eight to indicate the character transmission speed.

via phone system
to another modem

Phone socket

Computer   Modem   Telephone

Basic connections

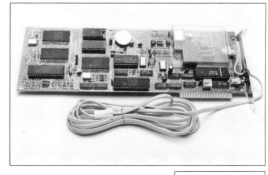

Internal modem

Acoustic couplers

You do not see many acoustic couplers around, but they are handy for portable computers because you can send and receive from just about any phone anywhere in the world.

An acoustic coupler is simply a modem that does not plug into a telephone socket. It's usually an oblong box with a couple of flexible cups on top into which a telephone handset can be placed. Some portable computers have a coupler built into their casing, but in most cases you attach the coupler to your computer in the usual way — via an RS-232 plug that goes into a serial-transmission socket on the computer.

To start communicating you dial the required number on your phone. When you get the high-pitched whine (the 'carrier tone') which means you have successfully made the connection, you just shove the handset into the cups on the coupler. The modem then takes over.

Acoustic couplers are mostly limited to 300 bps, because the connection is not good enough to accept anything faster — the modem is just replacing your ear, after all, and the presence of the telephone handset with its relatively crummy loudspeaker and microphone magnifies all the possible problems of interference. Couplers are not especially cheap, either. But they are genuinely portable, and easier to set up than most conventional modems.

Coupler with 'laptop' computer

The next speed you are likely to encounter is the 'split-rate' working defined by CCITT Recommendation V23. If you use a viewdata service such as Prestel, your modem *must* be able to receive characters at 1200 and send only at 75. The argument is that for viewdata you will be doing a lot more receiving than sending and the slower speeds are simpler and cheaper to implement.

The 1200/75 split-rate option (sometimes called '1275') is quite widely available in Europe, not least because the telecommunications authorities wanted to popularize viewdata as an easy modest-cost service. Now many information services and electronic mail suppliers also offer 1200/75. The potential is that the comms software you use has to be set to a particular speed. Since 1200/75 is not widely used in the States, software derived from the USA may not be able to work at that combination of speeds.

One step up is the V22 standard, receiving *and* sending at 1200 baud ('1200/1200'); these usually represent a pretty significant increase in price. The faster the modem can go, the fancier and more expensive the modem has to be — at higher speeds, data transmission becomes highly susceptible to glitches and electrical noise in the phone lines, and that means the modem must have lots of expensive in-built error-correction facilities.

Sending and receiving at 2400 baud (the CCITT's V22 *bis* standard) is the top limit permitted by British Telecom on the PSTN. This speed is used primarily for commercial data transmission, and many dial-up services do not bother offering 2400 baud access.

Beyond 2400 baud there are other, much faster, data communications speeds. Larger commercial users who can justify the expense of top-grade modems and high-speed transmission usually rent a special dedicated phone line of their own to handle the traffic.

CCITT

The *Comité Consultatif International Téléphonique et Télégraphie* issues 'recommendations' that are followed by most of the world's telecomms authorities and suppliers.

CCITT recommendations for data transmission over the telephone network have the prefix V, and in Europe modem manufacturers tend to characterize their products by reference to these standards (in America and US-influenced parts of the world, a different and non-compatible set of modem speed standards is used). A 'V22 modem' or 'V22-compatible modem' essentially means one that sends and receives at 1200 bits per second, because V22 is the CCITT recommendation for data transmission at that speed.

These are the key CCITT references that you might come across:

- **V21**   send and receive at 300 baud
- **V22**   send and receive at 1200 baud
- **V22** *bis*   send and receive at 2400 baud
- **V23**   receive at 1200, send at 75 baud (the viewdata standard)
- **V24**   interface standard for serial data transmissions — covers the pin connections and cabling between two data communications devices (typically a computer and a modem or printer); also known as RS-232
- **V25**   automatic answering by modems (and telephone answering machines, too, as it happens)

BABT

BABT is the *British Approvals Board for Telecommunications*. By law, any equipment connected to British Telecom's networks must have BABT approval — including modems. Since the BABT publishes quite detailed standards, it is not too difficult for a manufacturer to design and build something that *will* get approval. The BABT does not test the modem's specification or claimed performance in data transmission; it only checks to make sure that the equipment does not interfere unduly with the phone lines. So BABT approval is no kind of *consumer* standard.

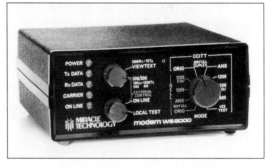

On-line. Externally-connected modems that cannot autodial will have a 'data' switch to move from local to on-line operation once the connection has been made; obviously that is done automatically by autodialling modems.

Data rate. Transmission speed on multiple-speed modems is also selected automatically on the fancier modems; the baud rate is set by software or keyboard entry, and the modem adjusts itself accordingly. Simpler modems will require you to twist a knob or push buttons on the modem itself to pick the desired speed.

Reset. The only other control switch you might find is a Reset button. This will clear all the settings the modem has taken from the computer, and usually runs the switch-on self-testing as well.

Indicators. You might get very few or a great many indicator lights. Apart from the on-off beacon, these lights usually relate specifically to what is happening on the RS-232 connectors. These are the most useful:

- DTR, Data Terminal Ready (may be labelled simply READY). This comes on when the computer is in contact with the modem, so they are both ready.

- DCD, Data Carrier Detect (may be labelled CD or CDT or CARRIER or ON-LINE). This comes on when the modem hears a carrier tone on the line, meaning it is picking up a remote computer — a service you've dialled, or someone calling in.

- RXD, Receive Data (may be labelled RD or RECEIVE). This flickers when incoming data arrives, so it indicates that something is being received from the other end.

- TXD, Transmit Data (may be labelled TD or TRANSMIT). This lights when data is being transmitted, so it indicates that something is being sent from your end.

The RS-232 specification has become the *de facto* standard for attaching modems. It tells the designers, manufacturers and users of computer equipment:

- The fact that a plug and socket are involved (though it does not actually say what shape they should be; the common D-shaped wide-mouthed connector originated from a West German standards organization — but IBM and Apple among others have used a different shape of plug and socket)

- The electrical characteristics of the signals being passed across the connection

- The functions of the signals on each of 21 connections (not all of the 21 possible signals are always relevant for computer communications — and in practice very few of them are actually used)

RS-232 was specifically designed for the connection of terminals to modems — the requirement was caused by the growth of multi-user systems with remote terminals that would want to connect to a host computer via phone lines. In practice, RS-232 works literally only for connecting a 'dumb' terminal (like a VDU) to a Bell-compatible modem (one that operates with the frequencies used by the phone lines of the US Bell network). Depending on the manufacturers' inclinations, a desktop computer may not be set up as a 'terminal' and a modem may not be a true RS-232 'modem' device. There's no unanimity on precisely what all of the wires will be used for; nor is there conformity on the usage of male or female connectors (males have the pins visible, female connectors have twin lines of socket holes). And that is just the start of the problems.

RS-232 is a specialized and complicated standard that today is being used on applications for which it was never intended. It owes much of its present popularity to the lack of any widely agreed alternatives.

Still, the existence of *any* standard is to be commended. In general, RS-232 has stood the test of time; and, truth to tell, it *is* usable. Besides, we are stuck with it.

Checklist: Modems

Compatibility

Will the modem work with the software —
in particular, if the software sends Hayes-
type control codes, will the modem recognize
them? If not, will it at least respond to
autodialling commands from your software?
And can the modem handle all the
parameters required by the destinations you
will be calling?

Speed

Can the modem operate at the optimum
speed for your requirements? Heavy use of
an on-line database service may rack up
large phone bills unless your modem can
transfer data quickly to minimize on-line
time.

Handling errors

Data transmission is prone to electrical
interference: the modem should have some
way of monitoring the quality of
transmission and automatically requesting a
retransmit if necessary (though most kinds of
error-checking rely on both ends of the link
agreeing on what they are doing). Look out
for ARQ or EPAD as a feature on your
modem.

Buffering

A 'buffered' modem includes a lump of
memory for temporary storage, enabling it to
accept input from the computer at one speed
and pass that data on to the phone line at a
different speed. This means, for instance,
that you can set up a computer to work at
1200/1200, while the modem communicates
with the remote computer at 1200/75 —
handy for communicating with V23 services
even though the computer or the comms
software does not support that.

Upgrades

Can the modem be upgraded? This is likely
to apply to increases in speed, but it may
also be relevant if you require additional
functions like automatic encryption for
security purposes of data sent and received,
buffering and additional error-checking
facilities.

Support

Few areas in computing can be as
troublesome as achieving successful
communications. This places a premium on
the quality and comprehensibility of
manuals, and the availability of a Hot Line
telephone support facility from the
manufacturer or a data centre.

For most business people, the telephone remains the most commonly used means of communication.

The program-controlled digital PBX has evolved considerably in the last few years; the advantages of all-digital operation have been extended from the operation of the PABX itself into the internal phone system, with analogue PSTN signals being converted into digital form for the extensions.

This has made a good many extra facilities available for voice calls, but it also has implications for data and fax communications.

Using a modem

There can be problems with conventional modem communications through a modern PABX:

- Warnings of incoming calls or reminders that a caller is still on hold are intended to be heard while the extension user is talking. That can interfere with data transmission; you may be able to kill the 'incoming call' signal, though, and some modern PABXs have a 'data protect' facility.

- Not all PABXs can cope with autodial modems, though in most cases the code to get an outside line can simply be tagged on to the start of the autodial number. Even so, the PABX may pause briefly before giving you the external dial tone; that pause might not be so easy to incorporate into an autodial sequence.

- Some older switchboards use dialling methods that are totally incompatible with any current modem. The only solutions are to use an acoustic coupler, employ a separate exchange line for the modem or replace the switchboard with one that *is* compatible with the modem.

The voice-handling facilities available on a digital PABX might include:

- *Queuing*. Incoming calls are stacked and put through in sequence.
- *Call redirection*. Incoming calls are diverted automatically to another designated extension when the user indicates he or she will be there.
- *Transfer-on-busy*. Calls are diverted to another extension if one is busy.
- *Call hunting*. Designated extensions are grouped so that any of them can take particular kinds of incoming call. 'Call distribution' or 'cyclic hunting' makes sure that the incoming calls for a department are distributed among the group of extensions; 'sequential hunting' assigns priority levels to concentrate calls on the early-choice extensions.
- *Call pick-up*. Enables users to answer calls on another extension.
- *Automatic call-back* (or 'camp-on-busy'). On finding an extension engaged, the exchange rings back when both parties are free.
- *Call warning*. Sounds a discreet tone during a phone conversation to advise of an incoming call.
- *Distinctive ring*. Distinguishes between internal and external calls.
- *Short-form dialling*. A library of numbers is maintained by the system and can be obtained by keying a short code.
- *Route restriction*. Limits are imposed selectively on dialling.
- *Route optimization*. Enables the PABX to route individual outgoing calls through lower-cost leased lines.
- *Call logging*. Information on individual calls is analysed (or stored for subsequent manual or computer analysis) to provide a basis for allocating telephone costs (and for checking British Telecom's billing).
- *Teleconferencing*. Several users participate in the conversation.
- *Voice mail*. Enables digitized voice messages to be stored in the system for later delivery to or collection by the recipient.

- Switchboards installed before the introduction of BABT regulations may exacerbate line attenuation under some circumstances, to the detriment of modem performance. 'Low-loss' exchange-switchboard lines fix this one.

- PABX operators are expected to answer all incoming calls; not all PABXs can automatically circumvent this for incoming data calls by detecting the carrier tone and switching the call to an appropriate extension.

  The only solution in some cases is to dedicate one or more lines to data and advise the operator that any calls on those lines should be transferred immediately to the relevant extension.

Modem manufacturers maintain lists of switchboards with which their products will work correctly. They can be remarkably coy about releasing this information, though a list (usually out of date) often appears in the modem manual. On the other hand, most users see the manual only *after* they have made the purchase.

All-digital comms

As well as improving voice communications and providing extra voice facilities, the digital PABX can theoretically handle data and image transmission as well. In principal, each telephone point connected to the PABX can reasonably be viewed as an information terminal on which data can be collected, enquiries made and a variety of communications links initiated.

The use of a handset as a data terminal extends the capability of a familiar device — and in doing this, the PABX behaves as a terminal concentrator and terminal switching unit. The PABX has the ability to act as a terminal concentrator or a message switching centre for the workstations of an electronic office.

Such an 'integrated service' PABX is able to multiplex a number of calls on to an outside line — to handle the switching and routing of voice, data and fax signals, and to interleave them to make optimum use of a leased line or a 64Kbps ISDN connection.

DPNSS

DPNSS is British Telecom's Digital Private Network Signalling System, a set of standards for linking digital PABXs via its present and future digital network services. DPNSS effectively aims to make available across a point-to-point network many of the facilities provided internally by modern PABXs; those include short-form dialling, auto redial, call forwarding and the like. The result should be a 'transparent' link, meaning that the end-users can utilize the same facilities as on internal calls without anyone having to worry about who actually made the PABX at the other end of the line and what facilities *it* provides.

This is fine in theory; but DPNSS is not an internationally agreed standard, and not all digital PABXs follow it. Still, it is a step in the right direction.

The PABX as data concentrator

There are several advantages to using PABXs as a concentrator for desktop data communications:

- The existing wiring is used.

- Even when new wiring is required, the purchase and installation costs of twisted-pair cabling are low.

- Data rates between the desktop and the PABX can be fairly high — considerably higher than a direct-dial modem connection.

- The PABX provides a single point of management and monitoring for all comms, voice and data (to assist in planning as well as allocation of costs).

- Individual modems are not required — the digital PABX already provides for digital communications internally.

At present, such a PABX will convert between its digital signals and the analogue signals required by the PSTN for voice, but not all incorporate the equivalent of a modem for data. Things will be greatly simplified when all point-to-point communication is digitized via ISDN, and the PABX will then come into its own as a standard interface to the outside world.

This should not imply that a digital PABX could automatically become a LAN controller, for instance. The PABX is good for only one thing — routing transmissions. It does not perform too well in managing resources. The most effective use is probably via a gateway, treating the PABX as one of several resources available to users.

The quality of decision-making depends on the availability and quality of information; the scale and range of the on-line databases available can significantly improve management performance.

An on-line database is the equivalent of a good reference library — except that the service will normally be available 24 hours a day, 365 days a year. It will also provide much *more* information — and more *specific* information — than the average library. You will be able to locate the facts you want more precisely, and you can take copies of the information you have found.

These services are operated by suppliers — often called 'hosts' — who do not usually generate the information themselves. The hosts run one or more computers (or they take space on another service's computers); they buy or rent the information from the database producer and make it available in on-line form. This will often mean the hosts have to get it into their computers in the first place. You will also find that the same databases are available from more than one host, and it can pay to shop around.

Most hosts run at least half a dozen databases from different sources, providing a common means of accessing and searching through the information. For instance, among offerings from Datasolve are a marketing and media service called MAGIC which includes the Mintel market research reports, Henley Centre for Forecasting reports (Leisure Futures and Planning Consumer Markets), the *Marketing Surveys Index* (a worldwide index to published market research) and the text of some relevant publications (*The Guardian*, *Financial Times*, *Media Week*, *Campaign* and *PR Week*) — which together can give a good idea of what is happening in the advertising and communications business.

What's available?

There are something over 2000 databases around the world, with more arriving every day — and the international nature of the

information need not be a problem, since there are economical means of accessing databases on the other side of the globe.

Broadly, there are two types of on-line database:

□ *Reference* databases usually contain bibliographic information, identifying relevant sources. Typical examples include scientific abstracts; the researcher will have to obtain copies of the documents separately, though often an order can be placed at the end of the search.

□ *Source* databases are a collection of facts that can be provided directly — company information, import/export data, commodity prices, details of investment grants and the like. (You may come across the term 'full text' database; this is one that gives the complete text in question, typically a newspaper or magazine story.) Source databases may have a reference-type index.

The range of topics covered is vast — scientific and technical matter probably constitutes the largest category of on-line information, mostly in bibliographic form: business-related databases run a close second, including company data and marketing information.

The panel on the next page gives an indication of what is available on just one service, albeit one of the largest. Dialog Information Services Inc., an on-line information service based in California but used in 75 countries, is one of the major suppliers; its KNOWLEDGE INDEX service gives access to more than 35 of Dialog's bibliographic databases at reduced rates, with a simple set of search commands, and at restricted times (basically the working day in California — so access times vary between time zones). The data for KNOWLEDGE INDEX currently runs to approximately 120 million records; four large computers are used for searching the database and a fifth keeps control of them.

Databases on KNOWLEDGE INDEX

AGRICULTURE
AGRICOLA
AGRIBUSINESS USA
CAB ABSTRACTS

ARTS AND LITERATURE
ARTBIBLIOGRAPHIES MODERN
ARTS LITERATURE INTERNATIONAL
BOOKS IN PRINT
MAGILL'S SURVEY OF CINEMA
MLA BIBLIOGRAPHY

BUSINESS INFORMATION
ABI/INFORM
HARVARD BUSINESS REVIEW
ICC BRITISH COMPANY DIRECTORY
STANDARD & POOR'S
TRADE AND INDUSTRY INDEX

COMPUTERS AND ELECTRONICS
INSPEC
INTERNATIONAL SOFTWARE DATABASE
MICROCOMPUTER INDEX
THE COMPUTER DATABASE

EDUCATION AND SOCIAL SCIENCES
AMERICA: HISTORY AND LIFE
GRADLINE [accredited US institutions]
HISTORICAL ABSTRACTS
PETERSON'S COLLEGE DATABASE
SOCIOLOGICAL ABSTRACTS

ENGINEERING AND MATHEMATICS
ENGINEERING LITERATURE INDEX
MATHFILE

MAGAZINES AND NEWSPAPERS
MAGAZINE INDEX
NEWSEARCH [current newspapers]
NATIONAL NEWSPAPER INDEX

MEDICINE
BIOSIS PREVIEWS
CANCERLIT
CLINICAL ABSTRACTS
CLINICAL ABSTRACTS
CONSUMER DRUG INFORMATION
DRUG INFORMATION
HEALTH PLANNING AND
ADMINISTRATION
INTERNATIONAL PHARMACEUTICAL
   ABSTRACTS
MEDLINE medical articles
MENTAL HEALTH ABSTRACTS
PSYCINFO literature

REFERENCE
ACADEMIC AMERICAN ENCYCLOPAEDIA
DISSERTATION ABSTRACTS ONLINE
GPO PUBLICATIONS REFERENCE FILE
HEILBRON [important chemical compounds]
IRS TAXINFO
LEGAL RESOURCE INDEX
NTIS [National Technical Information Service]
THE BIBLE
WHO'S WHO

In short, there are databases to cater for needs from the very general to the minutely particular; and whatever you are looking for, the chances are that you will be able to find it *somewhere*.

Marketing and media information

Marketing information can often be difficult or expensive to acquire. On-line services can do the job quickly, relatively cheaply and from your own office.

FT Information Services operates PROFILE, which contains the full text of some three dozen different periodicals and news agency reports. British Telecom's HOTLINE is a marketing facility using different sources — among them the Saatchi & Saatchi Media Facts series, giving information on media developments throughout the world, and EUROMONITOR ONLINE for marketing data in Europe. MAID (Market Analysis and Information Database) from Pergamon Infoline again provides similar information, and also has a weekly news update service based on the retail trade press.

Company information

Several on-line sources are available to find the kind of information that would otherwise have meant a trip to Companies House, if not the employment of a financial investigator. Many of these services give you nothing more than published information, usually from Companies House Annual Returns and the *London Gazette* (winding-up petitions), but they do make it available instantly, with quick and accurate searches, and they do pull together all the latest published information.

The ICC database (Inter Company Comparisons) is available from a couple of suppliers. It has information on 'approximately 1.8 million' limited companies in Britain; for 100 000 of them, more detailed financial datasheets are available. JORDANWATCH is also offered by more than one supplier; it provides more detailed financial data on only 55 000 'key companies'. KOMPASS ONLINE has the same kind of Companies House information, plus data drawn from sources such as the *Directory of Directors* and *UK Trade News*.

Patents

Patent searches can be particularly laborious, but as well as confirming the novelty of a particular invention they can be extremely useful in finding out what direction research is taking in a particular area and for indicating what competitors are doing.

The major source here is a bibliographic database, WORLD PATENTS INDEX, which has over three million entries — primarily from Europe, North America and Japan.

Access

There are three basic ways of calling an on-line service:

☐ The service may operate its own network directly, in which case you use the PSTN. After joining the service you will usually receive a copy of the *User's Guide* (which should describe the commands and the various databases provided), an account number, a password and the appropriate phone number to call along with the terminal parameters that will have to be set up in your comms software.

Most of these networks can accept access at speeds up to 1200 baud; some will take faster modems. It obviously makes sense to use the highest speed possible, as billing is on the basis of connect time.

☐ The service may operate a network with access via PSS. In some cases you may need a separate PSS subscription if your organization does not already use PSS, but a number of services include the PSS costs in their billing. Otherwise the service charge and information supplied will be much as for direct connection.

Using an on-line service via PSS is a good indication of the value of comms software with automatic log-on capabilities. When connected, you enter a PSS password which usually consists of ten letters and three numbers; you then have to enter the 'address' of the service — normally one letter and eleven numbers. That should get you to the information service itself, whereupon you will be asked to enter your

This illustrates the type of basic company information you would get from one of the reference services, KOMPASS ONLINE. The user's input here is shaded.

Select from the following files :
1   U.K. Companies
2   U.K. Registered Companies
9   END OF SESSION
Enter selection number or ? :

> 1

TYPE OF SEARCH - (U.K. Companies)

TYPE 1 Select companies by Product
TYPE 2 Select a company by Name
     9 RETURN TO OPENING MENU
Enter TYPE number or ? :

> 2

SELECT A COMPANY BY NAME
Enter company name or K-code or ? :

> APRICOT COMPUTER

4 companies selected
1.   APRICOT COMPUTER
     MAINTENANCE LIMITED
        Birmingham
2.   Apricot Computers plc
        Birmingham *HQ*
3.   Apricot Computers Ltd
        Glenrothes
4.   Apricot Computerworld
        Swindon

        * END of LIST *
Enter line number(s) or (S)top :

> 2

Enter (D)isplay, (P)rint or (R)eselect :

> D

Enter Format Option(s) or ? :

> ?

FORMAT A. Summary of Company Data
FORMAT B. Full Company Data
              (Summary Products)
Enter ?? for more detailed display options
Enter Format Option(s) or ? :

> A

Summary data
APRICOT COMPUTERS PLC
   Apricot Hse.,111 Hagley Rd.
   Edgbaston
   Birmingham
   W Midlands B16 8LB
Tel.   : 021-456 1234
Telex   : 334792
Fax.   : 021-455 8427
Emp.   : 650
Sales   : £75m — £125m
Business   : Microcomputer manufrs
Reg.No.   : 00844354
K-Code   : 1N2CT
Data   : H.Q. Location
           : Also on Infocheck
Updated   : 15.Sep.87

account number and then your password. The possibility of mistyping is considerable.

PSS means most UK users will be able to access an internationally-located database at local-call rates; KNOWLEDGE INDEX, for instance, is available through a PSS link.

☐ The database may be available through a 'gateway' from another service, typically one of the electronic mail systems — the panel shows some of the databases currently available on Britain's largest electronic mail service. Via a gateway, the database can normally be used on an *ad hoc* basis with no separate subscription required and charges included in the e-mail bill.

This is by far the simplest way to taste the waters of on-line information; the range of gateways is limited, however, there may be no user manual available and the costs can be high for frequent access.

Using an on-line service

Different services have different procedures, but this approach is quite common:

☐ Nominate a file or an individual database to be searched by a command such as SELECT or BEGIN followed by a database name.

☐ Select a topic with a command like GET or FIND followed by the text to search for. Such commands can normally be used with more than one topic to narrow the search to specific items; you can also demand that terms must be present or absent in an item, a paragraph or even in the same sentence. Wildcards, too, can be used and are particularly helpful where what you are looking for may be found under a variety of terms all sharing the same root: GET COMM* would find items containing 'comms, communications, communication, communicating' and so on.

Databases via Telecom Gold

OFFICIAL AIRLINES GUIDE
Airline schedules and fares

DATASOLVE
Full-text coverage of national and international newspapers and business periodicals

JORDANWATCH
Extensive company information, with fuller financial data on major UK companies

INFOCHECK
Company financial information with comment and credit ratings on over 160 000 UK companies

AIMS NEWS
Information on Government and EEC grants for UK businesses

KOMPASS ONLINE
Range of business directories with facility to print named mailing labels

INFOMATICS DAILY BULLETIN
Daily bulletin on information technology

FINTECH
Weekly Financial Times bulletin service on business aspects of new technology

PETROLEUM MONITOR
Daily bulletin on North Sea petrogas industry

You can mine a rich vein of information in on-line databases, but you may initially have problems in knowing where to start and which databases are appropriate.

Brit-Line

Directory of British databases, published twice a year. Lists databases by subject matter. A typical entry gives the provider's details, subject and content, on what services the database is available and charges.

PUBLISHER: Educational Data Information
ADDRESS: 23 High Street
Lingfield
Surrey RH7 6AA
TELEPHONE: 0293 773675

Online Business Information

Monthly newsletter with in-depth reviews of one or two databases per issue; details nature and depth of information provided, prints sample records, assesses search methods.

PUBLISHER: Headland Press
ADDRESS: 1 Henry Smith's Terrace
Headland
Cleveland TS24 0PD

TELEPHONE: 0429 231902

□ There may be a subsidiary command such as PICK to narrow down the search, and a variety of extras to make it even more specific by looking in very particular places for particular occurrences of the search terms.

□ Once the references are located, there will be commands that let you check what you have. In the PROFILE service, HEADLINE shows the source and the headline, CONTEXT displays the headlines plus paragraphs in which the search terms are present. Dialog uses different combinations of a DISPLAY command — for instance, DISPLAY S1/SHORT/3-6 would show the third to sixth reference of the first search to be displayed in 'short' form, with title and author(s) only. DISPLAY S2/M/ALL would display all references found by search 2 in a 'medium' format — with full title but no abstract. Dialog also has a useful EXPAND command which will give references near to the ones you have found — handy when you are not sure of the exact spelling of an author's name, for instance.

□ Alternatively or subsequently, you can read the full text of the entry. PROFILE'S TEXT command and Dialog's DISPLAY LONG would do this; typically, you would log the session on a disk file to capture the incoming information and read it later.

These are the basic operations. More sophisticated search techniques will probably be available, including searching by date, stepping back through commands to look at previously retrieved items and combinations of the more precise search commands. Other commands may provide an indication of the cost of this search, a recap of the searches you have carried out in a given session and (for bibliographic databases) a way of ordering hard copies of any references. A HELP facility is generally available as well to give a more complete description of the use of each command.

Principal commands for PROFILE

COMMAND	DESCRIPTION
filename	Nominates one of the available files for searching
group	Nominates one of the available file groups for searching
SELECT file[s]	Selects another file — or a group of up to five (separate file names with commas)
SELECT group	Selects a file group
GET subject	Search for items containing specified term(s) — multiple terms can be used, separated by plus signs
PICK subject	Narrow down a search from items already retrieved by specifying only those items containing particular term(s)
HEADLINE ALL	Display the headlines of all items retrieved
HEADLINE number	Display the headlines of specified item number from those retrieved
TITLE ALL	Display the titles of all items retrieved
TITLE number	Display the titles of specified item number from those retrieved
CONTEXT range	Display the headlines or titles, plus paragraphs of text in which search terms occur, for specified item or range of items from those retrieved
TEXT range	Display the complete text of specified items from those retrieved
END	Ends a session

Charges

Charges for on-line services vary widely. The components may include:

- A one-time *registration fee*.

- *Subscription* charged monthly, quarterly or annually.

- *Usage* or 'connect time'. The length of time spent connected to the database. In a few cases the subscription buys unlimited access, but hosts normally pay a usage royalty to the database providers and this is passed on. Charges are normally imposed for usage per minute or per hour (you may get a couple of hours' initial familiarization at no cost) and billing is generally on a monthly basis.

  Minimum charges are the norm; many hosts like to deter occasional usage, since the access capacity is always restricted and large-volume users are likely to be unhappy if they are unable to get on to the system. Equally, discounts for high usage are common.

  The bill will generally itemize accesses by database and by date.

- *Information retrieval*. A charge for the amount of data you select (for each reference you read, for example). Once the norm, this element is now becoming less common.

- *Orders* will apply if you request a copy of a document referenced. This relates particularly to bibliographic databases that contain only an abstract of the material, with the full text available by mail.

- *Communication costs*. In addition you will of course have to accommodate the costs of getting at the service, usually via PSS or the PSTN (some hosts include PSS costs in their billing). Suppliers who operate their own networks may additionally charge for usage of the comms link.

- *Manuals* are usually provided free with registration, but some suppliers charge for them. Additional copies will probably be billed.

- *Training and staff time* may not be negligible. Some hosts provide training courses at extra cost.

Billing can be direct or, for databases where occasional and/or personal access is more likely, via credit card.

Local information services

A number of local councils run on-line information services, usually using a viewdata format — that requires 1200/75 access, the same access parameters as Prestel (one stop bit, even parity, seven data bits), displays whole pages at a time, and typically uses a number-entry menu-selection system.

Most of this information is for the domestic user. This, for instance, is the main menu for the Berkshire Viewdata Service, one of the better-established examples:

```
        BCC — BVS    04/07/87 11.29
        Royal County of Berkshire

             BVS Main Index

Key>

  11  Local & Central Government
  12  Education
  13  JOBSPOT
  14  COMPANYSCAN
  15  Health/DHSS
  21  Tourism
  22  What's On
  23  Sport
  24  Leisure
  25  Disabled People
  26  Youth Info
  27  Roadworks
  31  Local Info
  41  BOOKSEARCH
  61  BVS STOP PRESS — free advertising
      for small businesses!!!
  77  KEYWORDS
  88  HELP pages
  99  All about BVS/How to contact us
```

Choosing BOOKSEARCH will take you to a method of scanning the catalogue for all 300 000 books in the county's 41 public libraries; you can search this using either an author's name or any two words in a book title.

At the time of writing about 7 000 pages of other local information is available. This includes local business information; the COMPANY SCAN option has basic details of 2 000 companies in Berkshire, including address, phone number and type of business.

Unlike the (somewhat limited) local information on Prestel, all the municipal

videotex services are free — apart from the cost of the telephone time. Most are designed to supply general local information. Some also offer advice, leisure activities and even electronic mail facilities for registered users. Because they are intended primarily for the public, they are much easier to use than most other on-line information services.

At the time of writing there is no comprehensive national directory of public local on-line services. This list summarizes services that are active:

Basildon DC	0268 294970
Berkshire CC	0734 875560
Bexley LB	01-304 6516
Essex CC	0245 267266
Gateshead MDC	091 4777047
Gloucestershire CC	0452 426471
Guernsey	0481 27121
Hackney BC	01-985 3322
Isle of Wight College	0983 521711
Kent CC	0732 845018
Merseyside	051-236 4212
Mid-Glamorgan CC	0443 853815
Milton Keynes	0908 662247
North Herts DC	0462 677177
Northamptonshire	0604 20441
Oxfordshire CC	0865 815768
Rochford DC	0702 546373

Electronic mail (often abbreviated to 'e-mail') is the transmission of textual material from one place to another using electronic means for capture, transmission and delivery of information. That information need never assume paper form.

As such, electronic mail services work rather like the Post Office — except that messages are stored electronically in a central computer. When you dial up the service, you are told if there are any messages waiting for you: and you get the option of reading them or waiting for a while. You can send messages to other subscribers — with copies, if required — by typing them directly or by loading previously prepared work.

What is electronic mail?

The term 'electronic mail' could literally apply to any electronic transfer, including simple transmissions between operator-attended workstations like the Telex service. In practice, e-mail more usually refers to a service that includes additional facilities:

- *'Store-and-forward'*. Messages are held until they are requested by the recipient. Direct person-to-person contact is not required, and the service can be used by either party at whatever time (and on whatever day) suits them.

- *Copies* can be sent automatically to names on a distribution list, including 'blind' copies (where the principal recipient is not notified that others have received the message).

- *Advise delivery*. The sender can be told (by a confirming message to his or her mailbox) when the recipient has read the message. An immediate *reply* can also be demanded.

- *Off-line working*. Text can be prepared in advance of transmission, and incoming messages can be saved for later consideration or for use within word-processed documents.

- *'Gateways'*. Most electronic mail services include access to other facilities. They include the Telex system, on-line information services, and electronic typesetting bureaux which accept e-mailed text and return phototypeset masters.

- *'Closed user groups'*. These are areas of the e-mail service with restricted access. In some cases they are available to anyone who pays an additional fee; usually they will include extra gateways and more services. Other closed user groups (CUGS) will be specific to members of a particular profession — Telecom Gold hosts CUGS for solicitors and accountants, for instance; and there are also CUGS for customers of individual companies (handy for disseminating and sharing information or making requests) and user groups for particular computer products.

Uses for e-mail

- *Business correspondence*. This may be the most obvious candidate, but in terms of replacing the mass of post received it will probably have little impact in the immediate future. Crucially, most offices do not yet have compatible text distribution systems; subscribers to different services cannot send messages to each other. The lack of formatting means that e-mail is generally unsuitable for documents where appearance is relevant for comprehension or corporate image.

- *Memos*. Instead, electronic mail is typically used for time-critical data or for brief memo-style messages: e-mail is tending to replace the telephone.

- *Document capture*. In cases where content is more important than appearance, incoming text can be saved on disk for subsequent editing and formatting. Internal reports can be circulated and the sender notified of receipt; where a document is being produced on word processors, e-mail can usefully distribute drafts for comment or amendment; a number of newspapers and other publications accept articles via e-mail rather than on paper; gateways to on-line information services can be used to 'capture' information for subsequent use.

Advantages	**Drawbacks**
□ Messages can be sent at whatever time of day suits the user (including times that take advantage of reduced charges). They can also be prepared in advance for subsequent despatch at convenient times. □ Messages will be in the recipient's mailbox within minutes. □ No need to speak to the recipient in person. □ Delivery of messages can be confirmed — the mailbox principle puts the onus on to the receiver rather than the sender. □ Messages can be marked as 'urgent'. □ A reply can usually be demanded. □ Copies can be sent automatically to everyone on a distribution list appended or previously defined. □ Messages can be read at the user's convenience. Access to the mailbox is available day or night; incoming mail can be stored locally for consideration later. □ Messages do not have to be read in full immediately — only the sender's name, date and subject need be displayed, allowing the option of reading now or later. □ Incoming messages can be saved (locally on disk, or in a file area of the e-mail service) for subsequent word processing treatment — for instance, to incorporate into a document. □ Electronic mail reduces the volume of paper that is to be processed. □ Telex services can be provided as part of the electronic mail facility. This removes the need (and the cost) for a dedicated Telex terminal, and it saves most of the ancillary Telex charges. □ On-line information services may also be available. □ Messages are generally more terse and to the point. Connect time charges, absence of formatting and the fact that the user probably has to handle the e-mail task him/herself all help minimize the number of characters per message.	□ Recipients must also be an electronic mail user — and they must subscribe to the same service as the sender, for as yet there is no inter-service communication between e-mail suppliers (but feasible in the future with X400 — see Chapter 30; and availability of Telex improves the range of contacts). □ Charges can be complicated. It may be difficult to get an indication of actual costs incurred before the bill arrives, and then it can be difficult to check the bill. □ Only text can be sent. It is normally difficult to transfer graphics files, spreadsheets and other non-text formats. □ Text formatting is restricted to the basic punctuation and alphanumeric characters. □ Though illegal on most services, there is occasional use of junk mail. Apart from the time and irritation this involves, there may be charges for unread mail accumulating in a mailbox. □ Until a mailbox is checked, there is no way of knowing that a message has arrived (unless there is an additional software facility for notifying receipt). As well as a computer, the user must have access to a modem and a phone line. □ Telephone links vary in quality. Messages may pick up interference and arrive garbled (or worse, with slight corruption that alters the sense); a lower data rate might have to be used, which can make e-mailing costly and irritatingly slow (interference is more likely at higher speeds); and sometimes it may be impossible to make the connection to the e-mail service in the first place because the line is busy or because the modem cannot detect a weak 'carrier tone' sent from the service to indicate connection (these are less likely now that modernization is improving the number and quality of lines).

Charges

Charges for electronic mail can be complicated. The overall cost may include some or all of these components:

- One-time *registration fee*
- Annual or quarterly *subscription* charge
- *'Connect time'* (how long you spend in communication with the mail service)
- *Character charge* (number of characters sent — and, just possibly, number of characters received)
- *Storage* (unread and/or undeleted messages in your mailbox)
- Fees for *additional services* like Telex
- *Telephone bill* (PSTN or PSS) for external connections

Communications services in general go for the lowest-common-denominator approach, catering for the simplest possible type of terminal and of transmission. In the case of electronic mail, this is reflected in the type of documents that may be sent and their content.

With an internal service, the likely range of capabilities and requirements will be known and the facilities provided by e-mail will be more extensive. Public services have to cater for the widest possible range of users, which means they have to offer the simplest types of transmission only.

In practice this will mean that only *text* can be sent — spreadsheets, for instance, cannot normally be e-mailed without first having been transformed into a text-like form. The range of *characters* will be limited to the basic punctuation and alphanumeric symbols, so not all the keys on your keyboard will produce a sendable character (even tabbing to indent text may not be sent), and few of the formatting functions of a word processor or other package will be acceptable (so some care must be taken to ensure that such controls are removed from a word-processed document before transmission).

What actually appears on your screen may also differ from what the electronic mail service can send. While you may appear to have a neatly laid-out document for transmission, the formatting could well be ignored during the e-mailing.

Using electronic mail

With the commercial e-mail services, you are generally given:

- A *password* that identifies you as a legitimate user. In most cases, individual subscribers can choose their own password.
- A mailbox *'address'* to which incoming mail is sent. This may be used for billing purposes by the system.
- A selection of *phone numbers* to call the service. The different numbers may provide alternative access when one line is busy; more likely, there will be a different number for different modem speeds.

The Dialcom service, owned and operated in Britain under the name Telecom Gold, is the UK's largest e-mail system by far. In most respects it is a typical electronic mail service. When the appropriate number has been dialled and the modem has made the connection, this is the kind of message you should see from the service:

```
Telecom Gold Network: For assistance type
'HELP LOGIN' at the prompt 'PAD>'.
This is Dial-up Pad 0. line 15 speed 300

PAD>    CALL 81
```

(The user's input in these examples is shaded.) Telecom Gold operates a number of 'systems', which in practice are separate computers on which an individual's mailbox is located; CALL 81 calls the system for this particular mailbox.

```
*** Call connected
Welcome to Telecom Gold's System 81
Please Sign On

>          ID
User id:   JET767
Password:
```

The 'user ID' is the mailbox number; the password does not appear on the screen when typed. A shorthand form is to enter ID JET767 [PASSWORD] on one line immediately after the 'Please Sign On' message.

```
TELECOM GOLD Automated Office Services
19.4I.177(81)
On At 8:55 13/10/87 BST
Last On At 8:48 13/10/87 BST

Mail call (1 Unread, 2 Read, 1 Read express,
Total 4)
```

If the password and mailbox ID match, the service indicates what if anything is currently in the mailbox: in this case there's one unread message and three that have been read but not yet deleted. Messages stay in the mailbox until the user specifically tells the system to delete them altogether. (An unread 'express' message is automatically inserted at the start of the mail list.)

```
JET>      MAIL
```

The JET> prompt invites the user to enter a command. A variety of options are available; MAIL enters the e-mail facility, but you can also call Telex or on-line information services at this point.

```
Send, Read or Scan:   SCAN

1    From:    INCOMING_TELEX (DEV011)
              Delivered: Mon 12-Oct-87
              11:56 BST Sys 10078 (72)
     Subject: Incoming Telex 334299
              DDTML G 9088DDT 871012
              B1C13 RIK440 ( GF ).
     Mail Id: IPM-10078-871012-107470001
2    From:    P.A.WREN (BTG171)
              Delivered: Thu 17-Sep-87
              15:49 BST Sys 10080 (26)
     Subject: DATABASE
     Mail Id: IPM-10080-870917-142350001
3    From:    P.A.WREN (BTG171)
              Delivered: Thu 17-Sep-87
              17:02 BST Sys 10080 (26)
     Subject: DATABASE continued
     Mail Id: IPM-10080-870917-142350001
4    From:    LAURENCE.HOMES
              (MMU216) Delivered: Sun 11-
              Oct-87 9:59 BST Sys 10081
              (6)
     Subject: Procomm
     Mail Id: IPM-10081-871011-089950282
Read or Scan:
```

The Scan shows the sender's reference, delivery date and time, subject and an internal 'mail ID' reference. Mail options now are to Read one or more messages; to Scan one or more again; to Send something; or to Quit.

At the end of each message read, the prompt ACTION REQUIRED appears. The main options are to press Return to move to the next message; or you can use D to delete it from the mailbox, R to reply, or A to read it again.

Sending messages

If you opt for Send, a prompt will appear on the screen for a mailbox address to receive the message and a 'subject' line. You can give an individual mailbox as the destination by typing a mailbox ID (or a name, if it has been set up for this by the subscriber). Alternatively, you can circulate the message to more than one user — in which case you may be able to specify one of several circulation lists that you have previously set up. You will probably be able to apply 'conditions' as well, so that a set of minutes for a meeting might be sent to everyone on a particular list only if they did not receive the last lot.

Thereafter you can type in the text or load on to the screen a previously prepared file from disk.

Once you have completed your message you can send it by typing .S — most Telecom Gold commands are preceded by the dot to distinguish them from text. Before despatch an urgent message can be marked as 'express' (.EX); other options are 'acknowledgement requested' (.AR), 'carbon copies' (.CC) or 'blind copies' (.BC).

Private e-mail

Users of in-house electronic mail systems outnumber subscribers to the public services by something like four to one. This is partly because DEC provides an e-mail system free with its Vax operating system; DEC users account for something like a third of the private mailboxes. Most of these systems run on multi-user minicomputers and mainframes; the market for e-mail on local networks is rather smaller, simply because LANs do not normally service enough users to warrant their having a messaging facility, but clearly there will be scope for e-mail as LANs are increasingly linked to larger computers.

Telecom Gold Mail: principal commands

READ options:

READ	read all messages in sequence
·READ ALL	read all messages without 'Action Required' prompt
READ [number]	read specified message
READ EXPRESS	read express messages
READ FROM	read messages from named sender
READ SU	read unread messages with subject nominated
READ UNREAD	read unread messages
READ [date]	read messages with the date(s) specified

SCAN options:

[as for READ]

ACTION REQUIRED options:

AGAIN	read message again
AGAIN HEADER	read message header again
NEXT	read next message
REPLY	reply to current message
FORWARD	send copy of message to named mailbox
DELETE	delete message
SAVE	save message in Telecom Gold file
DISPLAY DIR	display user directory

Text input options — editing:

.SP	run Telecom Gold spelling checker
.DISPLAY	display text entered so far
.JU	justify text to specified linewidth
.TO	add or delete recipients

Text input options — sending:

.S	send message
.TO	add or delete recipients
.CC	send carbon copies [to specified mailbox(es) or distribution list]
.BC	send blind copies [to mailbox(es) or list]
.AR	acknowledgement requested [done automatically when message is read]
.RR	reply requested
.EX	send Express [message goes to top of incoming mail list when recipient checks mailbox]
.DA	date-activated message [will not be delivered until specified date]

All bar the first of these can also be used without the dot at the TO: prompt.

Extra services

Many e-mail services offer some or all of these:

- *Radiopaging*. Your pager will bleep when an urgent message is received in your mailbox. Or you can bleep someone by sending a message to the service's radiopaging mailbox.

- *Telemessages*. This replacement for the old-style telegram can be sent from some e-mail services rather than by you calling the Post Office yourself. Delivery the next working day (including Saturdays, usually) is guaranteed for messages received by a set time (which can be as late as 10pm). The Telemessage service can include 'special occasion' formats for birthdays, anniversaries and the like; the delivery can also include a special reply-envelope to encourage an immediate reply.

- *Message translation*. Messages sent or received can be translated by the e-mail service into the recipient's native tongue.

- *Courier services*. A message placed by you on the e-mail service can be copied and delivered by hand or mailed.

International e-mail

There are 14 international licensees for the Dialcom system used by Telecom Gold, which means a UK subscriber can e-mail direct to users of these systems.

Country	System name
Australia	MINERVA
Canada	INFOTEX
Denmark	DATABOKS
Hong Kong	DIALCOM
Ireland	EIRMAIL
Israel	GOLDNET
Japan	KDM INC
Mexico	TELEPRO
Netherlands	MEMOCOM
Puerto Rico	DIALCOM
Singapore	TELEBOX
United States	DIALCOM
West Germany	TELEBOX

Despite the disadvantages, electronic mail can be a cost-effective solution where simple despatch and guaranteed delivery are required. It is quite cheap, not difficult to use, and despatch is fast — certainly faster than conventional mail or facsimile transmission, faster and more versatile than Telex.

The promise of electronic mail does, however, depend crucially on the availability of cheaper, simpler modems; on better, simpler comms software; on easier, more versatile electronic mail services; and, above all, on the ability for subscribers on different services to talk to each other. The situation is not unlike the early days of the telephone: there's little point in having one yourself if the people to whom you wish to talk do not have a phone.

There are several publicly available e-mail services, and the development of X400 interfaces should allow their subscribers to exchange messages; that will eliminate one key disadvantage of e-mail. There is little to choose between the principal suppliers in terms of the mailbox services they provide. The competition (and much of their income) comes from the other on-line facilities they offer — such as access to databases — and their ability to provide purpose-designed packages of services attractive to specific groups of customers. With the resources required for such 'value-added' services, it is likely that only the larger and more visible suppliers will survive as mass-market public mailbox services.

British Telecom's traffic statistics indicate that Telex usage has been growing annually at a steady rate between 7 and 10 per cent over the past few years. It is available in 200 countries; there are over two million Telex users in the world, something around 100 000 in the UK; and British subscribers are making 100 million calls a year within the country, another 80 million or so internationally.

Advantages of Telex

- *Coverage*. Telex is an established international service; international usage accounts for 50 per cent of UK traffic. Only the voice phone system can compete with that scale.

- *Cost*. Telex is relatively inexpensive in Europe, where the connect time charge is typically half the rate of a phone call and line rental is a quarter of the telephone line equivalent.

- *Confirmed delivery*. The most important plus for Telex is the automatic answerback that confirms delivery. The answerback is an alphabetical code which identifies the subscriber; the receiving machine responds to incoming calls by sending its answerback code, and if this is not the code the sender was expecting it can ring off and try again. It is possible to automate this check.

Telex users rely heavily on this invaluable device. It warns them when they have dialled wrongly; it confirms that a correctly dialled Telex has been properly delivered. No other public text messaging service can equal this — the 'advice of delivery' on electronic mail services is only sent when the recipient checks his/her mailbox.

Telex subscribers utilize a special network separate from the PSTN; connection is usually available 24 hours a day with direct dialling. When a call is set up a copy of the text being transmitted is produced simultaneously at both ends. In the UK, a dedicated Telex machine requires the customer to order a special line from British Telecom — BT charges on the same basis as for PSTN lines, installation plus a quarterly rental. Prices for the Telex terminals themselves have been falling since deregulation in the early eighties removed BT's monopoly of supply, but the norm is still well above £1000.

Disadvantages of Telex

- *Speed*. The basic system is slow — 50 bits per second is standard, with national variations allowing faster communication at premium rates for speeds up to 200 and 300 bps.

- *Text*. Only the Baudot telegraph code can be transmitted. This five-bit code allows for only the simplest character set, with no lower-case letters, punctuation, or pound, dollar and percentage signs.

- *Terminals*. To access the line and transmit the limited character set, special terminals are required. An ordinary unconverted computer or VDU cannot be used, and nor can a standard modem.

- *Performance*. The success rate for national connection is pretty good, but for international links it is much lower (because of shortage of lines and failures on the international network as well as simple subscriber unavailability).

Although the Telex system has its drawbacks, the speed is adequate for many users and the absence of fancy formatting will not distress the average subscriber.

Modern Telex machines are microcomputer-based and incorporate many of the easy-to-use features of other electronic office equipment; technology has built on the strengths of Telex (notably its simplicity and its large user base) while papering over its principal weaknesses (low speed and limited character set).

A desktop computer can be used to send and receive Telexes. The options are:

- Dial-up bureau services (mostly available on electronic mail systems)
- Direct access via an internal Telex adapter card
- Direct access via an external Telex box

Telex direct or via e-mail?

For the system manager, it will always be difficult to judge exactly when it becomes more economical to invest in dedicated Telex links rather than relying on e-mail bureau services. It is self-evident that any user who wishes to send Telexes can sensibly take advantage of the desktop computer's word processing and communications facilities. On present pricing, however, it seems likely that Telex traffic exceeding 50 or so inland calls per month would justify a dedicated line.

Using a Telex bureau or e-mail service has cost advantages when sending international Telexes. This is because bureaux can send the text of a Telex via the IPSS international data network; cost savings are achieved since data travels over this network roughly five times faster than over a dedicated Telex link. An associated bureau operation in the destination country receives the Telex and then forwards it via a local Telex line.

Telex adapters for the desktop computer

It is possible to buy special Telex adaptors (in fact they are specialized modems) which connect your computer directly to the Telex network and allow it to be used just as an ordinary Telex terminal. You have to pay the normal subscription and usage charges for the Telex line, but you do not have the expense of buying or renting a special Telex machine.

Facilities in Telex adaptors (modem plus software combinations) for the desktop computer may include:

- *Automatic dial and retry* (more or less standard now).
- *Priority allocation*. Messages from users with a high-priority code get preferential treatment in the 'send' queue.
- *Timed sending* to take advantage of reduced rates or the recipient's availability.
- *Distribution lists* (a Telex is sent to all names on a previously prepared list with a single command).
- Unlimited *storage of frequently used numbers* in abbreviated form.
- Detailed *analysis* of traffic by individual user.
- Simplified *menu-based operation*.
- In-built *text editor* for off-line preparation of Telexes.
- *Automatic conversion of text* into Telex format — putting all text into upper case, for instance, and expanding non-Telex characters such as the dollar and pound signs into text. Alternatively, illegal characters will be highlighted for alteration by hand.
- *Text merge* facilities which automatically insert commonly used phrases into a Telex message.
- *Password protection* — for instance to restrict access to usage statistics or to limit Telex transmission times.
- *Storage* for incoming Telexes — they are received and stored on disk automatically for subsequent consideration.
- *'Background' operation*. While the user gets on with something else, the Telex modem monitors the line for incoming Telexes and stores them.
- *Independent operation*. Some Telex adaptors are powered either from the mains or by battery, and continue to monitor the line when the computer is switched off to accept incoming messages. These are either output immediately on a connected printer or stored.
- More generalized *data communications* facilities, for instance to access electronic mail and dial-up information services.

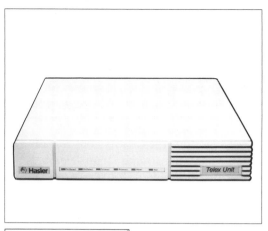

External Telex modem

These 'Telex modems' come as externally connected devices or (for certain computers) an internal plug-in circuit board. They are usually supplied with purpose-designed software to interface a computer (or a local network) to the Telex box; the software will also convert standard-text messages to and from Telex format.

Effectively such adaptors allow you to send and receive Telexes on your desktop computer (they are available primarily for Apple Macs and IBM-compatible PCs) while using the machine for other purposes.

Telex via electronic mail

A cheaper and usually more versatile option is to use the Telex facilities in an electronic mail service — virtually all e-mail services provide access to Telex, in practice by acting as a Telex bureau. Your electronic mail messages are directed to the service's Telex facility, which converts it into the format required for Telex and sends it out to a named recipient on behalf of the user.

This can be simple, efficient and cost-effective for the small or occasional user, since it removes the overhead costs of a dedicated Telex line and a Telex machine. You have to upload the text for a Telex only once. The system is able to forward it to as many different recipients as required.

There is also no waiting around for recipients to answer before you can get on with the transmission — the bureau handles

all the retries automatically until it gets an answerback, and when a message has been delivered an acknowledgement can be posted to the sender's mailbox. A user can also check the progress of sent Telexes.

The main drawback is the difficulty in discovering whether a Telex *has* been received — calling the e-mail service on a regular basis to check the progress of a missive is costly and time-consuming.

One solution is crude but simple: for a modest charge an operator at the e-mail service could ring up to inform the sender personally that a Telex has arrived.

Other measures tried by some e-mail companies include those noted earlier in Chapter 35. The radio-paging option or automated delivery using autoanswer modems at the user's end can be most effective.

Until recently, another serious disadvantage with using any bureau service was the absence of individual Telex numbers — subscribers share one of the bureau's numbers and ask senders to quote a reference that the bureau uses to direct incoming Telexes to the particular customer.

In the case of Telecom Gold, for instance, an incoming Telex would have to be addressed to 265871 MONREF G (a conventional Telex code which is the number of Gold's Telex bureau) but it would also have to cite the individual recipient's mailbox number as well — so a user would give a Telex number as '265871 MONREF G, quoting mailbox 72:MAG95610'.

The principal e-mail bureau services, including TextDirect, now offer individual Telex numbers to subscribers (normally ten digits rather than the standard six or seven) which are used to direct incoming messages automatically to the relevant mailbox.

BT's Prestel viewdata service also operates a Telex bureau within its MAILBOX e-mail facility (and it is very cheap). The software at the user's end requires a text preparation capability that can set up messages in Prestel format, however, and not all commercially available comms packages offer this. Facilities are restricted, too; Prestel is fine for single Telexes, for instance, but it cannot handle multiple destinations.

Telex management

Many companies have enough Telex usage to warrant an employee with the sole responsibility of looking after the traffic. This may be an opportunity for a Telex management system, typically a desktop computer set up to accept input from microcomputers or dedicated word processors, convert text to Telex format, check outgoing messages, pass them on to the Telex system via one or several dedicated lines it controls, monitor the answerbacks and advise senders of delivery.

Legal status

One drawback with Telexing via e-mail has until recently centered on the question of individual 'answerback' numbers.

A test case has, however, confirmed that in the UK a legal contract is deemed to have been made when the other party receives a Telex: the confirmed answerback shown on a hardcopy of the Telex has been regarded as admissible evidence.

The legal status of a document sent by facsimile or electronic mail has not been similarly clarified in court. Since most e-mail services do not provide individual users with a unique answerback number, the legal status of a Telex sent by electronic mail is invalid. BT's TextDirect customers do have a two-letter answerback code, and this service could well provide users with a legally acceptable method of receiving Telexes.

Teletex

Teletex is essentially an upgrade of Telex that is intended to provide a publicly available electronic mail service. The aim is to emulate Telex in providing a simple and accessible message transfer facility; but it will use phone lines rather than telegraph circuits, it employs a different code to provide a much wider character set that includes punctuation and lower case, and transmission speeds will be very much higher — 2400bps rather than 50 or 100 bps.

The Teletex specification laid down by CCITT also includes the requirement that communication takes place between terminals on a direct memory-to-memory basis, so any local work in progress at either end of the link is completely undisturbed; message transfer should go on 'in the background'. Establishing the call, transferring information and closing the connection at the end are all performed automatically by the terminal without operator intervention.

So far, so good. But Teletex terminals are relatively expensive, the telecomms service suppliers have been signally reluctant to get too involved in Teletex, and while there are so few users there seems no extra advantage to Teletex over commercial e-mail services. Teletex can provide specialist facilities for particular customer needs — a standardized system for transferring bulk text from one dedicated terminal to another — but it has failed to become established and it will not play a significant part in the future of messaging services.

TextDirect

TextDirect is an electronic mail service from British Telecom, similar in principle to conventional e-mail networks but offering *only* a Telex bureau facility. From the outset, subscribers were given individual Telex numbers; until the principal electronic mail suppliers started doing this as well, TextDirect had a major advantage.

TextDirect does have a potentially serious drawback. A positive answerback is generally regarded as a safe indication of a successful Telex contact. Conventionally, Telex users assume that the answerback code comprises a short sequence of three or four characters. All TextDirect subscribers have the same code for that part of the answerback (namely, the sequence =TD G).

In fact, the answerback code includes the whole number as well, so the literal definition of the answerback will be a sequence of fourteen or so digits for TextDirect. In practice, however, Telex users tend to assume confirmed delivery when the last few characters are seen; because the preceding number is not normally checked by the sender, the common answerback sequence for TextDirect users can lead to misrouted Telexes.

Apart from that, TextDirect compares well for cost and convenience when set against the bureau-style facilities offered by e-mail purveyors, and for the light Telex user it certainly looks very attractive.

The future for Telex

In the longer term, the spread of national and international X400 services will simplify inter-system messaging and expand the range of types of transfer; Telex will surely decline slowly, just as the telegram service has.

Telex may be characterized as an outdated system, but it clearly meets a real need for simplified operation with confirmed delivery. As long as there is no serious text messaging facility available internationally, the continued use of Telex for overseas transmissions and increased use of Telex by mailbox subscribers will maintain a respectable growth in traffic.

Viewdata — or 'videotex', as the international standards bodies would prefer — involves storing information on a computer for simplified and standardized access via telephone lines from a simple terminal (so simple in fact that it can be a modified TV set).

Features of viewdata

The original viewdata project was the then Post Office's Prestel service. Its design principles have influenced most other viewdata developments, not least because several national telecomms authorities have licensed the Prestel software outright to set' up their own services.

Prestel's aim was to generate more telephone traffic: the new service had to be quick and easy to implement. Viewdata provides easy, interactive operation for non-specialists via a simplified keyboard: basic operations can be carried out with the dozen or so keys on an ordinary telephone keypad. It involves low equipment costs, with a simple terminal (based on the TV set) and a simple connection to the computer (the telephone).

Rather than 'scrolling' past the viewer, as with electronic mail and other dial-up services, information is presented one 'page' at a time; the dimensions of the page and the size and style of the type on it correspond to the capabilities of a domestic TV set.

Inexpensive usage was another requirement for the mass-market ambitions of its developers — public systems are charged on a 'pay-as-you-use' basis and the essential simplicity of operation keeps down the running cost of private viewdata. Most organizations can afford it.

In short, viewdata has a lot going for it: a simplified interface, text-oriented display of information, ready availability at modest cost. Importantly, there is also universal local call access to the public viewdata service, Prestel.

A viewdata system, public or private, comprises:

- One or more *computers* to store and process information. This system will include appropriate software and hardware to manage viewdata-style information and to convert between viewdata format and the computer system's own internal data formats.
- A *communications link* with appropriate *modems* to attach the viewdata terminals.
- *Viewdata terminals*, which normally incorporate a purpose-designed *modem* and a *character generator* to produce viewdata-format text and graphics. Such terminals may be *adaptors* for a TV set, purpose-built screen-plus-keyboard *terminals*, or *modem/software* combinations for use with desktop computers or local networks.

Prestel also established two key *de facto* standards:

- *Character representation*. Viewdata does not utilize the ASCII character set that is now more or less universal in desktop computer communications. Instead a specialized character set was developed, incorporating many ASCII codes but adding some simple graphics symbols and permitting colour to be specified on the display.
- *Line speed*. To make the most efficient use of existing phone lines and to minimize the cost of modems, Prestel (and most other viewdata systems in Europe) adopts a split-speed approach. The principle was that most information would be coming from the computer to the terminal, so a reasonably fast data rate is employed for incoming information; on the grounds that very little would be going the other way, a greatly inferior rate was specified for terminal-to-computer link. In Prestel communications, data is received at 1200 baud but transmitted from the terminal at 75 baud. This has now been enshrined as one of the CCITT standards, Recommendation V23.

What you get

Prestel and systems like it are information-broking businesses that operate viewdata as a public service: Prestel just provides the framework in which 'information providers' offer free or charged-for facilities.

On Prestel at present there are several hundred such IPs, offering between them over 300 000 pages of information.

Most of these are available to any caller; if there is a charge for reading a page, it is normally notified to the user and will be included in the monthly Prestel bill.

When greater flexibility or some confidentiality is required, commercial users would elect for private systems. These can be provided by reserving a limited-access section of a public viewdata facility, which is what Prestel calls a 'closed user group' (normally available to anyone who pays the IP a fee) or 'Private Prestel' (usually a more restricted service available only to a particular business fraternity).

Prestel

Mention of British Telecom's public videotex service usually provokes one of two reactions. It is either 'one of the major contributions to the acceptance of technology by the computer-illiterate businessman' or 'one of the worst-marketed high-tech services of all time'.

These two apparently contradictory statements can both be regarded as accurate. The initial marketing of the service used phrases like 'a world of information at your fingertips' and 'the greatest thing since television'; in short, it was directed at the home user.

In the event, the home user was demonstrably unkeen. 'A technology looking for a marketplace' was one of the more polite criticisms of those early attempts to promote Prestel. Prestel belatedly discovered that what counts is the *value* of the information available, and that is down to the number, quality and marketing acumen of the information providers. Prestel and its IPs did not provide a cost-effective solution to the information needs of most people, and in any case those needs turned out to be surprisingly limited.

In the mid eighties, BT radically changed its marketing policy, partly by adopting the idea of the 'trigger product concept'. This reflected the view that most businesses were interested in industry-specific facilities rather than a generalized pot-pourri of services and data. The theory was that once the 'trigger product' had brought someone on to the Prestel system, that user would naturally feel inclined to exploit the 300 000-page general database — rail timetables, government information, local services, weather, games and the rest.

Hence the development of a variety of services such as CitiService for the financial markets, Prestel Travel for travel agencies, Farmlink for agriculture, BTIS for the insurance business. The domestic market was not dismissed, but it was given a lower priority and received its own set of 'trigger product' packages — teleshopping, Micronet for computer buffs, HomeLink for home banking.

Prestel itself was no longer marketed as an identifiable product, while the individual packages were sold with varying degrees of success. Prestel Travel became one notable success, and by 1982 was certainly used by some 95 per cent of all travel agents. Micronet was also an early performer, attracting some 15 000 subscribers within 18 months of its launch late in 1982.

The key to establishment in the broader marketplace was the realization that such 'vertical databases' alone would never provide enough incentive for massive increases in the number of subscribers. Prestel's record since this changed attitude reflects the relative success of the new British Telecom strategy.

A second factor in 1981-82 was the growth of *private* videotex — non-BT services that shared Prestel's technology, and ran mostly within the public sector (local and central government and nationalized industries).

The real pioneers of non-Prestel videotex services were actually conceived and

launched prior to this period, among them the Stock Exchange's mammoth TOPIC system, British Leyland's Stock Locator and the Debenhams store management reporting system. Major growth in this area saw some 300 individual systems operational across a wide range of vertical markets by the end of 1982, with a concomitant spread of specialist system developers.

A third and possibly more significant development around the same time saw truly interactive functions added to Prestel. Many of the early Prestel services did promote the two-way capabilities of the technology, for booking theatre tickets, ordering brochures, catalogues and so on. These were very cumbersome procedures, however, with Prestel receiving an end-user's message and then relaying it (as much as 24 hours later) to the service or information provider.

In March 1982 Prestel launched its GATEWAY facility to provide real-time interactive services. This built on development work done elsewhere, mainly in West Germany's Bildschirmtext system, to link videotex screens to the non-videotex data held on computers at banks, holiday companies and theatre booking agencies.

The GATEWAY software enables the end-user's terminal to be led directly and instantaneously from one 'field' — the Prestel computer — to the host computer that is storing the data to be manipulated or exploited, all without the user being aware of the manoeuvre. Even the format of the data transmitted from the host computer could give the same videotex appearance as the Prestel-stored data.

Overall, it could be argued that without the development of GATEWAY (or something similar) Prestel and videotex generally would probably have gone the way of the dinosaur by now.

Quicker Prestel?

One of the biggest problems in computing and communications is producing products that neither intimidate the novice nor frustrate the expert. In general, the bias is usually towards satisfying the expert.

That approach is not open to videotex designers. By definition, videotex is computer access for the common user, and simplicity invariably takes priority over functionality. So Prestel is almost always on a hiding to nothing when it tries to enhance its service.

For example, for some years it was obvious that Prestel just *had* to improve its indexing and search facilities. All that plodding through numeric page indexes and sub-indexes was pretty well essential when the emphasis was on the domestic user with TV and adapter with numeric keypad. As more advanced dedicated terminals began to proliferate in business and the PC-using audience became significant, page access just had to become a little more efficient, a lot quicker and probably alphabetic.

Prestel's research with various classes of users concluded that extended access functions just had to be kept simple. Constructs like 'ISLAND AND SPANISH BUT NOT MAJORCA' may be meat and drink to the computer fraternity, but 'SPAIN' followed by one or two accesses via lower level indexes has to be the Prestel approach.

Indeed, the Prestel KEYWORD facility (as you can find out by accessing page .1900) is little more than a list of common searchable terms, each of which is associated with a particular page (generally a menu page). If you strike lucky, you get quickly to what you want. If you are *fairly* lucky, you hit a synonym for one of the keywords with the same result (and that synonym base is updated regularly). If you miss out this time there's a chance that you will not be unlucky next time; failed keywords are being logged as an input to regular keyword updates.

The PAGEMARK feature lets you allocate your own names or codes to up to five pages. Thereafter you can re-access them using those names or codes. That would be very useful if the number of pages were larger and the marking were semi-permanent. As it is, the feature is no more than moderately useful, as pagemarks last only for the duration of the call.

In-house viewdata

Viewdata *as a technology* is not important, but videotex as a delivery mechanism for easy-to-use services could be a key element of many companies' communications and data strategies.

Applications for in-house viewdata

□ *External information access.* Viewdata systems can be used to retrieve business-oriented information held on external services such as Prestel.

□ *Internal information.* The kind of information that would be printed can be made available on a viewdata service — price lists, stock availability, product specifications.

□ *Bulletin boards.* A viewdata-based bulletin display could replace the company noticeboard and free the internal mail system from items of casual interest.

The main arguments in favour of viewdata — ease of access, low equipment costs and the page-based display — apply to a number of potential business applications. There may be a case, therefore, for implementing a viewdata system inside the organization — either by using existing files on an existing system or by buying a dedicated single-purpose computer.

Enthusiasts would also claim that the viewdata approach is also well suited to information retrieval of a more intense and detailed nature.

For example, with a viewdata system a manager can reference files: set up a database or contribute to one created by someone else; amend, delete or change information, send and receive messages; access other sources of information outside the organization.

At a basic level the terminal could access locally held files for information like departmental records, personal diaries, and phone lists. To reference information one level higher in the organization — like divisional inventory levels and production figures — the viewdata user would access centrally stored data via a PABX. To get at the larger amounts of data needed for management control and strategic planning the terminal would provide a window into existing corporate files on a computer elsewhere in the company.

For certain users there could also be another level of viewdata access, this being restricted to the private and public national and international database services that can supply for specific trade or professional information.

In practice, in-house viewdata scores over conventional systems when some or all of these criteria will apply:

- Low-cost access required to information
- Data entry and/or data capture only on a limited scale
- Relatively small amounts of information to be accessed
- Types of information which can sensibly be presented as single pages at a time
- Colour and restricted display width (40 characters per line) add to comprehensibility
- Use from varied locations
- Non-expert users
- *Ad hoc* usage — occasional, fairly brief accesses at unpredictable times (day or night, working day or weekend)
- No dedicated comms lines and no predefined terminal types required

On the other hand, viewdata looks inappropriate where the information required does not fit easily into the viewdata format; when larger amounts of data are requested, and when considerable user input is involved; and, perhaps crucially, when the user requires a degree of flexibility and is relatively experienced in the use of terminals or desktop computers. For many such users, viewdata can feel clumsy and unsophisticated.

Viewdata by desktop computer

The development of videotex has not been dependent on the parallel development of the business microcomputer. However, access to viewdata services can be a useful added facility on computers. Of the estimated

150 000 videotex terminals installed in the UK, something like a third are actually PCs rather than dedicated terminals or adapted TV sets.

In principle, any V23 modem and any comms package can be used to access Prestel — provided both are set up for the Prestel format of 7 data bits, even parity, and one stop bit. Many modem-software combinations will buffer the data transmission so that other speeds can be used.

The problem then is that your keyboard may not produce the right effects — the number and asterisk keys may work, but the hash sign may be difficult to find. More distressingly, the screen may show a jumble of garbage.

If so, this is because the comms package cannot handle Prestel correctly. If a viewdata option is claimed, the software should be able to cope with this:

- *End of line.* Some comms software cannot detect the end of Prestel's 40-character lines and attempts to run a whole display across the screen as a single line.

- *Block graphics.* All Prestel pages, including those from IPs, make the most of the system's display capabilities by using 'block graphics' — mostly simple square or rectangular slabs. Many packages cannot cope with the graphics — they appear typically as rows of asterisks. This may seem no more than irritating, but many Prestel displays are virtually useless without the graphics; some menu options in particular are totally unreadable. Genuine Prestel-compatibility should include at least some attempt to reproduce the block graphics.

- *Enhanced text.* Another feature of Prestel displays is the use of flashing text, double-height characters, and the like. A comms package may not be able to reproduce these, but it should at least make some attempt to display them legibly.

Prestel in practice

CHARGES

Telephone bill. Calls to Prestel are not identified separately from other phone usage. Local-call access is available to 'about 99 per cent' of the UK, however.

Standing charge. Payable quarterly in advance. There may also be additional subscription charges for particular services.

Access time charge. Payable quarterly in arrears; applies only during Prestel's own Standard Rate period (0800-1800 Monday to Friday, 0800-1300 Saturday: note that this is not necessarily the same as BT's Standard Rate period for phone charges). Access at all other times is free.

Frame charge. Payable quarterly in arrears; a fee to see a page of an IP's information. The charge is determined by the IP and flagged on index or menu pages.

ACCESS

☐ Dial the relevant Prestel number.

☐ The carrier tone should be followed by a sign-on display requesting your 'customer identity'. Enter a ten-digit ID (notified when you sign up, along with Prestel numbers to call and a password).

☐ You will then be prompted for a four-character password.

☐ This should produce the Prestel 'welcome page', which includes notification of any electronic mail waiting.

DIRECTORY

Moving around Prestel pages involves entering numbers, asterisks and hash signs (#); entering up to seven digits will take you direct to a readable page. The full Prestel Directory is available from the main menu on page 7; it is also published in paper form as a supplement to *Connexions* magazine, and is available at no charge to subscribers.

FREE TRIAL OFFER

Prestel has a no-charge trial access facility with some sample pages. When you are on-line, enter 4444444444 (ten 4s) for the customer identity and 4444 (four 4s) for the password.

Teletext

Developed in Britain in the early seventies, teletext is a one-way information retrieval method that uses existing television broadcast signals to broadcast data. Teletext services are currently provided by the IBA under the name CEEFAX and by the BBC as ORACLE.

Teletext effectively gives the user an electronic magazine: its pages may be displayed on an appropriately equipped domestic TV set. The information is transmitted simultaneously with normal television broadcasts. It uses spare capacity on the TV signal, being carried on unused lines of the broadcast that are not normally visible on the TV receiver.

In order to convert data signals to a television image, the TV set must be provided with a decoder to demultiplex the data from the broadcast television signal. The decoder is used to 'turn' to the required page of the teletext 'magazine'.

Viewdata is distinguished from teletext primarily in that the user gets a considerably more powerful tool for interactive communication, the keypad. This in turn means a user can make finer discriminations, and so much larger amounts of information can be provided in a viewdata service.

Teletext is limited to a few hundred pages; Prestel was initially designed for several thousand. The intended use of the two systems is therefore quite different: teletext provides current general-interest magazine/newspaper-type information such as news, weather, sports and Stock Exchange reports.

- *Dynamic pages*. This effect involves switching rapidly (and automatically) between pages to give the impression of animation. Few packages can handle this, but it tends to apply only to the home-oriented sections of Prestel.

- *Colour*. Prestel IPs also make extensive (and effective) use of colour — different colours may, for instance, be used on the text of a stock exchange listing to indicate whether the price is rising or falling. When a monochrome display screen is being used on the computer, most Prestel-compatible systems can at least ignore the colour to produce readable text; but actually displaying the colour is likely to require special facilities (maybe even a special replacement graphics controller chip), even when the computer has a colour screen.

Facsimile is the electronic transmission of a copy of a document from one point to another. The key points are that it uses existing comms links (the phone system) and it transmits an *exact* copy of the source material.

Because facsimile systems reproduce a whole page rather than just encoding the data written on it, they can be used to send non-textual information — such as graphs, maps, signatures, Japanese and Chinese characters — which are difficult or impossible to transmit using other electronic systems.

Fax has several attractions:

□ *Familiarity*. It requires little or no change in work habits. Documents are still written, typed, or drawn; they are still filed, handled, *seen*.

□ *Speed*. With current fax machines an A4 document takes less than 30 seconds to send.

□ *Authenticity*. An *exact* copy is sent.

□ *Competitiveness*. Fax is simpler than Telex, cheaper and faster than messenger services, more reliable than the posts.

□ *Accessibility*. No matter how many people subscribe to the various electronic mail services or possess dedicated Telex terminals, there will always be people you wish to reach quickly who eschew anything that involves a QWERTY keyboard.

□ *Simplicity*. Instead of a series of access codes and passwords, the fax user merely has to enter a telephone number to get the word (and pictures) out. The rest of the process is not very different from feeding a photocopier. At the other end, a facsimile rolls out of the receiving machine — without requiring the owner to load a comms program, log on and query an e-mail service.

□ *Compatibility*. Though formerly there were few fax standards, the current situation is that any fax machine can communicate with any other in the same CCITT Group.

□ *Phone lines*. An ordinary phone line will do.

Against that, there are still some significant disadvantages:

□ *Price*. Although 'compact' models cost from just over £1600 (and discounting is rife), a full-featured fax machine will more than £2000 — and it usually requires its own telephone line. The principal alternatives are charged for (primarily) by the word; fax transmissions are charged per page and can include a lot of white space. A lot of the built-in paid-for capability is under-utilized, especially the pictorial ability of fax — some three-quarters of all faxes are estimated to be text only.

□ *Reproduction*. Less crucially, fax machines are currently unable to transmit in colour — and they will not pick up light shades (particularly of blue, green and grey) on the original.

□ *Document size*. Most fax machines cannot handle anything larger than A4 (a few higher-priced models can cope with A3 input, though that has to be reduced before it can be output — at the time of writing, no fax machines can print on to A3 paper). This restricts its appeal for large-format plans and diagrams.

□ *Dependency on paper*. The need to have a piece of paper at both ends of the link might not appeal to a user organization that is attempting to reduce the volume of paper in the office. In any case the technique presupposes that the page itself is an important part of the communication, whereas for most communications the paper is in fact no more than the *medium* — a page of text sent via fax scan requires up to 40 times as many bits as a similar page encoded as characters and sent by e-mail or Telex.

Features on Group 3 fax

The appeal of fax is being strengthened by the kind of sophisticated facilities now being built into fax machines. Some of these are not part of the CCITT standards and will only apply when both fax machines are the same make and model.

Retry on busy. The fax machine will automatically try an engaged number (twice at five-minute intervals if it follows the CCITT Group 3 standard).

Timed send. An autodialling machine can send at preset times — in some cases, a queue of multiple timed sends can be built up.

Short-code dialling. Abbreviated diallers work just as on memory phones. You can usually store between 20 and 100 numbers for single- or two-digit dialling.

Group codes. Some machines let you set up a distribution list of numbers, such that a document can be transmitted to multiple destinations just by entering the group code.

Line speed changes. The fax machine monitors the quality of the transmission line (the amount of interference on it) and reduces the transmission speed to obtain the best possible quality — from 9600 baud successively to 7200, 4800 and 2400 (if it cannot assure transmission at 2400 baud the terminal usually aborts the connection). Some can also *increase* the data rate automatically if the quality of the line improves. In practice, automatic speed changing may not be too useful — it can only be done at the end of a page, and the line-testing procedure can add seconds to the transmission time.

Identification. The phone numbers for sender and receiver can automatically be included on the copy.

Automatic answer. A 'polling' facility allows a user to activate the remote fax machine to start it sending, for instance to take advantage of cheaper phone rates — though obviously the remote machine has to be switched on.

Transaction reports. A log can be produced showing mode (Group 2 or 3), number and ID code of the sender and receiver, page count, and an indication of errors (usually total number of pages with detected errors, perhaps the page numbers in question too).

Resolution selection. Some machines have a 'fine mode' for maximum readability — the scanning resolution is increased. So, too, is the transmission time, of course.

Talk mode. Pressing a 'Talk' button temporarily suspends the transmission and signals to the remote machine that the operator should pick up the phone for a voice conversation.

Automatic document feed. Most fax machines have a paper feed rather like that on a photocopier, so eliminating the need for constant supervision.

Copying. As on photocopiers, a multiple print of incoming documents can be requested. Since the image is sitting in the memory of a microprocessor that controls the fax machine, it is also available for a subsequent repeat print until something else arrives or until the machine is switched off.

Background control. This facility can 'white out' a coloured or shaded background to improve readability.

'Light original' option. As on photocopiers, the density of the image can be stepped up.

Fast mode. A number of facilities are available to improve throughput. The two most common methods are for the scanner to skip over white space and for a sophisticated data compression method to 'abbreviate' parts of the transmission. Speed improvements of around 25 per cent are usually claimed.

Automatic line check. The fax machine applies a degree of 'filtering' to remove interference on the transmission line.

Error correction. A sophisticated fax will include extra error-checking information in the transmission, much as most data transmission now does. The receiver can verify the accuracy of the incoming data, deduce the existence of some errors and perhaps make the likely correction, and request a retry automatically if significant errors are detected.

Reduction. As on a photocopier, an A3 image can be reduced to A4 before sending. More usually, a B4 image (257x363mm, the size of many computer printout sheets) can be resized to A4.

A3 into A4. An A3 machine can send an image as two A4 sheets to be matched up.

Still, the number of facsimile terminals is currently rising at around 30 per cent annually in the UK, where fax users are already over the 150 000 mark; worldwide there are more than two million.

This growth is expected to continue as prices continue to fall and as the number of terminals reaches the stage where fax begins to be perceived as a standard business communications tool.

How it works

The technology is inherently digital. A scanner steps over the original, deciding whether or not it can detect a dark area at each point of reference.

This information is transmitted as a stream of yes/no decisions for each point in sequence: at the other end of the line the receiving unit uses this to recreate a pattern of dots, rather as happens in newspaper photographs.

Current fax machines incorporate a specialized modem to handle the conversion between digital data and the phone system's analogue signals; fax terminals for ISDN operation will not need the modem, of course.

Some of the simpler fax machines use thermal printing for output. The signals are decoded into electrical charges that are applied to a sheet of special paper, causing an electrochemical reaction which burns off portions of the top white coating to expose the dark surface beneath and so produce a copy of the original.

Thermal printing does not really produce a very black image, however, and the paper feels very flimsy. It can also deteriorate with time.

More modern (and more expensive) fax machines use plain paper and thermal transfer technology borrowed from photocopiers; at the receiving end, the image is recreated on a photosensitive transfer medium that can then print on to plain paper.

For the immediate future, laser-printing technology will probably be the norm for fast, high-resolution output.

Standards

The principles of fax actually date back to 1842, but the technical limitations plus competition from the better-developed transmission media like telegraphy impeded its development until recent years.

Fax was notoriously slow, produced poor copies, was unreliable in terms both of the transmission itself and the equipment at the line ends, and was by no means cheap. It was also characterized by an almost total absence of standards, which meant that you could transmit safely only between identical fax machines. So it had been used only in very specialized applications where there were few alternative methods of getting an image fairly quickly from one place to another.

The principal consideration is the resolution. Obviously, the more dots per square inch, the better the image will be. However, that complicates the location of the points, and great precision is naturally required. Because of the increased transmission load that results, great emphasis is placed on the availability and quality of appropriate high-speed transmission links. (With current fax scanners, the standard resolution is 200 horizontal by 100 lines per inch.)

Improving technology has solved most of the problems with high-resolution digitizing devices and high-speed international transmission links.

Crucially, standards have now been established by the CCITT for fax machines. *Group 1* and *Group 2* are for analogue facsimile (the electrical signal varies with the intensity of the image from black to white through greys): Group 1 fax machines could take up to six minutes to send an A4 page; Group 2 halved the transmission time and meant that fax could realistically compete with Telex.

The important *Group 3* specification (*circa* 1980) applies to most fax machines sold today. It covers *digital* facsimile; the electrical signals represent picture elements of either black or white without grey tones. Transmission time is reduced to a minute or less, for a data rate of 9600 baud is used. Most Group 3 fax terminals can alternatively be used in Group 2 mode when necessary.

There is also a *Group 4* specification for use with digital phone lines — with ISDN, in other words — that will permit speeds of at least 19 200 baud. There are some Group 4 faxes on the market in advance of ISDN. Until ISDN becomes available, though, Group 4 machines are expensive and largely irrelevant.

In general, the quality of the output image for Group 1 and 2 machines is such that anything smaller than 6pt type will not be legible. Group 3 machines are better, but the quality still compares unfavourably with that from a photocopier; it is, however, good enough for practically all purposes — even HM Customs and Excise will accept faxed forms for cross-channel goods traffic.

BT Merlin HS-20 incorporates a phone

Fax direct to the desktop computer

In some cases, a faxed document will have to be retyped or redrawn on a desktop computer for local editing and revision. There are some solutions to this, notably the facility to connect a fax directly to the computer such that it can act as an input device — both machines do after all use digital encoding. An incoming fax can then be printed normally and/or passed on to the computer.

Most modern fax machines towards the upper end of the price range now include an RS-232 socket to permit this kind of direct connection to a computer. It is a relatively expensive option, however, for special format-conversion software will almost certainly be needed at least to receive faxes.

The main appeal of linking fax terminals to a computer system will probably lie in the scanning. Page scanners are used to input documents into a computer without having to rekey them; the scanner converts the physical image into a digital form. That is exactly what a fax machine does, and with suitable software it seems reasonable that a fax could double as a scanning device for data entry.

Fax adaptors

Removing the need for the fax terminal altogether has proved a feasible alternative for transmissions that are not too graphic, and for that a specialized fax adaptor is used.

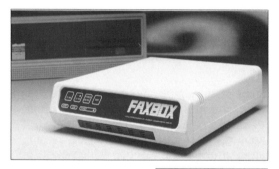

External fax modem

There are a number of fax adapters available for the desktop computer, both as externally connected boxes or internally located plug-in circuit boards. As usual, the internal options apply only for IBM-compatibles with a couple of products for the Apple Mac too.

Most of these adapters offer good Group 3 fax at prices from around £500. They function somewhat like a modem, connecting to the phone line and (in the case of external fax adapters) to the computer's RS-232 port. All can send and receive ASCII text; most can handle the kind of images produced by graphics packages. Once installed, they are used like a conventional fax machine — the destination number is dialled and the material for transmission is entered (though obviously it comes from a prepared disk file rather than from a physical document).

Such adapters can also receive faxes, in which case they usually assume that incoming material will be output on a laser printer. As with any printing software, there will be restrictions on precisely what printers are supported — the market leaders (Canon, Hewlett-Packard) will certainly be covered. It is not usually worth trying to output a fax image on anything but a laser printer, though other printer types will of course be adequate for straight text.

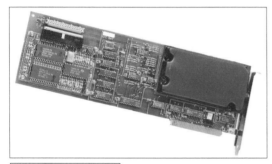

Internal fax modem

Since a page scanner is basically a fax machine without the built-in fax modem, it seems reasonable to suppose that a page scanner acquired for direct data entry (to a desktop publishing setup, say) could be used with a fax modem. This multi-purpose arrangement will probably become the norm for fax when integrated with computer networks.

At present, there are still technical drawbacks which limit the value of the fax modem:

□ The computer probably cannot reproduce a fax image accurately on screen or on a laser printer — the 400 dots per inch used by most fax scanners is much finer than the resolution offered on most displays.

□ Even a single A4 page represents a lot of data — around a megabyte. That places a strain on the memory and disk

capacity of most desktop computers, and the image will be too big for many software packages to handle for further editing work on it.

□ A megabyte of data takes a long time to transfer from fax receiver to the computer, particularly when an external cable-connected fax adapter is connected via the obvious link — an RS-232 line. Most RS-232 links are limited to 9600 bits per second, so just getting one A4 page from the fax line into the computer could take a quarter of an hour.

Still, fax adaptors can be an effective way of transferring text and simple graphics:

□ When the other end of the link has a fax but no computer (or no modem) or
□ When the fax transmission is destined to be incorporated into a computer-processed document of some kind.

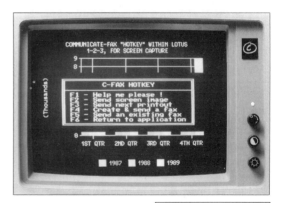

Fax software at work

INTELPOST

The Post Office (and *not* British Telecom) provides a fax bureau service under the name INTELPOST. You are billed on a usage basis only — no joining fee, no minimum monthly bill.

Copy can be accepted over the counter at some main Post Offices or it can be taken from your own fax machine, Telex terminal or computer. Obviously in the case of the last two options, only text can be sent.

It is facsimile-transmitted to its destination — which could be the recipient's own fax machine. Alternatively, INTELPOST can hold the message for counter collection at a local Post Office, it can deliver it by messenger or it can mail the documents on.

In other words, INTELPOST acts like other business bureaux — providing facilities for which one or both ends do not have the necessary equipment.

For the customer with a desktop computer and modem, direct access to the service is possible only via Telex (or through Telex facilities within an electronic mail service).

This requires an account number for billing purposes, usually available with no problems to creditworthy applicants. Then all you have to do is Telex your material to be fax-forwarded to the Post Office at 913058 RMAIL G. It must include 'header' information in exactly the right format, as follows (everything in capitals must be sent as it is, everything in lower case is supplied by the user):

```
INTELPOST
sender's account number
sender's name
up to six lines for sender's address
END
recipient's name
up to six line of recipient's address
END
recipient's country
F
fax phone number
fax machine's 'group-number' code
MESSAGE
your message
END OF MESSAGE
INTELPOST
```

Voice messaging (sometimes abbreviated to VM — or DVM, for 'digital voice messaging') is a spoken version of electronic mail: voice messages can be entered by users, stored in the system and passed on verbally to the recipients. Some VM systems can also convert other stored information into speech for the caller.

Advantages of voice messaging

- *Familiarity*. The spoken word is the preferred means of communication for most people. Voice messaging promises a familiar and readily-understood means of depositing or retrieving information.

- *Simplicity*. The only equipment required at the user's end is a telephone. Commands are entered as speech or by keypresses on a touchtone phone's number pad.

- *Efficiency*. Something like one in four telephone calls fail for one reason or another to reach the recipient on the first attempt. Time-zone differences complicate international communication as well. As with electronic mail, voice messaging offers a means of communication that does not rely on personal contact.

- *Automatic distribution*. A spoken message can be relayed to multiple recipients.

- *Information access*. Voice messaging can provide quick *ad hoc* access to information where a hard copy or displayed text is unnecessary. Some systems can retrieve digitized information from a database and convert it to natural-sounding speech.

Voice messaging has long had the air of a technology looking for applications; the main drawbacks to date have been the poor state of the technology for digitizing and reproducing the voice and the high cost of the equipment required. Advances in the technology and the falling cost of computer components — especially memory (digitized speech requires a lot of memory), processors (speech digitization is complex, and high-speed processing is required) and programming (more memory and faster programming permit the use of more sophisticated software) — suggest that at the very least some niche markets may be appearing. In particular, there are applications within organizations that have many frequent telephone users, and perhaps they could be used for consumer information such as train times and airplane schedules.

Voice messaging is typically provided in three ways:

- As a facility built into or added on to a PABX to store and forward messages

- As a facility within a local network, when a workstation terminal or desktop computer is able to receive messages and relay them as speech

- As a public service.

The kinds of facilities provided are illustrated by one of the existing commercial services.

To contact the service

Dial the phone number. You will be asked to enter your ID as a series of numbers on the telephone keypad (some systems additionally allow users to set up passwords for additional security). If that is accepted, you will be told whether your mailbox contains any unheard messages and any previously received messages that you have saved. Thereafter you can dial a single digit to send or listen to messages.

To send a message

Key the 'send message' number and wait for the 'ready' tone. Enter the voice-mailbox address of the recipient followed by an 'end of address' code; speak the message; key an 'end of message code'.

Keying the appropriate digits should enable you to go forward or back through the message to do some simple 'editing' before it is sent. Other facilities may include:

- Notification of delivery for critical messages
- Distribution lists for bulk messaging
- Timed delivery, with the system releasing your message into the recipient's voice mailbox at a specified time and date in the future

To listen to messages

Press the 'receive message' button and wait for the 'ready' tone. The messages you chose to hear can be new messages or those you have previously saved. For new messages, you can listen to it; then key appropriate digits to save the message, erase it, reply, and/or redirect it to another subscriber. In the last two cases the 'send message' procedure is followed, with the option of adding your spoken comments to a redirected message; you can then save or delete the message.

Keying the appropriate digits should enable you to go forward or back through the message list to select a message to hear. Other facilities may include:

- 'Scan' waiting messages before hearing them in full, in which case you will just hear the sender's name and/or a few words giving the subject
- Date and time stamping, to indicate when the message arrived in your voice mailbox
- Diary functions, with the system reminding of appointments and the like that you have previously recorded

'Conferencing' (or sometimes 'teleconferencing') has been technically feasible since the seventies. The essence is some kind of link between geographically dispersed individuals by electronic means, and a number of possibilities are available. For many applications, there are obvious advantages in replacing the conventional face-to-face meeting — particularly savings on travel costs and time.

Audio-conferencing, an extension of the person-to-person phone call, is now provided as the norm on many PABXs. Technology advances, new possibilities, declining capital costs, increasing pressure on management time and the emphasis on quality in decision-making have combined to make the more sophisticated options attractive.

Some approaches to teleconferencing are extremely expensive, justified only when quite large groups are assembled in some kind of studio at either end of the link. The potential benefits are further eroded by the nature of the link itself — there's no opportunity for discussion to continue informally after the meeting has broken up, for instance, and conferencing can actually stimulate travel and the need for face-to-face contact by highlighting the deficiencies of remote communication.

Perhaps the main problem has always been the organizational issue — it is difficult for individual managers and whole systems of working to move from a situation where face-to-face meetings or exchange of memos is the norm.

Video conferencing

The use of video cameras and microphones for purpose-built conferencing has long been predicted as a feature of organizational life for the eighties, but in fact the take-up has been slow. The basic technology has been available for some time; but video conferencing in particular has suffered from the organizational reluctance to change.

In fact, there is some justification for this. In particular, there are two rival standards for the 'codec', the modem equivalent that compresses video signals into digital form for transmission and then converts them back again at the receiving end. The CLI standard is established in North America; most of Europe follows a CCITT standard.

Video conferencing is also an expensive option; to set up just two private conference rooms in Britain complete with monitors, lighting, cameras, sound equipment and the link between them could easily cost over £250 000. For a private system using studios, there may have to be a specialist operator at each end; a simpler system will still require some technical expertise, given the current state of equipment.

On the other hand, the investment may not have to be made by the end user — a number of private video conferencing service suppliers have appeared, with conference rooms in key centres. British Telecom, for instance, has ten of its Confravision centres around the country (but then Confravision was first introduced back in 1971 and hasn't exactly been a howling success).

Savings identified by early users centre on the cost and time of travel, particularly when European managers have to confer with counterparts based in North America. A more sophisticated approach can yield other benefits; a video shot in the production or R&D facility can be spliced into the link so that two or more widely dispersed groups can watch problems or procedures more or less at first hand.

The immediate future might see significant cost reductions for private systems — the CCITT has a draft standard for a low-speed codec that will work on more economical links, and a number of manufacturers are interested in development of a colour videophone that will work with it on standard ISDN lines.

On-line conferencing

Video conferencing has an obvious appeal when visual contact is important — meaning anything from eye contact to adding a separate video or film into the proceedings. Not all situations require that, however.

Computer conferencing is a relatively recent phenomenon. The simplest version is the special interest group 'areas' on bulletin boards: qualified users — meaning those who have paid their subscription — exchange information with each other, read the accumulated messages, and add their own messages for public consumption (a request for information, say) or private viewing (such as a personal e-mail message for another user or a very specific response to a query that would only clutter up the public-access area).

A more advanced form of conferencing is available on commercial systems, typically offering more options to select messages to read. An active conference may have accumulated several hundred messages, which necessitates some scanning and selection facilities. The commercial services can also store more; the messages take up space on the supplier's computer (or rather on its disks), so there will have to be some housekeeping from time to time — but the commercial suppliers can set up archive files of old messages that may possibly be relevant to users, while the bulletin board SYSOP will have to delete them.

The first commercial conferencing option, called PARTI, is available on The Source (a giant multi-user multi-faceted on-line service based in the States) and TTNS (The Times Network Systems, a closed user group run on Telecom Gold); PARTI is awkward to use, however, and more recent systems are a lot more friendly. That applies particularly to COSY, produced in 1985 and used notably for BIX (the Byte Information Exchange — technical conferences run for subscribers by the US computer magazine *Byte*) and for CIX.

CIX is the Compulink Information Exchange. Compulink was one of the earliest UK user groups for owners of the IBM PC and compatibles, and it set up a bulletin board

system for members. There are several dozen 'open' conferences, to which all subscribers can have access, but any subscriber can set up a conference, and a conference can be designated as 'closed' — meaning access is restricted. CIX also includes a separate e-mail facility.

Most conferences on most systems are technical and oriented towards computer enthusiasts — there are CIX conferences for virtually all the popular microcomputers, operating systems and data comms considerations, for example. There's also a miscellany of special-interest conferences with subjects like chess, lonely hearts, jokes, the game *Diplomacy*.

Conferences are usually set up by keen individuals, but there is considerable scope for corporate organizations to set up closed conferences for staff and/or customers. Computer companies such as Borland International are already using this approach to provide 'hot line' technical support and to enable users to share information.

In-house computer conferencing

Conferencing is also feasible on in-house multi-user systems, though as yet this has not become widespread. The key features of any conferencing system will apply:

- Simplified access for non-technical users
- No time-of-day restrictions on access
- Contributions from any and all users, including possibly useful input from individuals who might have been left off a conventional distribution list and those who couldn't attend a meeting in person
- Free-format exchange of information (suitable, for instance, for 'brainstorming')

One of the features of the small-computer revolution of the eighties has been the development of electronic 'bulletin boards'. Although set up by and for enthusiasts, there is a general relevance to many of these systems — of which there are now several thousand around the world, mostly in Britain and the States.

Why use a bulletin board?

Bulletin boards are intended for public access by like-minded people who want to share opinions and concerns and who support the principles of cooperative non-profit communication. The individual business user may well qualify on a personal level, but in any case there can be real benefits for users.

- ☐ *Messaging*. A bulletin board with 'private message' facilities (which in practice means virtually all of them) can be used as an economical electronic mail system.

- ☐ *Support*. Most BBSs are run and patronized by enthusiasts. The 'public message' areas and SIGs are excellent opportunities to broadcast specific technical problems and seek advice at no charge from individuals who will probably be more experienced and more competent than most commercial consultants.

- ☐ *Entertainment*. Quite simply, browsing the boards can be *fun* — if you are that way inclined.

A basic bulletin board system (BBS) is a kind of electronic noticeboard on which messages and other information can be 'pinned'. In other words, people call up the BBS to post messages and read other people's; the first bulletin boards were intended as exact replicas of those school noticeboards that everyone checked to see if they were in the school team.

Most boards offer rather more than that, however:

- ☐ *Electronic mail*. You can leave messages for public consumption, which is useful for small-ad style sales or for exchanging information, or you can specify that the message is 'private', in which case the BBS effectively provides an electronic mail service. When your recipient signs on to the BBS — giving a unique name and frequently a password — the BBS software will be able to spot him or her and check for 'private' mail messages.

Since nearly all boards are free or make only a modest charge for user registration (there will rarely be any charge for access), this can be a very economical way to pass messages.

You can also send e-mail (electronic mail) messages from one BBS to another if they are linked, as the FIDO boards are — 'FIDO' is the name of the BBS software used by many boards. The links may be international, too.

- ☐ *Special interest sections*. The board is likely to have a number of different 'areas' in which you can leave a message. So as well as a kind of general noticeboard, there may be sections intended for messages on particular subjects. Often termed SIGs (special interest groups), these might have information about a certain make of computer, particular sports, games, jokes, golf, art history, VW Beetles, UFOs, home computers, women, men, pets, or cake-making (all actual examples). There are even computer-dating areas on boards which have resulted in romance, marriage, and the like. Bulletin boards are ideal for exchanging information with like-minded people on just about *any* subject; if you are not interested in the topic, you do not bother browsing around the messages in that area.

In some cases the BBS will restrict access to one or more of these areas — you may have to prove that you really *are* interested before you are allowed in, or you may have to pay a (typically small) fee to get at them.

These restricted areas often form into what are called closed user groups (CUGs).

□ *Free software.* Many BBSs also have a collection of public domain files for all sorts of computers. These are programs or text files for which the author makes no charge, and at the last count there were well over 10 000 programs in the public domain. The quality varies greatly, but there's some really good material around. They can be 'downloaded' to your computer from the BBS; often you are requested to contribute something of your own in return — a good idea that benefits all users of the service.

It was due to the bulletin boards in the USA being used as the main source of PD software that the first 'Shareware' products were launched. These packages are not exactly in the public domain; if you like and use the software, you are invited to pay a small sum to the author of the program.

The commercial version of the BBS costs money — a one-time registration fee and/or an annual subscription, with access charges thereafter. Such services usually provide a good deal more than the facilities listed above — notably sophisticated e-mail arrangements, access to on-line information, and Telex facilities. Examples include those that are primarily electronic mail purveyors (like Telecom Gold and Mercury Link 7500), as well as the more generalized services such as Compuserve, The Source and CIX.

A non-commercial BBS may make a small charge to defray expenses — *someone* has to cover the cost of the equipment, after all — but the principal motive will not be profit. Such systems will actually comprise one or more small computers with disk storage for the messages, one or more incoming phone lines with modems attached, one or more individuals who run the facility (the 'system operator' or SYSOP) and some software that controls everything.

The software that runs the BBS is likely to be quite sophisticated. It will be able to handle multiple tasks (and multiple users) simultaneously. It usually has some kind of registration or access system (you will often have to give a name and assign yourself a

password before you can get on to a BBS). There is also likely to be a menu, or a series of them, which offers the user access to the various areas of the board.

Calling a BBS

It is the SYSOP's role as the managing director-cum-janitor of the BBS to handle the maintenance of the service, to register new users, to set up open and closed areas of the board, to keep a backup of the information on the board and to maintain security of the system.

Frequently the boards operate 24 hours a day, although all have a certain amount of downtime — when they are disconnected from the telephone lines — for essential maintenance. (The commercially run systems like Compulink's CIX have multiple machines which are shut down one at a time, so the service appears to be uninterrupted.)

Smaller boards use smaller computers and less sophisticated software. At the other end of the scale to the 24-hour 365-day BBS you will find boards that operate only at weekends or only in the evening; often these have a 'ringback' number — the SYSOP does not have the kind of modem that can operate unattended, so you have to ring first and ask him/her to plug in the modem at that end.

A major problem with browsing the boards is knowing where to start; there are more than 200 BBSs in the British Isles, so personal recommendation is the only alternative to trawling around the options (at some cost to your phone bill).

Connecting to a BBS may itself require some experimentation. All boards are restricted in terms of the comms parameters you have to use. Specifically, you will need to set up your software and your modem for the following parameters (you do not have to understand *why*, just enter the relevant information):

□ *Speed.* Access at 300 baud is usual, 1200/75 is quite common, 1200/1200 is becoming more so, 2400/2400 is relatively rare.

□ *Stop bits.* The number of stop bits can be '0' or '1', and it is usually '1'.

□ *Parity.* This can be 'odd', 'even' or 'none'.

□ *Data bits.* The number of 'data' bits can be '7' or '8'.

FIDONET is an electronic mail network with no on-line charges and dial-up points all over Europe, Australia and the USA — it has 1700 public access points worldwide. Any user on FIDONET can send to and receive from any other. The system can transfer ASCII files (text) or binary files (programs), offers a total of seven alternative protocols to upload and download files, and produces a free on-line newsletter read by 70 000 users every week. What's more, it is all run by amateurs.

FIDONET began in the early eighties when two computer enthusiasts living at opposite ends of the States became frustrated by the fact that neither commercial nor amateur electronic mail systems allowed them to send messages irrespective of the computer they happened to be using. So one of them, Tom Jennings, developed a piece of software that could operate during the day as a machine-specific electronic mail system — and which would exchange its electronic mail with another similar system for one hour every night.

The result was FIDO. It is available on a public-domain basis to anyone with an IBM-compatible computer and a Hayes-compatible modem.

At the time there were several packages around for running bulletin boards. FIDO followed many of the traditions laid down by its predecessors, built around the movement associated with public domain and user-supported software. However, there were important differences.

During the day FIDO operates as a good conventional bulletin board: users can call the board, read notices, upload or download software, and leave messages for other local users.

There is also the network interface FIDONET: a FIDO system can be told via a configuration file that at certain times of each day it must accept calls *only* from other FIDOs. During this process, FIDO SYSOPs can exchange information; updates to FIDO and FIDONET can be passed on from Jennings and his cohorts; and, crucially, messages from users on one FIDO can be passed to another.

The first FIDOs were exchanging messages reliably in the USA in the spring of 1984. By August the first major snags turned up: there were just too many FIDO systems trying to exchange information, and a two-tier system was established with 'concentrators' linking local FIDO 'nodes'.

The other significant difference between FIDO and other bulletin board systems from the user's viewpoint is the wide range of material stored locally. Often public domain software is first released in the USA on FIDONET; it will appear on UK FIDO systems within 24 hours, thanks to FIDONET's very own (amateur) high-speed modem links running on the international PSTN.

Making telephone calls costs money, though. FIDO has an extensive range of data-handling protocols to move files between far-flung systems with a minimum of errors and subsequent retransmissions.

Standards that FIDO has engendered and/or enforced in this way have been documented and are now being accepted outside its own bailliwick; System Enhancement Associates, for instance, has developed a new commercial mail system for PC owners called SEADOG that effectively adapts any bulletin board system (including commercial implementations) to cater for FIDONET mail exchange.

A new generation of bulletin boards is building on FIDO. One of the first has been OPUS. FIDO's bulletin board features are its weakest element; its message-entering services are poor compared to more commercially oriented non-networked systems. OPUS rewrote FIDO to improve the usage of the board, notably to add support for colour graphics.

Most BBSs were programmed by hit and miss, evolving into highly individual systems; some achieved a degree of stability and uniformity that led to quite widespread adoption of the common software. FIDO imposes a wider discipline and is considerably more structured; Jennings insisted on keeping control of the actual source code of the program. As a result of the provision of common and specific BBS features, FIDO has set some important standards in bulletin boards — reliability, in particular.

FIDO's success does not lie in providing a spectacular user-friendly environment. Rather, it has provided a standard base on which others can build a second generation of bulletin board systems. FIDO has become a standard to be matched or beaten.

This list is by no means comprehensive — being largely amateur operations, bulletin boards appear and die with disconcerting frequency. It does, however, include some of the more stable and longer-established boards, those with a track record of usefulness and entertainment.

You will find that the boards here include examples run by:

☐ Computer enthusiasts (the majority)
☐ Independent user groups for particular computers and packages
☐ On-line typesetting firms (who take text over a data link and return typeset copy in ready-to-use form)
☐ Computer suppliers (for support and promotion)
☐ Computer and other magazines
☐ Local Itecs and colleges
☐ Local authorities

Aberdeen Itec	0224 641585
Access FIDO	0905 52536
Avon FIDO	0934 29570
Banat Board	0865 882872
Basildon Itec	0268 25122
Brixton Itec	01-735 6153
Bulletin AT FIDO	0792 297845
Cardiff Itec	0222 464725
CATS FIDO	0628 824852
Colchester FIDO	0206 561898
Communitel	01-968 7402
Cyberzone	01-638 2034
Cymrutel	0492 49194
Dark Crystal	01-207 2989
Dataflex FIDO	01-543 7020
Dr Solomon's FIDO	02403 4946
Dublin FIDO	0001 854 522
FBBS Swansea	0792 203953
FIDO Bangor	0247 467863
FIDO Compulink North	051-220 3761
FIDO Gamlingay	0767 50511
FIDO Manchester	061-773 7739
FIDO PD Software	0342 315636
FIDO Teesside	0642 784819
Forum 80 Hull	0482 859169
Gnome at Home	01-888 8894
Gosport Apricot BBS	0705 524805
Hackney BBS	01-985 3322
Haunting Thunder	0752 364059
Health Data	01-986 4360
Hendon FIDO	01-200 7577
Hole in the Wall	0742 350319
Hughs FIDO	0534 36433
ITCU Exchange & Mart	01-960 4742
Link FIDO	01-659 6992
Liverpool FIDO	051-260 5607
Log On The Tyne FIDO	091-477 3339
London Underground	01-863 0198
Mailbox 80 Liverpool	051-428 8924
Mailbox 80 Warley	0384 635336
Medway BB	0634 815805
Oxford Poly	0865 68585
PBBS Adult BBS	04862 25174
PCW	0483 573338
PD-Sig FIDO	08926 61149
Personal Computer Plc	01-265 1265
Poly FIDO	01-580 1690
Staines BB	01-816 5794
Stoke Itec	0782 265078
Swafax	0622 850442
TBBS London West	0895 52685
Techno Line	01-450 9764
TeePee Link FIDO	061-494 6938
Twilight Phone	01-624 5338

If in doubt, set up for 8 data bits, 1 stop bit and No parity; if that does not work, try 7 data bits, 1 stop bit and Even parity. Most BBSS follow one format or the other.

As for speed, try 300 bps to get on to the board first time around — all offer at least that speed. The sign-on message will usually indicate if a higher speed is permitted; or you can send a message to the SYSOP and ask.

Restrictions

Because the BBS cannot anticipate exactly what kind of computer you are using, and because most of them therefore try to cater for everyone, there's a lowest-common-denominator approach: most boards are text-based — no pretty graphics, no fancy windows — and the way they present information makes no assumptions about the capabilities of a particular computer.

There are limits to the number of communications ports on the average microcomputer, and one port is required for each modem and phone line. The number of people wishing to 'log on' to a popular BBS will frequently exceed the number of comms ports and phone lines available. Then you have to keep trying to log on until there is a phone line free — and you will discover one of the advantages of having an autodialling modem, one that can dial a number (and re-dial it) automatically.

It is because of the limitations of smaller systems that most bulletin boards impose a time limit on each call. The time you spend on the board, downloading software or flicking from message to message, is monitored by the system; you will be disconnected when your time is up. Sometimes you will not be allowed access again until 24 hours have elapsed. In this way, more people are more likely to get a chance at the BBS.

The nature of mainframes — fast, sophisticated processing; massive memories to run complex software; very large data stores — means that the mainframe will continue to be the only practical repository for large databases.

On the other hand, the advent of the desktop computer has meant a proliferation of local computing at the level of departments and individual workstations. More users and increasing sophistication can lead to disorganization, incompatibilities, and a lack of standardization; the departmental computing can get out of step with the larger requirements of the organization.

It makes sense to impose a degree of order by connecting local systems in a way that does not limit their activities too much.

More pragmatically, there will be an obvious requirement in many applications for the local computing to utilize corporate information held centrally. Equally, there will be a need to pass local departmental information to the mainframe for consolidation into the corporate data base.

The tricky aspect of this is designing the systems for control. The easy part is actually making the connection.

Direct connection

The most basic form of communication between two computers is asynchronous; this is the method used for simple connections, such as one desktop computer to another or to an e-mail service. The start and end of a message are indicated by special characters.

The alternative is synchronous communication, where the start and end of a message are determined by pulses from a crystal clock. This permits much more economical transmission, and it usually allows higher speeds.

For those reasons it is used as the normal comms medium for mainframes — the quickest, simplest and generally safest way to access a mainframe computer is to follow its synchronous protocol.

That protocol will be highly specific. The async protocol is more or less standardized,

and there is little variation in it. The only standards in synchronous protocols are *de facto* — they have arisen simply because they are there and because lots of people need some kind of standard to follow.

In practice, most communication will be with one of very few mainframe types; and nearly all offer IBM-compatible synchronous comms. In practice this requires appropriate hardware (normally in the form of a plug-in board) and suitable software that emulates a particular terminal.

In the case of IBM-type communications, the likeliest emulation is of the 3270 terminal — the genuine IBM 3270 is intended for interaction with a mainframe while providing a degree of local computing and controlling its own local disks and printer, which is generally how the desktop computer will want to operate. The software and hardware that provide the local PC with 'emulation' effectively make the mainframe think it is dealing with a 3270.

Partly because 3270 emulation has become a *de facto* standard, and partly because emulation products are now so widely available for desktop computers, many mainframe manufacturers have adopted those protocols as a standard option for communications — the *only* such option, in some cases.

For popular computers there are specialized packages for appropriate emulations. Users of ICL personal computers, for instance, have a good selection for emulators using ICL's CO1, CO2 and CO3 protocols.

Communicating via a network gateway

The other likely option is for a departmental local area network system to access the mainframe via a 'gateway' — normally a direct connection to the mainframe's communications controller through a purpose-designed link.

As far as the end-user is concerned, passing information to and from the remote mainframe is greatly simplified because the gateway handles all terminal emulation and protocols.

There is more to information technology than the catalogue of tools and services that may or may not be available. This section provides some pointers on the design, implementation and successful use of information systems.

There is no simple correlation between investment in information technology and any gains in performance and productivity. In fact, IT can make good management better — and it can exacerbate any failings.

That is because information systems can and should become central to the organization. Such a key factor cannot survive anything less than a rigorous approach to design and implementation. In short, information systems need proper management if they are to benefit management.

1. Establish objectives

Any project needs a clear statement of goals from the outset. This is particularly true of a project with potentially far-reaching effects, such as an information system. The problem is that it may not immediately be possible to quantify those goals in anything more than the vaguest terms.

☐ *Determine goals*, particularly in terms of meeting corporate objectives — both in the long and short term. This may have to cover an analysis of what exactly the corporate goals *are*.

☐ *Establish the support of top management*. Experience suggests that this is absolutely crucial, not least because many organizations obtain their style and attitudes from the top. Key arguments might centre on cost savings (including intangibles like management time), productivity improvements and corporate benefits that could accrue.

2. Analyse existing systems

At this stage it should by no means be clear that the only or the best solution would be investment in information technology. Other options, including leaving well alone, should be available.

To check out those alternatives, a thorough analysis of existing procedures will be required.

The overall aim is to understand the office, identify activities and hopefully establish some measures of office productivity. A formal O&M work measurement programme could be involved.

☐ *Assess the performance of present systems*. Once the corporate objectives have been established, the current systems can be evaluated in terms of how they meet the goals — and how well. This should highlight deficiencies and provide pointers to change.

☐ *Investigate non-technical issues* — in particular, how the organization operates. This will include assessment of the types of information the organization uses, where and how it moves, the degree to which tasks are centralized, present methods of monitoring management performance, the level of formality in operating procedures and reporting, and the etiquette of office life. This should indicate areas of potential difficulty and set guidelines for how and where any new system might fit in.

☐ *Explain and involve*. Measurement techniques can be intrusive, to say the least, and there is widespread antagonism towards work measurement, particularly among white-collar staff. A tactful approach is called for. As well as explanatory meetings and other channels of information to explain what is going on, middle management should ideally be involved actively in the assessment process — and other personnel may be able to contribute. There has been some success in adopting a team approach, inviting departments to provide the first-stage analysis both to supply basic input and to prepare the ground for statistical assessments.

3. Establish opportunities

It should now be possible to identify areas where change is desirable, and to indicate benefits for different levels of restructuring.

☐ *Identify possible benefits.* This should be done strictly in terms of corporate objectives. Cost reductions, for instance, may be a chimera; saving on management time is valuable only if the manager can utilize that extra time effectively. Such goals may range from a low-level approach like the desire to reduce the number of systems installed and maintained, through operational specifics like the requirement for an extra competitive edge and more generic considerations such as productivity improvements, to a complete support for corporate strategies. Here, for example, are three different levels of approach:

| LEVEL ONE |
[no integration with corporate strategy]
Primary objective: operational efficiency
Secondary objective: management information

| LEVEL TWO |
[limited integration with corporate strategy — supports policy]
Primary objective: aid decision-making
Secondary objective: appreciate problem areas better

| LEVEL THREE |
[complete integration with corporate strategy]
Primary objective: open new markets
Secondary objective: change decision-making process

☐ *Design a system to fit those objectives.* This may require the use of outside consultants, if they have not been involved before. Select experienced, appropriate consultants: in-house staff often cannot see the wider picture — they tend to specify systems to fit the organization's current needs rather than future development.

A checklist of objections

In many organizations, management is reluctant to consider an information system. These are among the concerns that should be met by any system design:

☐ Inadequate, superficial understanding of the aims and role of new technology
☐ Fear of new technology, based on a suspected inability to handle the new tools
☐ Inability to match any new system to personal, departmental or corporate goals
☐ Doubts that the new operating concepts can be sold to staff
☐ Doubts about the claimed benefits — especially when they are set against time and effort required to implement any new system
☐ Concern that new technology will disrupt company relationships and the chain of command
☐ Lack of confidence in the likelihood that accurate cost-benefit analyses will be attainable
☐ Belief that much retraining will be necessary'

Human factors

☐ *Radiation* from CRT screens is almost certainly not a serious hazard, particularly given the shielding most manufacturers build into their monitors. The early research produced some scaring results, particularly on the incidence of miscarriages among VDU operators. None are conclusive, however, and in some cases the researchers have actually retracted their conclusions — particularly because they took insufficient account of other factors like alcohol and smoking. (There may, however, be a correlation between VDUs and the kind of stress that encourages the use of alcohol and tobacco.)

☐ *Visual discomfort* is much more of a problem — eyestrain leads to headaches, stress and fatigue. Factors at work here include several considerations relating to the equipment itself:

— The height, shape and spacing of characters
— Speed of scrolling
— Persistence of the original image after the display has changed
— Flickering
— Glare on screens and from the keyboard
— Keytops too small, too grubby or too worn

Previously tolerable problems with slight visual deficiencies and even mild epilepsy can certainly be exacerbated by using VDUs. The immediate answers include:

— Eye tests for anyone who will have to sit in front of a screen for long periods at a time
— A compromise between a good level of general lighting and glare on screens and keyboards (fluorescent lights cause headaches in many people)
— Selection of ergonomically appropriate equipment

□ *Posture* problems leading to fatigue, stress, backaches and the like. The main causes are adopting an awkward posture to compensate for unadjustable furniture, poor workstation layout, visual factors, and the like; and the fixed posture of sitting in one working position for a long period. It is almost always poor economy to avoid purchasing adjustable furniture.

□ *System design* is probably the key area for attention, however. To some extent the VDU and the non-adjustable office chair have become the whipping-boys for inadequate workplace conditions. The user's attitude to the information system itself can be a major cause of tension that impairs performance and aggravates other physical symptoms. Factors to consider include:

— A psychological need to 'possess' paper
— Sheer technophobia — fear of the system largely due to a suspected inability to cope with it, to utilize it effectively
— Jargon jars
— Opaque and unhelpful error messages are as much likely to be the fault of the designer, who failed to consider the user's fallibility and unfamiliarity

Basics

The BSI has a six-part *Draft British Standard Recommendations for Ergonomics Requirements for Design and Use of Visual Display Terminals in Offices.*

Importantly, this draft does not follow the prescriptive approach of existing and influential standards like the West German DIN 66234; laying down over-restrict criteria can inhibit innovation and become irrelevant as technology moves on. Instead, BSI takes a task-oriented approach, emphasizing user performance.

There is considerable detail on formal assessment methods for ease of use of a keyboard and the legibility of a display; those sections are primarily intended for hardware designers.

But Part Two is potentially the most important section, covering the design and management of work at display terminals. It includes no specific figures and offers no conformance tests; it does, however, represent a sane approach for designers and installers to follow.

The UK has one of the world's leading centres of expertise on human factors design in information technology. The Human-Computer Interface Service is based at Loughborough University, publishes a good deal of sane advice and research, and provides consultancy services as well.

How information technology is sold

The computer business is second only to holiday companies in the number of complaints received by the Advertising Standards Authority. The Information System is not a short-term project; the organization will benefit from a long-term relationship with a supplier, so it makes sense to pick the people you business with almost as carefully as the system you do business on.

□ *Manufacturers* who sell through a direct sales force are encountered less frequently these days. This is partly because of the investment they have to make in marketing and selling; in particular, they are concerned to protect the corporate image. This means they will have to pay their sales people the highest available salary, partly in order to keep them (particularly with relatively few career advancement opportunities) and partly to motivate them correctly (most direct sales forces do not work on commission).

Accordingly, most manufacturers at least operate a two-tier system. Larger blue-chip sales are handled direct — because the order value will be high and because the corporate image will suffer if a third party screws things up. Smaller clients are passed to local dealers.

□ *Distributors* perform a middleman function for dealers, usually taking equipment from a variety of manufacturers and offering the dealer one-stop shopping for all the components that make up a system. The manufacturers are happy with this because it means a guaranteed level of production and income without requiring too much expensive support from them. The dealers might be happy because they do everything their customers could need: the distributors' terms can also be fairly flexible. The dealer might also get no choice — some manufacturers will not supply them direct, insisting that they take their order to a distributor.

□ *Dealers* represent the sharp end of the business. There is considerable attrition among smaller dealers, who are usually underfunded and short of management expertise. There is also a wide range of dealers. At one end are mail-order 'box shifters' offering maximum discounts and absolutely no support; at the other you will find companies of considerable sophistication and a heavy investment in the products they handle.

□ *VARs* are value-added resellers, sometimes termed '*system houses*'. The VAR specializes in one style of product and often one type of customer; in principle, the VAR adds something extra to a manufacturer's basic machine, usually by offering a complete service with software and support. VARs usually look for a long-term relationship with a customer to maximize the investment they have had to make in knowledge and development of a product, in marketing and in a relatively long period between initial contact and signing an order.

Assuming the system has been specified so as to meet specified goals, and allowing for some groundwork in changing staff attitudes, much of the hard work has been done.

Plan for implementation

Implementing any new technology will require that people are asked to change the way they do things. A good deal of the early implementation program should therefore be based on dispelling doubts and fears.

- *Establish new operational procedures*, new work routines to replace the existing systems that are probably unstructured and have grown up in a strictly *ad hoc* fashion to meet immediate needs.

- *Establish procedures for audit and control* of the system in advance of implementation.

- *Establish and publicize support facilities* — particularly a 'hot-line' to provide quick answers to queries.

- *Set up training* — preferably 'hands-on' training using the new technology and the systems themselves (or accurate simulations). The supplier and any external consultants should be able to help.

- *Provide end-user documentation*. Even if the new equipment comes with voluminous manuals, they will not relate to the specifics of operation within the organization. Besides, customized documentation will help to dispel worries about a foreign system being imposed. Documentation should include short quick-reference cards, instruction guides, 'how-to' answers to common requirements, an ongoing set of published responses to users' queries and on-line help available from the system itself.

- *Evaluate health issues* and dispell or attend to them.

- *Set up pilot projects* to identify actual benefits and establish guidelines for operation; such pilots can be selected to get key end-users familiar with the new systems. They should also ensure that the proposed new technology works (and that it works better).

- *Build a foundation of enthusiastic support*. Good-natured and respected individuals who become converts can do a lot of the propaganda work for new systems.

- *Explain what is going on*, using all available means of communication — house journals, noticeboards, personal interviews for doubters, hands-on seminars to educate and involve staff at all levels. Promote the benefits: facts win minds.

- *Encourage participation*. Invite and reward proposals for extension or (minor) alterations to the proposed systems, encourage practice. Provide feedback. Above all, do not bully staff into sullen acquiescence — the system should serve the organization, but it must do that by serving the end-users.

- *Plan for parallel running*. There are arguments for and against a quick changeover from existing systems. As a rule, it makes sense to implement the change gradually and run the two systems in parallel for some time. This can lead to a duplication of effort, but a phased introduction could more effectively introduce users to the high-benefit features while permitting the control and support systems to settle down.

Implementation

Once the system is running, there are two key considerations:

- *Encourage continuing involvement*. It is the end-users who will most quickly spot the blemishes and the additional opportunities in the system.

- *Monitor the system*. Audit attitudes as well as costs, benefits and performance.

Security

The FBI says the average loss from computer fraud in the States is $600 000; the average loss from non-manual fraud is $23 000. UK insurers are said to have made an £85 million provision in 1985 for claims relating to computer frauds. Over half the 400 UK organizations polled by Ernst & Whinney in 1985 had been victims of a computer fraud.

The boom in computer-related crime is caused by a combination of opportunity — more computers are being used, more people know how to use them — and the increasing dependence of organizations on computerized files.

The problems are exacerbated by the lack of security controls. That is a management question, for nearly all but the smallest computer systems will already incorporate security facilities adequate for their needs. The problem is that they are not used. Moreover, much of the investment in computer security is wasted — partly because the resulting systems are not used either, and partly because they cater for the more esoteric and least likely manifestations of computer crime.

The emphasis on fraud is probably misleading; it is just easier to quantify than commercial espionage. Most criminals go for the easiest option that will deliver the greatest reward: a copy of the organization's strategic plans for use on the stock market or for sale to competitors is more likely to appeal to the criminal than abstraction of funds — which will be more risky, more laborious and probably more time-consuming.

Since commercial espionage is most easily done simply by copying the disks that happen to be next to a manager's desktop computer, the elaborate precautions of encrypted data communication seem to have missed the mark. As one security consultant puts it: 'the real hazard in computer security is the mundane, not the exotic'.

Security options

□ *Physical access control*. A variety of devices are available — among them *card readers*, access-code *keypads*, *physical recognition* (a digitized image of authorized personnel is compared with a video picture of the would-be entrant), *palm print* readers, and unique *signature* recognition.

□ *User authentication for dial-up systems*. Options here include a *dial-back* (the user calls the computer and asks for contact, the security modem at the other end calls back and establishes access if the caller's number is authenticated), *smart cards* containing unique and undecipherable access codes (a card reader is required at the user's end), and *tone generators* which play a series of security tones down the phone line to be authenticated.

□ *Data communications encryption* requires special security modems at both ends of the link; they respectively scramble and unscramble the data being transferred over the line.

□ *Software locking* involves password-protected access to files and programs. The amount of authentication the software demands before allowing access can be extensive.

□ *Software encryption* for programs and files is usually done by a purpose-built utility package that renders the original useless to anyone without the authenticated decoder.

Assessment

A.T. Kearney's research project *The Barriers and Opportunities of Information Technology* estimates that UK companies invested some £5 billion in IT during 1984 — on which fully one-fifth was wasted. The reasons seem to lie quite simply in a lack of direction and control, compounded by a reliance on traditional DP practices.

The major problem in monitoring any information system is the difficulty of assessing true costs and real benefits. The hangover from the early days of information technology, the introduction of centralized computer services, is that the performance of systems was more easily judged; the tasks being automated (payroll, stock control, management accounting) were tightly structured, with predefined requirements and a measurable processing time. Measuring intangibles like the improved quality of decision-making is not easy; it places considerable stress on the preliminary stages of an information system project, where office procedures and corporate goals have to be evaluated.

At a more pragmatic level, however, the information system is amenable to close control that will not adversely affect its operation.

The answer is to impose an information system policy in the form of standards. The information centre is best placed to develop and implement those standards. They may include:

□ *A restricted choice of hardware and applications packages*. In this way a degree of familiarity and expertise can be built up to support end-users, and transferability of data is assured. Such standardization may also produce benefits in cost terms (bulk purchasing attracts discounts) and in improved support from the supplier (large customers are favoured).

□ *The requirement that users document all applications they develop*, from spreadsheets to expert systems. A copy of this documentation should be lodged with the information centre for reference. A detailed example might feature:

— *Configuration required*
— *File format*
— *Sources of data*
— *Calculations performed*
— *Results expected*

— *Operating instructions*
— *Expected error messages and responses*
— *Specimens of output*

□ *Standardized working procedures* — in particular, to enforce regular backup copying. This can be done by providing 'how to' guides for new users.

□ *Standardized procedures on individual packages*. A classic illustration: all spreadsheets should be checked with one of the spreadsheet auditing utilities to ensure their internal consistency and accuracy (and a copy of the results should be included with the documentation).

□ *Hardware monitoring*. All hardware should be logged with serial numbers and warranty details, and all service calls should be notified to the information centre (or the centre should be the sole authority for them). Tracking engineering calls will highlight problem machines, can be used in negotiations with the supplier and will have relevance to future equipment purchasing.

Insurance

A computer will add substantially to the total value of your office contents, and should therefore be specified precisely in a normal 'office contents' policy. This should pay out on fire, theft, flooding, malicious and accidental damage. In addition to those physical risks, there may be some cover for the cost of getting back to normal — 'consequential loss'.

The 'office contents' policy may not provide sufficient cover, however:

□ Accidents and theft when the equipment is away from the office may not be covered.

□ There may be limits on the maximum cover for individual items.

□ A general contents policy may not include software and disks, and the cover might not extend to recreation of the files. Such policies are intended primarily for the replacement of *items*.

Because of this, it is preferable to take out insurance policies specifically for computing. These normally provide for physical losses, including cover for equipment in transit, and consequential losses as well. Losses arising from operator error are usually excluded, as is public liability.

Many computer policies can also be extended to provide cover for the cost of maintenance. This kind of insurance can in fact be cheaper than a conventional maintenance contract; and unlike the contract, it will include the consequential loss sections.

What the policyholder does not get is any guarantee of response. The user will have to make the arrangements for repair, pay for the service and claim subsequently from the insurer.

Accidental damage and the cost of hiring a temporary replacement machine are usually covered as well; both are normally excluded from a maintenance contract.

Maintenance

For hardware problems, there are four options:

- *In-house servicing* is not usually practicable for any but the simplest maintenance. Apart from the technical skills required, most servicing consists of straight replacement of parts.

- An *annual maintenance contract* is available from a number of specialist third-party maintenance companies. Such contracts should at least provide a quick repair or a replacement machine if an on-site fix is not possible. Different types of contract are available, usually by offering different levels of response to service calls — the maximum cover aims at response within four hours, seven days a week; the minimum cover is a 'return to depot' with the user taking the equipment to the service company.

- For *ad hoc* repairs on a time-and-materials basis, costs are incurred only when repairs are necessary. Most third-

party maintenance organizations will offer such a service; but *ad hoc* arrangements provide the least security, and maintenance companies give priority to contract-holders.

- An *insurance policy* that includes recompense for maintenance charges can be combined with assured maintenance cover from independent service companies who charge a low annual fee in return for guaranteed 24-hour response. The user still pays for parts and labour, and those costs are claimed from the insurer.

Preventative maintenance

Maintenance contracts do not generally cover *preventative* maintenance, and agreements usually state that the contractor reserves the right to make an extra charge for repairs resulting from misuse, neglect or accident.

Preventative maintenance is the equivalent of a regular car service. The checks and adjustments will apply particularly to disk drives, especially the read/write heads. They can go out of alignment over time, which means they will no longer sit exactly above the information on the disk's surface. That in turn can cause problems with trying to read information that was put on to the disk before, when the head was operating with a slightly different alignment. Realignment is just a matter of adjusting a few screws, though to get the positioning right takes some specialist equipment and technical knowledge.

Preventative maintenance should also include a regular cleaning for the disk heads. As they actually touch the disk's surface, they can pick up a patina of dust, grime and a fine scraping of the brown oxide coating from the disks. This can interfere with the reading and writing, much as the detritus on a cassette unit's play/record heads can interfere with recording and playback.

The user should also do this personally as a matter of course to minimize the problem.

It is possible to take some measures that at the very least will delay the requirement for formal maintenance. These are usually no more than good working habits.

- Above all, *regular backup copies of files should be taken*. This might seem a time-consuming irritant, but it would take a lot more time to key all the information in again. The copies should be kept somewhere safe, well away from the workplace.

- *Floppy disks should be handled correctly*. Disks should be replaced in their envelopes, never stacked flat, and kept well away from contaminants like coffee, cigarette ash and paperclips.

- Consider a *surge protector* or even an *uninterruptible power supply* if variations in the power supply are at all common. Sudden power cuts will be rare, but even the best-regulated electricity supply shows some voltage fluctuations. Computers will die with loss of data if there's no power at all, but they can also react quirkily to fluctuations, and there may be some scrambling of data on disks being used at the time.

- *Static electricity* is another aspect of modern office life that can be as irritating to the computer as it is to people. It is caused by a lack of humidity in the air — central heating is a major culprit — and is generated by friction (walking on nylon carpets produces an amazing amount of it). In theory static can result in internal malfunctions, but most computers are well-shielded; the effects are more likely to be seen in the way dust clings to the computer. Antistatic mats and aerosol sprays are available, but a better solution is to use a humidifier. (That can benefit people too, since low humidity can cause headaches and nasal problems as well as static shocks.)

- *Cable protectors* should be used if the cable has unavoidably to cross the floor. These are rubber strips with a non-slip backing and a strengthened channel inside to take the cable.

- *Cleaning the screen* regularly will get rid of the smudges, smears and dust that impede legibility. There are several proprietary screen-cleaning fluids or cloths; they should be used in preference to normal domestic or office cleaning materials, which can leave a residue on the screen.

- *Cleaning the inside of the keyboard* with a vacuum cleaner or aerosol can of 'clean' air will help to keep the key contacts clean. If it is possible, and if it does not invalidate any warranty, the keyboard can also be dismantled and the contacts wiped with an alcohol-based cleaning fluid on cotton buds.

- *Keep contaminants away from floppy disk drives*. Dust and even cigarette smoke can impair the accuracy of reading and writing.

- *Use disk head cleaners occasionally*. Proprietary disk head cleaning kits use an abrasive cleaning disk (to scrape off the detritus) or one that is impregnated with a special cleaning fluid (which dissolves the contaminants). There will not actually be very much rubbish on the heads — most of the accretion in fact is likely to be a minute build-up of oxide particles from the surface of floppies — but the precision with which disk drives operate is such that even a fractional coating can impair the head's ability to read or write.

- *Have the alignment of floppy disk drive heads checked from time to time*. They do tend to move slightly out of alignment as mechanical parts wear. The first warning of misalignment is an increased level of read errors; this is happening because the information was written on to the disk's surface in a fractionally different position.

The development of information systems will have far-reaching consequences for the organization — even before all the building blocks for full integration and proper control of such systems are in place. But future-gazing seems possible.

More interconnection

ISDN and the widespread adoption of standards like the OSI model will simplify communications at the technical level between different services, different devices and different applications. The theoretical result could be the ability for all forms of communication to be passed between any devices in any country. Practicalities will provide a limitation, but it is not impossible to envisage an image-producing device like today's fax machines being able to receive, decode and print a voice message.

More computing, more digitization

Virtually every tool used by people — in the home, office, education, leisure — can economically and sensibly include a microcomputer. (How about the intelligent pen, which evens out the flow of ink as it writes? Or checks your spelling as you go?) Virtually all forms of output from those devices will be digitized for decoding into other types of signal (voice, image, etc.) as required. Miniaturization makes this feasible, though that is no guarantee it will be required or even desirable.

More interactivity

Advanced programming techniques and the availability at low cost of miniaturized components will enable end-users of information systems to design those systems themselves. Personalization will be feasible without destroying standards and compatibility; each workstation can have as much functionality as it needs; the design tools will be intelligent enough to guide the user through the design process. Thereafter,

the system will be intelligent enough to help the user actually *use* the system, with advice on possible options and a good deal of anticipation and 'intuition'. Natural speech will be used for communication between the human and the machine.

More management

With the increasing automation of clerical functions, improved access to information and better tools for management, the emphasis will continue to shift from hierarchical, bureaucratic organizational structures on to decentralized team-oriented systems. The nature of offices will change, with less requirement for in-person attendance at a centralized facility. The nature of management will change as well; today's emphasis on formal reporting and *supply* management will be replaced by *demand* management that can support corporate goals.

More skills

Information centre staff will develop new skills in the design and implementation of integrated, application-oriented systems. The information centre will become the most critical element of most organizations, reflecting its central role; management of the information centre will be a natural route to Managing Director or CEO.

This glossary is intended as a practical guide to terms that may be encountered; it does not provide the same kind of comprehensive and literal definitions you should expect from a dictionary, but it should help to clarify some of the terminological obfuscations.

Where more description is available from the main body of the book, a reference to the relevant section is given. All cross-references are in *italics*.

1-2-3 (properly **Lotus 1-2-3**). Market-leading IBM-compatible *spreadsheet* package

24-pin. Indicates the number of dot-producing elements in the *printhead* of an *impact dot matrix printer*. With 24 pins, the printer will be able to print dots close enough for very good quality graphics and near letter-quality text. *More information: Chapter 13*

4GL. See *fourth-generation language*

80286. The Intel *microprocessor* chip used in the IBM AT and becoming the norm for desktop computers of a reasonable capability. *More information: Chapter 18*

80287. A *maths co-processor* for use with the 80286

80386. The Intel *microprocessor* chip used in the IBM PS/2 Model 50 and many other high-powered desktop computers. *More information: Chapter 18*

8086. The Intel *microprocessor* chip used in many of the IBM PC clones — faster than the original PC's 8088 but otherwise completely compatible. *More information: Chapter 18*

8087. A *maths co-processor* for use with the 8086 and 8088

8088. The Intel *microprocessor* chip used in the original IBM PC and many clones. *More information: Chapter 18*

abbreviated dialling. Also called short-form or short-code dialling — a facility whereby regularly called numbers are stored and used by entering a short code. Many modern telephones, PABXs, Telex and fax machines, and modem/comms software combinations include this time-saver. *More information: Chapter 31*

abbreviation. A facility in word processors and DTP packages for inserting prestored text automatically by use of a short abbreviation. Avoids repetitive typing; can be used to impose a 'house style' or a preferred format for specific terms. *More information: Chapter 24*

access barring. Prevents specified users from sending or receiving voice, data or fax calls

access time. Indicates how quickly a specific item stored in memory or on disk can be referenced. *More information on disk access times: Chapter 9*

accounts payable. Same as *sales ledger*

accounts receivable. Same as *purchase ledger*

acoustic coupler. A type of portable modem that is used with an ordinary telephone handset rather than connecting directly to a phone line. *More information: Chapter 32*

activities. In project planning, refers to operations involved in a project

add-in. A piece of hardware inserted into a computer or other device (*more information: Chapter 12*); or (just possibly) a software facility that can be incorporated into an existing package

add-on. A hardware or software facility that can be added on to an existing system. Often used interchangeably with *add-in*, though obviously the latter should refer only to something that is added internally

address. Coded identification of a source or destination in a comms link. Also (more technically) the identification of a particular location in memory

AI. Abbreviation for *artificial intelligence*

ALT. Engraved on one of the keys on many desktop computer keyboards — signifies an 'alternate Shift' key, normally used in combination with another key to provide a specific function. *More information: Chapter 11*

analogue. Representation of value by means of a physical variable, such as voltage or frequency levels — as opposed to *digital*, where values are represented as numbers

ANSI. American National Standards Institute — the US standards-setting body best known (in computer terms) for the ASCII *character set*, a specification of what bit patterns relate to which characters

answerback. A Telex facility whereby delivery of a message is notified to the sender. For this purpose, Telex messages include a sender's 'answerback code' — which itself is often termed 'the answerback'. *More information: Chapter 36*

applications environment. A piece of software that sits on top of the operating system and provides a simplified approach to using system facilities (copying and deleting files, running programs, etc.). Most of these *front-ends* feature *windows* and *icons*. *More information: Chapter 14*

applications packages or **applications programs.** Task-oriented software which does something for the user (as opposed to system software, like the operating system, which does something for the computer). *More information: Chapter 19*

arrow keys. The keys that control the movement of the *cursor*

artificial intelligence. Exhibited when a computer system apparently displays human attributes — notably a combination of learning by experience and (to some degree) intuition. *More information: Chapter 27*

artwork. Catch-all term used for the graphics or images (sometimes the text too) involved in the production of a printed page

ASCII. American Standard Code for Information Interchange — the almost universal *character set* employed for text, equivalent to the *CCITT* standard V3 (also known as 'International Alphabet No.5')

Assembler. A style of programming language that enables the programmer to control the operations of the computer in very precise detail. More precision would require the use of 'machine language', where programs are entered as binary numbers; Assembler at least replaces this with more or less comprehensible mnemonics. Because the programming does operate at such a detailed level, Assembler programming is usually machine-specific and it is still unintelligible to the layperson

async. Popular abbreviation for *asynchronous*

asynchronous. The simplest and most popular form of data transmission, in which the start and end of a character transmitted is denoted by special start and stop characters. Cf. *synchronous*, where the start and end of transmission is synchronized such that time intervals between characters are of equal length

AT. IBM's extension of the original PC line, featuring a faster processor (Intel 80286), improved keyboard and a hard disk as standard. *More information: Chapter 18*

attribute. Literally, some characteristic of an item of data — so a variable or a record's field may have the attribute 'integer'. More usefully, it indicates some characteristic of displayed or printed text that distinguishes it from the norm; as such, it usually applies to typeface variations such as italic, underlining or emboldening

audio-conferencing. Enables many participants in a telephone call as a substitute for in-person meetings. *More information: Chapter 40*

audit. Ascertain the validity of data or procedures

audit trail. A method of tracing the path of a transaction through a system from beginning to end

autoanswer. A facility whereby a modem or other comms equipment can operate unattended to receive incoming calls. *More information: Chapters 31 and 32*

autobaud. A facility in some modems that can detect the transmission speed required by the other end of the line and adjust accordingly. *More information: Chapter 32*

autodial. A facility within a *modem* and/or a software package that provides for automatic dialling of another computer or a comms service. *More information: Chapter 31*

auto log-on. A facility within a *modem* and/or a software package that provides for automatic *log-on* to another computer or a comms service

auto-sync. A feature provided in some colour graphics monitors that enables them to adjust to a variety of different *graphics controllers*

b. Abbreviation for bit(s), usually used in Kb or Mb

B. Abbreviation for byte(s), usually used in KB or MB

BABT. British Approvals Board for Telecommunications, the body that decides whether comms equipment meets the required standards for connection to British Telecom lines

background operation. The ability of a computer system — more specifically, of an *operating system* — to perform one task at the same time as another. Typically this is restricted to a maximum of two concurrent tasks — and in practice they are not *really* concurrent, for the computer will wait for a few milliseconds of spare time during the 'foreground' task and then execute a small part of the 'background' job before handing control back. The usual facility is for background printing, where one document is being printed (in somewhat staccato fashion) while the user works on something else

backing store. Anything that extends the computer's memory — typically, *disk* storage devices

backlit LCD. A method of improving the legibility of an *LCD* display by including a light source in the screen to counter reflections. *More information: Chapter 10*

backup. A duplicate for security purposes of files on disk

BACS. An on-line direct-debit facility run by the clearing banks for transferring money from one account to another

balance-forward. An accounting method whereby payments are allocated to the total outstanding balance. Cf. *open-item*

bandwidth. A measure of the range of frequencies that a transmission medium can carry, measured in hertz. In practical terms, the bandwidth indicates the number of different channels that can be supported for different functions; and/or the speed of data transfer. *More information: Chapter 15*

banner. A heading or title extending the width of a page

barchart. As *histogram*

barcode. A printed code that can be read as encoded data by a device called a barcode reader. Barcodes are commonly employed in retailing as the panel of vertical bars found somewhere on the label of purchased goods

bar graph. As *histogram*

baseband. A frequency *bandwidth* of around 300Hz or less for data transmission, particularly encountered in local area networks, that restricts communication to relatively low speeds and only one type of data. *More information: Chapter 15*

BASIC. Beginners' All-purpose Symbolic Instruction Code — the programming language most widely encountered on home computers and in computer instruction. Because of that background it is still widely used for desktop computer programs, despite the availability of superior alternatives

Basic Input/Output System. See *BIOS*

baud. A measure of data transmission speed. Literally it means 'signals per second', but in most cases can be taken as synonymous with 'bits per second'

Baudot. A five-bit code used for telegraph and Telex transmissions. Similar in some respects to the ASCII character set, except that the possible combinations available in only five bits do not provide enough codes for a full alphabet (including lower-case letters as well as capitals) and the extra control codes in ASCII

BBS. Bulletin Board System — a public-access dial-up noticeboard and electronic mail facility, usually run by enthusiastic amateurs. *More information: Chapter 41*

bell. A ring or beep from the computer

Bell. A US *common carrier* and telecommunications system that has given its name to a number of modem standards utilized in North America in preference to the *CCITT* recommendations followed in Europe and most of the rest of the world

benchmark. Some kind of practical test for equipment, software or systems

Bernouilli box. A type of high-capacity removable disk

binary. Literally, 'composed of two elements'. More generally, the simplest possible numbering system using only two digits ('to the base 2')

binary digit. One of the two digits used for binary, and abbreviated to *bit*

binary file. A *file* in non-ASCII form, which usually means non-text material like programs or graphics

BIOS. Basic Input-Output System — that part of MS-DOS which mates the generalized operating system functions to a particular computer

bisync. Abbreviation for *bisynchronous*

bisynchronous. A *synchronous* IBM comms protocol

bit. Contraction of *binary digit* — a single digit in a binary number. By extension, an individual component of the binary code

bit error rate. A measurement of the quality of a transmission line in terms of the number of wrong bits received

bit image. A dot-by-dot representation of something to be displayed or printed, one bit being the equivalent of one dot

bit map. A common technique in computer systems for defining the content of a printed page or a display by breaking it down into the component dots and setting aside an area of memory corresponding on a dot-by-dot basis to that output

bits per second. Usually *bps* — a measure of transmission speed

block graphics. Images created from shapes built up within the normal dot matrix used for characters (rather than treating the whole screen or page as a matrix of possible dot positions). The limited number of dot positions available obviously restricts the size, shape and flexibility of the graphics that can be created in this way

block operations. Moving, copying or deleting a chunk of text at a time in WP or DTP editing

board. As *printed circuit board*

body type. The main style of typeface used for text in printing (as opposed to styles used for headings or emphasis)

boilerplating. Constructing a new document by assembling sections of previously created and previously stored text. *More information: Chapter 24*

bold. Text with a heavier, darker appearance, normally used for emphasis and achieved by making the characters thicker (**extra bold** is even heavier). Also describes extra-bright ('high-intensity') characters displayed on a screen

boldface. As *bold*

boot. To start up a computer system

bootstrap. A small program that actually starts up a computer, typically by checking out the hardware components and then loading the operating system from disk

BOS. Business Operating System, a business-oriented *operating system* produced for a variety of computers by the British company BOS Software

BOS/LAN. A version of *BOS* for local networks

box shifter. A largely pejorative term applied to vendors of computer systems and components who usually provide no pre-sales advice and no after-sales service or support — a fact which is reflected in the discounted prices they typically offer

bps. Bits per second — a common measure of data transmission speed

Bps. Bytes per second — a rarely used measure of data transmission speed

breakout box. A tool for checking RS-232 connections and hopefully overcoming problems

bridge. An interconnection (usually between a LAN and an external facility) that enables selective data transfer with no protocol conversion. *More information: Chapter 15*

briefcase computer. A *microcomputer* compact enough to fit in a briefcase

British Approvals Board for Telecommunications. See *BABT*

broadband. A frequency *bandwidth* usually in the range 300-3000 Hz for data transmission. Encountered particularly in local area networks, this permits communication at relatively high speeds and for several types of data. *More information: Chapter 15*

BSC. Binary synchronous communications — an IBM comms protocol

BSI. British Standards Institution, the UK standards-setting body

BT. Abbreviation for British Telecom

buffer. A small chunk of *ROM* used for temporary storage, typically to even out the different processing speeds of two devices — a buffer can take data from one high-speed device and feed it out at a lower speed to another

bug. A fault or error, usually in software

bulletin boards. See *BBS*

bullets. Text marks used for emphasis in a list — round blobs, usually

bus. The electrical connection between components of a computer system along which data is transmitted

business graphics. Business information presented in graphic form. *More information: Chapter 21*

Business Operating System. See *BOS*

bus network. A type of LAN utilizing a single line with devices attached along its length. This is the most basic and the most widely used of the LAN configurations. *More information: Chapter 15*

byte. A group of eight bits, which almost invariably is used to hold a single character (a letter, numeric digit or part of a control code)

C. Technically complex but function-filled programming language originally developed for the *Unix* operating system.

cable protectors. Rubber strips containing a channel for cables such that they can run across the floor without causing a dangerous obstruction

cache or **cache memory.** A method of speeding up disk access by setting aside an area of memory as a *buffer*

CAD. Computer-Aided Design

CADCAM. Computer-Aided Design and Manufacturing (the computer-produced design is generally used to produce production plans)

CAL. Computer-assisted learning

call logging. Recording detailed information about telephone usage and costs

call redirection. A facility whereby incoming calls are automatically redirected to another designated destination. *More information: Chapter 33*

CAM. Computer-Aided Manufacturing — usually as *CADCAM*

Cambridge ring. The best-known type of *slotted ring* local area network

camera-ready artwork. As *camera-ready copy*, though usually the term implies the addition of graphics to text

camera-ready copy. Pages of text that are ready for a litho printer to begin the film and platemaking process

camp-on-busy. A PABX facility whereby calls are automatically repeated until a number is no longer in use. *More information: Chapter 33*

caps. Short for capital letters

Caps Lock. A keyboard facility that locks the alphabetic keys into upper-case — the equivalent of Shift Lock, except that only the alphabetic keys are affected. *More information: Chapter 11*

CAPTAIN. Japanese viewdata standard

CAR. Computer-assisted retrieval (for automated microfilm storage)

card. A *printed circuit board*

carrier. Literally, a signal for sending messages. More generally used as a short form of *common carrier*

carrier tone. A high-pitched tone that indicates a public network is available for data transmission use

cartridge. A slot-in package of some kind. Tape streamers use tape cartridges; removable hard disks usually come in a cartridge; many laser printers have font cartridges, a plug-in package that contains one or more complete typefaces (which are actually held in ROM on a miniature circuit board) to add to any fonts already provided

CAV. Constant angular velocity — one of two methods of laying 'tracks' on a laser disk. CAV disks have a number of concentric-ring tracks, do not have to vary the spin speed, can access stored data more quickly than the alternative CLV method, but do not hold as much data. Though not as widely used as CLV, and not currently part of the Sony/Philips standards for CD, CAV is likely to become the preferred technique for interactive and information applications of laser disk

CBL. Computer-based learning

CCD. Charge-coupled device — a solid-state memory technology that in theory fits between RAM and disks in terms of price and performance. In practice, CCD has never realized its early promise — CCDs first appeared in the early seventies, and they are still both expensive and rare.

CCITT. Comité Consultatif International Téléphonique et Télégraphie, the committee of the International Telecommunications Union that recommends standards for data communications. *More information: Chapters 30 and 50*

CD-I. Compact Disk — Interactive, a laser disk technology aimed at education and entertainment. CD-I can mix text, sound, and video (by contrast, CD-ROM cannot handle moving pictures) with interactive selection of options; a CD-I player is hooked on to a TV set just like a video cassette recorder. *More information: Chapter 16*

CDLC. Cellular Data Link Control — a *protocol* for data transmission over cellular radio links

CD-ROM. Compact Disk — Read-Only Memory, a laser disk technology offering high storage capacities and reasonable access time with extremely long working life for storage of digitized data. Because the content of a CD-ROM cannot be written or altered by the user, such disks will presumably be used for 'electronic publishing' of reference information and the like. *More information: Chapter 16*

CD-V. Compact Disk — Video, a laser disk technology that effectively combines current VCR playback features (fast and slow-motion replay, freeze frame and the like — but not recording) and the music facilities of audio compact disk. It can be connected to a standard TV or hi-fi system. *More information: Chapter 16*

CEEFAX. The BBC's *teletext* service

cell. In a *spreadsheet*, one 'box' in the worksheet grid where a number, text or a formula can be entered. *More information: Chapter 20*

Cellular Data Link Control. See *CDLC*

cellular modem. A *modem* specifically intended for data transmission over cellular radio links (for instance, from a carphone). *More information: Chapter 32*

Centronics. A once-successful printer manufacturer that popularized a plug-and-socket method of connecting printers to computers. This *parallel interface* has now become a *de facto* standard

CGA. IBM's Colour Graphics Adapter for the PC and AT, a means of producing limited medium-resolution graphics in colour on a suitable display. *More information: Chapter 18*

character. Any printable or displayable letter, digit, punctuation mark, technical or arithmetic symbol, or space

character generator. Circuitry which translates data into dots on a display screen.

character set. A set of codes corresponding to characters

checksum. A method of adding verification characters to data to test for errors

chip. A thin sliver of silicon or other material on to which miniaturized circuits are etched or engraved. More colloquially, the whole package including connectors (the 'legs') and protective plastic coating

circuit board. As *printed circuit board*

clip art. Ready-to-use graphics that can be incorporated into documents — originally in the form of cutout images for pasting on to masters, but the term has been borrowed by desktop publishing for the electronic equivalent of loading images from disk to insert into a page on the screen

clock speed. A measure of the speed of a processor. Many other factors affect the overall throughput, but clock speed can be used as a broad indication of performance. *More information: Chapter 6*

clone. A compatible (usually, IBM-compatible) computer

closed user group. A private members-only facility provided on a public-access service

CLR. A command or key that (probably) has the effect of clearing the screen

cluster. A group of *terminals* connected to a comms line at a single point

CLV. Constant linear velocity — one of two methods of laying 'tracks' on a laser disk. CLV disks have a single spiral track, increase the spin speed towards the centre of the disk, and are generally used for most digital compact disk applications. Cf. *CAV*

CMOS. A type of memory *chip* that does not lose its contents when power is removed

CNTRL. Sometimes engraved on a keytop instead of *CONTROL*

co-ax. Abbreviation for *co-axial cable*

co-axial cable. A type of cable familiar from TV aerials with a conductor wire running inside a metal sheath to shield out interference. *More information: Chapter 15*

COBOL. A widely used *high-level* programming language with facilities oriented towards business applications

code. A representation (usually in binary form, in this context) of a character or command. Also used to mean the instructions in a program (and by extension 'to code' means to write a program)

codec. A device that combines encoding and decoding of a signal; usually applies to conversion between video signals and digital form for transmission

Colour Graphics Adapter. See *CGA*

COM. Computer-Output Microfilm — produces microfilm directly from the computer

common carrier. A supplier of a public telecommunications service, such as British Telecom

comms. Abbreviation for *communications*

comms server. A LAN controller that handles external communications facilities on the network — which may be one or more *modems, gateways* or *bridges*. The server will accept material to be transmitted, decide which facility to use and send it; incoming material is received and directed to the appropriate workstation. *More information: Chapter 15*

communications. The movement of information

communications server. See *comms server*

compatibility. The ability of two devices to work together, or for software to work on particular computers

Compuserve. A US-based public-access information and electronic-mail service — the main competitor to The Source. Compuserve charges a subscription and connect-time fees

computer. Basically, a fast rule-following idiot using solid-state technology and featuring a method of input, output and storage for data and programs

computer-assisted retrieval. See *CAR*

computer conferencing. Enables many participants in an on-line messaging facility as a substitute for in-person meetings. *More information: Chapter 40*

concurrency. An *operating system* facility that enables two or more tasks to run simultaneously

Concurrent DOS. A Digital Research operating system providing *concurrent* operations for computers utilizing the Intel 80286 or 80386 processor

condensed. A typestyle with a squashed appearance, with minimum spacing between characters

conferencing. Electronic substitute for in-person meetings. *More information: Chapter 40*

connect time. Length of time connected to a remote computer or comms server — usually meaning *chargeable* time

consequential loss. Costs involved in recovering data, programs, etc., and otherwise restoring the normal working conditions after some mishap that warrants an insurance claim. *More information: Chapter 45*

consolidation. Generally, merging two or more *spreadsheets*. More specifically, it is an accounting term that indicates the incorporation into group accountants of figures from subsidiary operations

contention. The simplest LAN protocol, where any user can try to utilize the network if there is no traffic currently on the LAN. If two users try to send at the same time, they both back off and try again a fraction of a second later. *More information: Chapter 15*

context-sensitive help. On-screen assistance that is relevant to the particular operation currently being performed

continuous stationery. The type of paper for computer printers that consists of a long strip of paper with holes down the sides (to engage in the sprockets of a *pin* or *tractor feed*) and perforated horizontally at regular intervals so that it can be folded concertina-style. Also called *fanfold* stationery

control character. A character that usually cannot be printed or displayed but has some specific function in controlling a device or software facility

CONTROL key. Like *ALT*, this usually signifies an 'alternate Shift' key that is normally used in combination with another key to provide a specific function. *More information: Chapter 11*

controller. A hardware facility, typically provided as in-built circuitry or an add-in board, that enables the system to utilize the specific characteristics of a device or some component

copy-fitting. Adjusting text such that it fits a given area of a printed page, usually by *variable leading*

correspondence-quality. As *near letter-quality*

corruption. Distortion of data during transmission, such that the data received is not what was sent

CPA. Abbreviation for *critical path analysis*

CPU. Central processing unit. Usually synonymous with *processor*; indicates the key element of a computer system, which actually decodes and executes instructions

crash. Sudden and unexpected failure — of a particular operation, a software package, the whole computer system, or a network

CRC. Cyclic redundancy check — a widely used method of detecting errors in data transmission

critical path analysis. A professional method of monitoring and controlling projects

crosstalk. Interference in a transmission caused by signals from another

CRT. Cathode ray tube — the display technology familiar from domestic TV sets that puts an image on to the screen by using a beam of electrons to illuminate a phosphor coating on glass

CSMA. Carrier-Sense Multiple-Access — the commonly used method of detecting whether there is traffic currently on a *contention* LAN. *More information: Chapter 15*

CSMA/CA. Carrier-Sense Multiple-Access with Collision Avoidance — extension of *CSMA* with a technique for avoiding 'collisions' between two LAN users trying to utilize the network at the same time

CSMA/CD. Carrier-Sense Multiple-Access with Collision Detection — an alternative technique that for practical purposes is identical to *CSMA/CA*

CTRL. Sometimes engraved on a keytop instead of *CONTROL*

CUG. Abbreviation for *closed user group*

cursor. A mark on the screen that indicates where the next character typed will appear or what effect the next command will have

cut-and-paste. A facility within some packages for moving or copying a block of text or graphics. This may be identical to a 'block move', but that operation usually applies to whole lines; a true cut-and-paste will allow *any* rectangularly shaped area of the display to be moved

cut sheet. Single sheets of paper

daisywheel. The removable print element in a daisywheel printer, comprising fully formed characters mounted on stalks around a central hub. *More information: Chapter 13*

daisywheel printer. A printer using daisywheel print elements

data. More or less synonymous with *information*, except that data does not necessarily have any inherent meaning

database. Generally, a pool of related information

Database Management System. A *package* providing facilities for the creation and use of a database. The term is normally reserved for the more sophisticated types of *file manager*, those capable of handling database structures with many-to-many relationships. *More information: Chapter 23*

data processing. Can be used to describe the operation of any computer, but more generally refers to the work of a *data processing department* — in other words, use of computers by professional staff not directly concerned with the use of any results from that processing

data processing department. A service facility within an organization that provides computer services

data rate. As *line speed*

daughterboard. A small circuit board positioned on top of another, larger, *PCB*

dB. Decibel(s) — a measure of the volume of sound

dBASE. Best-selling file management package

DBMS. Abbreviation for *Database Management System*

DDL. Document Description Language — a rival *page description language* to POSTSCRIPT, developed by Imagen Corp. and popularized by Hewlett-Packard

DDP. Abbreviation for *distributed data processing*

dealer. A company that will actually sell computer products to end-users, buying the goods from the manufacturer or a *distributor*

debug. To remove errors or faults

decimal tab. A word processor facility for aligning columns of numbers around a decimal point. *More information: Chapter 24*

decision support (usually **decision support system**). Software facilities intended to provide direct assistance for management decisions, typically in assessment of priorities and allocation of resources. *More information: Chapter 27*

decryption. Decoding material that has been encrypted for security purposes

demultiplex. To separate incoming *multiplexed* communications

desktop computer. A full-function *microcomputer* intended for more or less static use. *More information: Chapter 6*

desktop publishing. The use of a desktop computer, laser printer and appropriate software to produce printed material of a quality approaching that obtained from phototypesetting. *More information: Chapter 25*

device. Generally, any equipment connected to a computer or participating in a LAN

device driver. A software facility, typically provided within the operating system, that enables the system to utilize the specific characteristics of a device

device handler. As *device driver*

Diablo. The early market-leader in *daisywheel printers*. By virtue of that, the control codes used by Diablo have become one of the *de facto* standards for print formatting

diagnostic. A software facility that checks the correct operation of hardware (or, occasionally, of certain software functions)

Dialcom. The US company that produced the software employed by most of the world's electronic mail services. Now owned by Telecom Gold, Dialcom's first and largest licensee

dial-up. A call initiated on a public telecommunications service

digital. Pertaining to the representation of information in numeric form (rather than *analogue*)

digitization. Conversion of information into *digital* form. *More information: Chapter 2*

digitizer. Usually synonymous with *scanner* — a device for converting images or text on paper into digital form for subsequent use by the computer (typically for incorporation into WP or DTP documents). *More information: Chapter 25*

DIN. West German standards organization, and usually encountered as part of the identification for standards it has set

dingbats. Miscellaneous print characters used for emphasis or adornment that are not part of a normal *font*

DIP. Dual in-line package, the correct name for a *chip* package including connectors and protective covering

DIP switch. Small switches mounted on a *DIP*, most frequently encountered in printers or add-in cards for selecting options

direct sales. Computer products are generally sold through middlemen — dealers and distributors — but some manufacturers do sell direct from their own sales force. This particularly applies when the customer has a large and complex order, or when the supplier's corporate image could be adversely affected by any hiccups in the deal

disk. A storage medium using circular discs coated with magnetizable material. *More information: Chapter 9*

disk drive. Motor-driven component that also includes read/write heads

disk file. Any discrete item stored on *disk*. The term therefore covers programs, text documents and graphic images as well as conventional files of records

disk swapping. Taking out one *floppy disk* and inserting another

display. Often synonymous with *monitor*; by extension, can refer to material displayed. *More information: Chapter 10*

distributed processing or **distributed data processing.** Data processing tasks performed at geographically dispersed locations

distributor. A middleperson. Most computer-related products sold in the UK are bought in bulk from the manufacturers by distributors, who in turn sell on in smaller quantities to individual *dealers* to service the actual end-user

document. Loosely, any text and/or graphics destined to be printed or transmitted

documentation. The aggregation of user manuals, 'how-to' guides, tutorials and other materials supplied with hardware or software that is intended to help the end-user *use* the product. Some of the documentation may be on paper, some of it may be in the form of disk files

Document Description Language. See *DDL*

document template. Predefined layout and formatting considerations that can be applied to a particular document at printing

dot matrix printer. A printer that works by creating dots on the paper in the shape of characters or images. The term usually refers to an *impact dot matrix printer*. *More information: Chapter 13*

double-density. A way of doubling the amount of storage on a *floppy disk* by doubling the number of 'tracks' on the disk's surface. This demands appropriate formatting and disk drives, and it may require special disks; a single-density disk can be used with a double-density disk drive, but the reverse is not normally the case

double-sided. Another way of doubling the amount of storage on a *floppy disk* by using both sides of the disk's surface. Again, appropriate formatting, disks and disk drives are required. A single-sided disk can be used with a double-sided disk drive, but not *vice versa*

download. Transfer a file to a local device or from a remote computer

downloadable font. An alternative laser print font stored on disk and loaded into the laser printer's memory as required (as opposed to *cartridge* fonts; both of them supplement the fonts already provided within the printer). *More information: Chapter 13*

downtime. A period of inoperation for a system, usually due to failure or maintenance

dpi. Dots per inch — a measure of *resolution*, usually referring to printed output and thus being the hardcopy equivalent of *pixel*

draft mode. The fastest printing possible from a dot matrix printer — usually contrasted with *NLQ* mode, which is slower but produces printing of better quality. *More information: Chapter 13*

DRAW disk. Digital Read After Write laser disk — synonymous with *WORM* disk

drop-down menu. A *menu* that when called up by the user overlays anything already on the screen — without affecting that existing display. Such menus usually appear from the top of the display

DTP. Desktop publishing

DVM. Occasionally used abbreviation for digital *voice messaging*

EBCDIC. Alternative to the *ASCII* character set, used by IBM for its larger computers

ECMA. European Computer Manufacturers' Association, a largely defensive and not particularly active grouping formed originally to counter the influx of American and Far Eastern computers but now most relevant for its occasional determination of standards

edge connectors. The connectors on the edge of add-in circuit boards, usually visible as strips of gold plating. These make contact with equivalent strips inside an expansion slot to link the add-in device to the *bus*. *More information: Chapter 12*

EDI. Electronic Data Interchange, a style of service offered by several independent companies for the transfer of lengthy commercial documents over public or private communications networks between geographically dispersed sites. In practice, EDI systems work like electronic mail services — except that the material to be transferred will be much longer, and many fewer subscribers will be involved

editing. The process of amending text (and, by extension, other material)

EFT. Electronic Funds Transfer, the transmission of money by electronic means

EFTPOS. Electronic Funds Transfer at the Point of Sale — direct debiting of a customer's account when a purchase is made

EGA. IBM's Enhanced Graphics Adapter for the PC and AT, a means of producing high-resolution graphics in colour on a suitable display. *More information: Chapter 18*

Electronic Data Interchange. See *EDI*

Electronic Funds Transfer. See *EFT*

electronic mail. The transmission of text using electronic means for capture, transmission and delivery of information. Electronic mail involves a *store-and-forward* approach and is typically geared to relatively short messages. *More information: Chapter 35*

electrosensitive printer. A type of *dot matrix printer* that builds up a character on paper by using electricity to create the pattern of dots, usually with paper that has a special coating which disappears or changes colour to black when an electric charge is applied to it

electrostatic printer. A *page printer* technology that creates an image on a photosensitive surface which subsequently attracts toner ink that is transferred to paper. *Laser printers* are the best-known example of this, but by no means the only one. *More information: Chapter 13*

em. A unit of measurement used in typesetting. Literally it is the width of a capital M in a particular typeface; in practice, it is generally taken to be one-sixth of an inch (and as such is synonymous with *pica*)

em dash. Printer's term for a dash (as opposed to a hyphen)

e-mail. Conventional abbreviation for *electronic mail*

embedded codes. Special characters placed in text for the purpose of controlling how printed output will appear. In other words, such characters will appear on a screen display; when it comes to printing, they will disappear having been used to set formatting and emphasis

emboldening. Making characters bold

emulation. A software and/or hardware facility that enables one device to mimic another and so perform more or less identically. *More information: Chapter 42*

encryption. Encoding for security purposes

end-user. The individual who makes direct use of the facilities of an information technology system. (The term 'user' may be synonymous, but it may also refer to a workstation or desktop computer that is part of a larger system such as a network)

Enhanced Graphics Adapter. See *EGA*

Enter. A key that may appear in place of one labelled Return and has the same effect — in text it may start a new line or paragraph, in command mode it indicates that input has finished and the computer can try acting on the input. *More information: Chapter 11*

envelope. Control characters, routing information and the like that may surround a transmitted message

EPAD. An error-checking and correcting method developed for data communications by British Telecom

Epson. Brand name and subsidiary of the Japanese Seiko group which has established market leadership in small dot-matrix printers. As a result, compatibility with Epson control codes has become a *de facto* standard for such printers

ergonomics. The study of people in relation to their working environment. *More information: Chapter 44*

ESC. Engraved on one of the keys on many desktop computer keyboards — sometimes signifies an 'alternate Shift' key like *ALT* and *CONTROL*, more usually employed by particular packages for some kind of 'cancel' or 'abort' effect. *More information: Chapter 11*

escape code. Special control codes that can be produced by the printer to affect the operation of the display, printers and other devices. There are usually simpler methods provided for achieving the same results

EtherNet. The most common style of *baseband CSMA local area network*

European Computer Manufacturers' Association. See *ECMA*

expansion slot. Sockets inside a computer for the *edge connectors* on a circuit board, thus enabling additional circuit boards to be plugged in there. Expansion slots are typically used for adding memory, local area network controllers, alternative displays (for colour and graphics, usually) and extra devices like hard disks and modems. *More information: Chapter 12*

expert system. A software package that provides the same kind of specific information as a human expert. *More information: Chapter 27*

expert system shell. Software for producing *expert systems*

export. Transfer files created by one package to another

face. Short for *typeface*

facsimile transmission. Transmission of images. *More information: Chapter 38*

fanfold stationery. The type of paper for computer printers that consists of a long strip of paper with holes down the sides (to engage in the sprockets of a *pin* or *tractor feed*) and perforated horizontally at regular intervals so that it can be folded concertina-style. Also called *continuous* stationery

fax. Common abbreviation for *facsimile transmission*

fax modem. A modem purpose-designed to receive (and possibly send) *facsimile transmissions*. *More information: Chapter 38*

fibre-optics. A transmission medium involving light pulsed down bundles of fine glass filaments. *More information: Chapter 15*

FIDO. Popular and well-specified software for running a *BBS*. *More information: Chapter 41*

FIDONET. The system whereby *FIDO*-based *BBSs* communicate with each other. *More information: Chapter 41*

field. A discrete component of a *record*

file. Usually synonymous with *disk file* — any discrete item stored on disk. The term therefore covers programs, text documents and graphic images as well as conventional files of records. In the latter case, the file comprises a collection of related *records*. *More information: Chapter 23*

file locking. A facility that prevents more than one user in a multi-user or LAN system from attempting to alter the contents of a file at the same time

file manager. A package that allows a user to set up a format for records in a file (and to set up different formats for different files); to enter information, to amend, sort, select it; and to output all or part of the information in a variety of formats. *More information: Chapter 23*

file server. A LAN controller that handles one or more storage devices on the network. The server will schedule requests for file access from workstations when two or more require simultaneous access to files. *More information: Chapter 15*

file transfer. Movement of *files* from one computer to another

find-and-replace. As *search-and-replace*

firmware. As *microcode*

fixed disk. A non-removable *disk*. *More information: Chapter 9*

flat-file system. The simplest type of file manager, with records organized very like a manual card index. *More information: Chapter 23*

floppy disk. A type of *disk* that uses a flexible base (though it is encased in a card envelope or plastic package). *More information: Chapter 9*

flowchart. A representation of a system or process in diagrammatic form, hopefully indicating the steps required to arrive at a solution

folio. In printer's terminology, a printed page number or a completed page in its correct sequence

font or (less usually) **fount.** A complete set of characters in a particular typeface — including all combinations of size and style (bold, italics, different sizes, etc.)

footer. A running line of text at the foot of each printed page

format. The arrangement of data (usually on a disk) or information (on a display or printed page)

formatting. Usually *disk* formatting — the preliminary procedure that sets up a blank disk for use by a particular operating system. Without this, data cannot be read from or written to the disk. *More information: Chapter 9*

formula. A problem-solving or calculation statement — generally one that is entered in a *spreadsheet* or a financial model. *More information: Chapter 20*

FORTRAN. High-level programming language oriented towards numeric (scientific and technical) applications

fount. Alternative spelling of *font*

four-function arithmetic. Including facilities for addition, subtraction, multiplication and division

fourth-generation language. A style of programming language that promises easier and faster development of applications by reducing the number of lines of program code required and simplifying the design of programs such that (in theory) an end-user is able to do the programming work. There are many products that claim to fit this description; the term covers program generators, command languages in file managers and spreadsheets, expert system shells and purpose-designed languages. *More information: Chapter 29*

freeware. Software in the public domain for which no charge is made or expected

friction feed. Mechanism that moves paper through a printer by pressing it against a rotating *platen*. *More information: Chapter 13*

full point. Printer's term for a full stop

function keys. One or more keys that do not have an immediately obvious effect, unlike the alphanumeric keys. Different programs utilize the function keys for different tasks; their effect varies from one package to another. *More information: Chapter 11*

galley or **galley proof.** Output from a typesetting machine before it has been corrected and placed in position on a printable page

Gantt chart. Representation of time required for different activities in project planning. *More information: Chapter 26*

gas plasma. A flat-screen display technology, widely used for portable computers

gateway. An interconnection (usually between a LAN and an external facility) that usually involves massaging the data transferred so that relatively incompatible networks can communicate. *More information: Chapter 15*

gender. The characteristics of one end of a plug-and-socket connection. 'Male' implies a protruding connector; 'female' connectors are correspondingly recessed

general ledger. Same as *nominal ledger*

gigabytes. One thousand million bytes

goal-seeking. A facility in some spreadsheet packages and all financial modellers that indicates what input data will be required in getting to an optimal solution. Sometimes called 'reverse calculation'

Green Book. A standard set jointly by Philips and Sony for the physical aspects of *CD-I*, and in practice the *only* such standard currently available. *More information: Chapter 16*

Group 1. *CCITT* standard for analogue facsimile transmission, now outdated — Group 1 fax machines could take up to six minutes to send an A4 page. *More information: Chapter 38*

Group 2. *CCITT* standard for analogue facsimile transmission permitting faster transmission speeds. *More information: Chapter 38*

Group 3. *CCITT* standard for digital facsimile transmission using a data rate of 9600 baud. *More information: Chapter 38*

Group 4. Proposed *CCITT* standard for digital facsimile transmission on *ISDN*. *More information: Chapter 38*

gutter. Empty space between columns on a printed page

half-tone. A photograph or other graphic image converted from grey tones into black dots (a half-tone contains no grey as such, but the weight and density of the dots can provide an impression of varying tone)

hand-held computer. A *microcomputer* in a package small enough to be held in one hand and operated with the other

handshaking. Hardware and software rules enabling devices at the two ends of a comms link to communicate

hardcopy or **hard copy.** Printed paper output

hard disk. A type of *disk* that uses an inflexible base and is sealed inside a casing

hardware. The physical components of a computer system

hash or **hash mark.** The American sign for 'number' — #

Hayes-compatible. Following the commands utilized by Hayes Microcomputer Systems that enable software to control the operation of a modem. In the absence of any alternative, these have become a *de facto* standard for suitably equipped modems and comms packages. *More information: Chapter 31*

header. A running line of text at the top of each printed page

Hercules graphics. A *de facto* standard for IBM-compatible systems that allows graphic display in high resolution on a monochrome screen. *More information: Chapter 18*

hertz. See *Hz*

high-level language. A programming language that is available in more or less

common form on a variety of different computers

highlighting. Applying *attributes* to emphasize text

High Sierra Group. An informal group of people in the laser disk business who are proposing standards for the format of information on CD-ROMs with a view to complete interchangeability of disks. *More information: Chapter 16*

hi-lo graph. A graphic display that summarizes different values on a single line. *More information: Chapter 21*

histogram. A graphic display with solid bars reaching up from the base of a chart. *More information: Chapter 21*

home (position). The top left-hand corner of the screen

home banking. Use of electronic services (usually viewdata) to check a bank account and (perhaps) initiate cash transfers

HOME key. A key that (probably) has the effect of moving the cursor to the home position

horizontal justification. Giving equal length to printed or displayed lines by varying the inter-word and inter-character spacing

host. The computer on which some kind of dial-up comms service is provided; or the supplier of such a service, an organization which will not usually generate the actual information available itself

hot-line. Support service provided by a supplier to answer *ad hoc* queries from users, usually via an office-hours telephone call

housekeeping. Routine functions associated with use of a computer system, such as deletion of unwanted files from disk and regular backup copying

HP. Abbreviation for Hewlett-Packard

Hz. Abbreviation for hertz, a measure of cycles per second (and therefore equating to 'signals per second' or 'bits per second' in most data communications usages)

I/O. Abbreviation for *input/output*

IA5. International Alphabet No.5. See *ASCII*

IBM-compatible. Indicating software that will run on one or more of IBM's computers (and therefore on IBM-compatible computers); or computers that emulate IBM models sufficiently well to run any and all software sold for the equivalent IBM machine, that have expansion slots of the same size and with the same connections, that follow IBM's use of memory and the MS-DOS operating system and that employ the same kind of keyboard layout. *More information: Chapter 18*

icon. A graphic representation that appears on the screen to indicate a particular function or operation

iconographic printer. Alternative name for *ion-deposition printer*

ID. Abbreviation for identification

IEEE. Institute of Electrical and Electronic Engineers, a US body responsible for some important interconnection standards

imagesetter. Alternative term for *phototypesetter* used by some vendors

impact dot matrix printer. A *dot matrix printer* that works by striking paper through an inked ribbon. *More information: Chapter 13*

import. Using one package to read files created by another

indent. Print all or part of text such that lines begin further in than the standard left-hand margin

index field. As *key field*

index hole. Small hole found near the hub of some *floppy disks* and used by the drive to locate data on the disk. *More information: Chapter 9*

information. *Data* in usable form

information centre. A facility within an organization that provides *information technology* services

information provider. The organization that makes dial-up information available. The supplier of such a service will not usually operate the computers on which that information is available or the telecomms facilities by which it may be accessed

information technology. Electronic and digital technology as applied to the handling of information

inkjet printer. A dot matrix printer that works by spraying fine droplets of ink on to the paper. *More information: Chapter 13*

input. Information entered into a computer system

integer. A whole number with no fractions or decimal portions

integrated package. A *package* providing functions for more than one application

Integrated Services Digital Network. See *ISDN*

Intel. US manufacturer of electronic components, notably of the microprocessors most widely used in desktop computers

INTELPOST. British facsimile transmission bureau service. *More information: Chapter 38*

intensity. A character *attribute* — 'high intensity' is emboldening on screen or in print; 'low-intensity' is a dim display or faint print

interactive video. Use of videotape or videodisk with computer control, such that a user can affect what appears on screen

interactive videodisk. Interactive video using videodisk

interface. Literally, a boundary between two items of hardware and software; usually a plug-and-socket connection

International Standards Organization. See *ISO*

Interpress. A rival *page description language* to POSTSCRIPT, developed by Xerox Corp.

inverse video. As *reverse video*

ion-deposition printer. An alternative to laser print technology among the electrostatic page printers, using a different method of 'writing' the print image on to a photosensitive drum. *More information: Chapter 13*

IP. Abbreviation for *information provider*

IPSS. International Packet Switched Service — British Telecom's service for international data-only packet-switched communications. *More information: Chapter 30*

ISDN. Integrated Services Digital Network, an all-digital public telephone network that will carry voice, data and image. *More information: Chapter 30*

ISO. International Standards Organization

IT. Abbreviation for *information technology*

italic. Sloping version of a typeface normally used for emphasis

JIT. Just-In-Time manufacturing, a technique in production scheduling

justification. Giving equal length to printed or displayed lines by varying the inter-word and inter-character spacing

K. Literally, a mathematical constant for 1024. For practical purposes it denotes 'thousands' (though correct scientific usage would have the prefix in lower case); so '8KB' is '8000 bytes'

Kb. Kilobits — thousands of bits

KB. Kilobytes — thousands of bytes

Kbps. Thousands of bits per second

KBps. Thousands of bytes per second

kerning. Varying the spacing between printed characters to give a more pleasing effect

key field. A *field* of a *record* that can be use to search for and/or sort the data in a file. Obviously, the more key fields the better

keytop. Literally, the top of a key (would you believe). More generally, the character(s) engraved on the top of a key — or the key itself. *More information: Chapter 11*

kHz. Abbreviation for kilohertz, a measure of thousands of cycles per second (and therefore equating to 'thousands of signals per second' or 'thousands of bits per second' in most data communications usages)

kilobytes. Thousands of bytes

LAN. Abbreviation for *local area network*

laptop computer. A *microcomputer* with a full-size keyboard and a screen large enough to display readable text. *More information: Chapter 7*

laser card. An information storage medium that employs a high-powered laser to burn minute pits into a reflective coating on a piece of plastic the size of a credit card. A low-powered laser is subsequently used to 'read' the data thus stored. *More information: Chapter 16*

laser disk. An information storage medium that employs a high-powered laser to burn minute pits into a reflective coating on a disk; a low-powered laser is subsequently used to 'read' the data thus stored. *More information: Chapter 16*

LaserJet. Trade-name for Hewlett-Packard's laser printer, one of the early market leaders in low-end laser printers without POSTSCRIPT-compatibility

laser printer. A printer that uses laser imaging with photocopier-type technology to produce whole pages with a variety of typestyles and graphics printed on them. *More information: Chapter 13*

LaserWriter. Trade name for Apple's laser printer featuring POSTSCRIPT-compatibility

layout. The physical appearance of a printed page — and by extension the task of designing it

LCD. Liquid crystal display — a flat-screen display technology

LCS printer. Liquid crystal shutter printer — an alternative to laser print technology among the electrostatic page printers, using a different method of 'writing' the print image on to a photosensitive drum. *More information: Chapter 13*

leading (pronounced 'ledding'). Printer's terminology for the space between printed lines, usually expressed in terms of the point size used for the text — so 9/10 is nine-point type with an inter-line gap one point wider than the type size

leased line. A private comms link provided by a *common carrier*

LED. Light-emitting diode, effectively a miniature lightbulb

LED printer. An alternative to laser print technology among the electrostatic page printers, using a different method of 'writing' the print image on to a photosensitive drum

letter-quality. Generally synonymous with *near letter-quality* — approaching the print quality produced by a printer using a solid fully formed type element. *More information: Chapter 13*

light-emitting diode. See *LED*

line graph. Graphic representation with a line moving through different points on an *XY* axis . *More information: Chapter 21*

line justification. As *horizontal justification*

line speed. Measure of the speed at which a data transmission link can transfer information

liquid-crystal display. See *LCD*

litho. Abbreviation for lithography or lithographic printing

lithography or **lithographic printing.** See *offset lithography*

local area network. Basically, a means of connecting by cable two or more computing devices — which may be separate computers, or shared devices like large hard disks and printers, or access points that give network users the chance to call external services. *More information: Chapter 15*

local network. As *local area network*

log. A record of activity. Often used more specifically in comms to mean capturing a session on a disk file for later consideration

log off. Terminate a comms session

log on. Initiate a comms session, typically by entering access codes after contacting a comms service

Lotus 1-2-3. Market-leading IBM-compatible *spreadsheet* package

lower-case. Small (i.e. not capital) letters

luggable or **luggable computer.** A full-function desktop computer that can easily be moved — though not too far. Conventional displays and mains power are the norm. *More information: Chapter 7*

LV-ROM. LaserVision — Read-Only Memory. A Philips brand name for digital storage on videotape. *More information: Chapter 16*

macro. A programming-like facility within some packages — a sequence of commands that would normally be entered individually at the keyboard but which can be stored and subsequently called up with the minimum of keystrokes for execution

mailbox. A storage area in an *electronic mail* system's computer that holds messages for an individual user. *More information: Chapter 35*

mail-merge. A word processing facility to create individualized letters or reports by merging standard text (such as a letter) with a previously stored file of variable information (like names and addresses). The standard text contains marker points of some kind at which the variable information is automatically inserted. *More information: Chapter 24*

mainframe. Basically, a big computer usually operated by a *data processing department* for an organization

main memory. As *RAM*

maintenance contract. A contract for the repair of faulty equipment. *More information: Chapter 45*

management workstation. Loosely, the computer system used personally by a manager. *More information: Chapter 5*

MAP. (1) Microprocessor Awareness Project, a scheme funded by the British government to promote the use of microprocessors in industry via grants and information. (2) Manufacturing Automation Protocol, a *protocol* sponsored by General Motors to link hardware from different vendors in a LAN installed for a manufacturing environment

MAPCON. Part of Microprocessor Awareness Project that provides funding for external consultancy advice on the use of microprocessors in products

mass storage. Anything that extends the computer's memory — typically, disk devices. Usually synonymous with *backing store*

master. In publishing, the finalized original from which a plate can be made for printing

mastering. The process of producing a prewritten compact disk

maths processor or **maths co-processor.** An additional processor available for some computers that takes the burden of mathematical functions from the *CPU* with consequent benefits for overall speed

matrix. A rectangular array of values — of possible dot positions, in the case of printers and displays

Mb. Megabits — millions of bits

MB. Megabytes — millions of bytes

MBOS. Multi-user version of Business Operating System from BOS Software

Mbps. Millions of bits per second

MBps. Millions of bytes per second

MCA. Abbreviation for Micro-Channel Architecture

MCGA. Colour graphics controller on IBM's entry-level PS/2 Model 30

MDA. IBM's Monochrome Display Adapter, the simplest standard for text-only displays

on the PC and AT. *More information: Chapter 18*

media and **medium.** The material on which data is stored or presented. Usually refers to *disks*

megabyte. See *MB*

megaherz. See *MHz*

memory. The storage capabilities of a computer system — usually synonymous with *RAM*

memory access speed. See *access time*

memory-mapping. As *bit map* — a common technique in computer systems for defining the content of a printed page or a display by breaking it down into the component dots and setting aside an area of memory corresponding on a dot-by-dot basis to that output

memory-resident program. A program that is loaded just once and sits there in memory to be called up when required — without interrupting the current task, which is what normally happens when one program is loaded after another. Such programs are sometimes described as *TSR* or *terminate-and-stay-resident* programs after the operating system function that allows this to happen

menu. A list of options presented to a user

message. Loosely, any information passed from one person to another

message switching. The technique of sending messages over a network, usually implying no direct point-to-point contact between sender and receiver

messaging. Generally, the process of passing messages between individuals

MHz. Abbreviation for megaherz, a measure of millions of cycles per second (and therefore equating to 'millions of signals per second' or 'millions of bits per second' in most data communications usages)

micro. Popular abbreviation for *microprocessor* or *microcomputer*

Micro-Channel Architecture. The *bus* system used in the IBM PS/2 family of desktop computers. *More information: Chapter 18*

microcode. Program(s) held in *ROM*

microcomputer. A *microprocessor* provided with the extra components necessary for acquiring data to act upon, storing programs and outputting results. Microcomputers usually have all the basic electronics on a single circuit board

microfiche. A sheet of photographic film, usually about 6x4in, on which a number of printed pages are recorded in a reduced form (reduced by a factor of 48 or more)

microfilm. A roll of photographic film, usually about 6x4in, on which a number of printed pages are recorded in a reduced form

microfloppy. Occasionally used term for a 3½in *floppy disk*

microform. As *microfiche*

micrographics. Generic term for the reduction of printed documents on to photographic film

microperforated. *Continuous stationery* on which the perforations are so fine that separating the sheets leaves virtually no evidence of their provenance, thus making them suitable for normal correspondence use

microprocessor. A miniature *processor* — an electronic component with the ability to execute programs. On its own it cannot do very much; it needs some means of acquiring data to act upon, some way of storing its instructions and some method of acting on them. Adding those facilities produces a *microcomputer*

microsecond. One millionth of a second

Microsoft. US software supplier responsible for MS-DOS

milestone. A checkpoint in a project

millisecond. One thousandth of a second, abbreviated as *ms*

mini. Abbreviation for *minicomputer*

minicomputer. Loosely, a computer that services several users at terminals connected to it. There was once a genuine technical distinction between minis and micros in that the latter crammed more functions into fewer chips with a penalty in performance; in practice this no longer applies

model. A representation on the computer of some activity, process or organization

modeller. A financial planning package, where representation of all or part of an organization is used for calculation and evaluation of alternative business strategies. *More information: Chapter 22*

modem. Acronym for modulator/demodulator — a device that converts data from digital to analogue form for transmission and converts it back again on reception. *More information: Chapter 32*

monitor. A complete display unit — comprising screen and image-producing mechanism. *More information: Chapter 10*

monochrome. Display or printing in only one colour

Monochrome Display Adapter. See *MDA*

motherboard. The main *printed circuit board* in a device

mouse. A hand-moved device for controlling the position on screen of a cursor. *More information: Chapter 19*

MRP. Minimum Requirements Planning, a technique in manufacturing scheduling

ms. Millisecond(s)

MS-DOS. The *operating system* (or rather, a family of operating systems) originally produced by Microsoft for the IBM PC and subsequently the *de facto* standard for all IBM-compatible systems that follow the PC and AT specifications

MTBF. Mean Time Before Failure — an average period of use before equipment failure is to be expected

MTTR. Mean Time To Repair — the average time for equipment repair to be effected

multi-function card. An *add-in* board that contains more than one extra facility

multiplex. To carry more than one communication at a time on a single transmission link

multiplexer or **multiplexor.** A device for handling *multiplexing*

multi-tasking. The ability of a computer system (or, more specifically, its *operating system*) to run two or more tasks at the same time

multi-terminal. As *multi-user*

multi-user. Descriptive of a computer system (or, more specifically, its *operating system*) that permits several users to utilize the computer at the same time

MUMPS. A multi-user *operating system*

mux. Abbreviation for *multiplexor*

NAPLPS. North American viewdata standard — incompatible with the Prestel/CCITT standard

narrow band. As *baseband*

near letter-quality. Approaching the print quality produced by a printer using a solid fully formed type element (such as a *daisywheel* or a typewriter's golfball). *More information: Chapter 13*

needle. The component in a *printhead* that actually puts a single dot on to paper. *More information: Chapter 13*

NETBIOS. A standardized facility in *MS-DOS* computers that enables software to operate on a local area network

network. Any set of points connected by a comms link

network interface adapter. A method of connecting a device to a *LAN* — usually an add-in card

network interface card. As *network interface adapter*

NIA. Abbreviation for *network interface adapter*

NIC. Abbreviation for *network interface card*

ni-cad. Nickel cadmium — a type of rechargeable battery

nine-pin. Indicates the number of dot-producing elements in the printhead of a dot matrix printer. *More information: Chapter 13*

NLQ. See *near letter-quality*

node. A connection point on a *LAN* — and by extension, a device connected thereby

noise. Interference in a signal

non-impact printer. A printer that works without something actually hitting a bit of paper. *More information: Chapter 13*

NTSC. TV transmission standard used in North America, Japan and some other countries

number-crunching. Descriptive of a computer system optimized for handling arithmetic operations

numeric keypad. A separate block of keys on a keyboard, featuring numeric digits and symbols for four-function arithmetic and arranged in the style of calculators or adding machines

numeric processor or **numeric co-processor.** See *maths co-processor*

OCR. Optical character recognition, a technology for scanning printed or typed material and 'reading' text thereon by converting it into digital form

OEM. It actually stands for 'original equipment manufacturer' and ought to refer to component suppliers. In practice the computer industry uses the term to mean system builders — the middlemen who rarely manufacture anything and who only occasionally do anything original

office automation. Broadly synonymous with *information technology* in most usage; more specifically, the application of *IT* to the office with the aim of improving white-collar productivity

offset litho. Literally, offset lithography or offset photolithography — the printing process more commonly used these days. A photographic image is made of a page *master*; the negative is used to etch a plate to which ink is applied; this is rolled over the paper to transfer the image

OHP. Overhead projector.

OHP foils. Sheets of transparent acetate on to which images can be drawn for subsequent projection

OMR. Optical mark recognition, a technology for scanning printed or typed material and 'reading' marks thereon by translating them into digitized information

on-board. Located on a *printed circuit board*

on-line. Successful connection via a comms link

on-line conferencing. As *computer conferencing. More information: Chapter 40*

on-line database. A public-access dial-up information service. *More information: Chapter 34*

open-item. An accounting method whereby payments are allocated to specific invoices (as opposed to *balance-forward*, where payments are allocated just to the total outstanding balance)

Open Systems Interconnection. See *OSI*

operating system. The software that controls the operation of a computer system, effectively fitting between the user and the electronics

OPT. Optimized Production Technology, a technique in manufacturing scheduling

optical character recognition. See *OCR*

optical fibre. See *fibre optics*

optical mark recognition. See *OMR*

OPUS. A package for running a *BBS*, derived from and superior to *FIDO. More information: Chapter 41*

ORACLE. ITV's teletext service

orphan. One word or a short line left at the bottom of a column or a page. Cf. *widow*

OS/2. The multi-tasking operating system used by the IBM PS/2 and other desktop computers featuring the Intel 80286 or 80386 processor

OSI. Open Systems Interconnection, a set of *ISO* standards theoretically covering the interconnection of any digital devices

outline processor. A style of software *package* that enables the user to structure a text document prior to word processing

output. Information produced by a computer system

PABX. Private automatic branch exchange, a device for linking several users (usually telephone users) to one or more external comms lines

package. As *application package*

packet. A technique for data transfer over local and wide-area networks that separates information into discrete 'packets' of identical size. This makes more efficient use of the network. *More information: Chapter 30*

Packet Switched Service. See *PSS*

page. A single printed sheet, obviously, but also used by analogy for a screenful of text; and as a verb, 'to page' means to step through text one screenful at a time

page composition. As *page make-up*

page description language. See *PDL*

page make-up. Assembling the different elements of a printable page — text, graphics, headings, columns, dimensions, etc.

page printer. A printer that prints complete pages at once — as opposed to a more conventional line or character printer, which prints a line or character and then moves the printhead and/or the paper before continuing. *More information: Chapter 13*

page scanner. A device that converts an existing text or graphic image into digital form for subsequent use, typically in desktop publishing or fax transmission. *More information: Chapter 13*

pagination. Separating a piece of text into pages (but not necessarily numbering them)

PAL. TV transmission standard used in Britain, West Germany and many other countries

paper-white. A display that shows black characters on a white background

parallel. A type of *interface* for connecting devices to a computer, where data in eight-bit form is passed along eight parallel wires (one per bit of data) such that it all arrives at the same time. Parallel interfaces are fast and effective over short distances and are used primarily to connect printers

parameter. A variable element that is assigned a specific value to achieve different effects

parity or **parity check.** A simple and widely used method of detecting errors in data transmission

Pascal. Popular and versatile *high-level* programming *language* used primarily on microcomputers

password. A security access code

paste-up. Traditionally, the assembly of a final printable page master by pasting text and artwork on to a sheet. The term has been borrowed for the electronic equivalent in desktop publishing of assembling a final page on the screen by mixing text and graphics

PBX. Private branch exchange. A generic term, these days more usually encountered as PABX (private *automatic* branch exchange). *More information: Chapter 33*

PC. Personal Computer — specifically, IBM's first *desktop computer*. More generally, any desktop computer

PCB. Abbreviation for *printed circuit board*

PDL. Page description language — a set of format commands sent by WP or DTP software to a page printer to define the precise look of a page. Best-known example is POSTSCRIPT. *More information: Chapter 13*

pel. Rarely encountered alternative form of *pixel*

pen plotter. A *plotter* that uses a pen to draw (as most do)

peripheral. Loosely, any *device* connected by cable to a computer

personal computer. See *PC*

personal computing. Use of a computer by an individual for his or her own benefit. Contrast the work of a *data processing department*, which provides services for such end-users but does not normally utilize the results of application-oriented computing itself

PERT. Project Evaluation and Review Technique — a professional method of monitoring and controlling projects

phosphor. The coating on the inside of a *CRT* screen that illuminates to form a dot of light when struck by a beam of electrons

photosetter. As *phototypesetter*

phototypesetter. A device that produces high-resolution text for subsequent use in *offset litho* printing

pica. A unit of measurement used in typesetting — roughly equivalent to one-sixth of an inch. Also the name of the most common typewriter typeface (in which case it is usually 'Pica', with an initial capital)

Pick. A multi-user *operating system*

pie chart. Graphic display with different entities shown as proportions of a circle. For emphasis, one or more slices of the pie can usually be 'exploded' — separated from the circle. *More information: Chapter 21*

pin. As *needle*

pin feed. As *tractor feed*

pixel. A 'picture element' — literally, the smallest element in a graphics display that a program can address directly. In practice it is used to indicate the resolution of a screen in terms of the number of dots that can be displayed (usually, per square inch). *More information: Chapter 10*

plasma. As *gas plasma*

platen. A rubber-covered roller in some types of printer against which paper is pressed. As the roller moves, so does the paper; this is *friction feed. More information: Chapter 13*

plotter. An output device for producing continuous-line graphics

point. In typography, a standard unit used to measure size of type — 1/72 of an inch

pop-up menu. A *menu* that when called up by the user overlays anything already on the screen — without affecting that existing display

port. A socket

portable computer. A *microcomputer* with all the capabilities of a desktop computer but light enough to carry. Flat screens are used, battery power is the norm. *More information: Chapter 7*

POSTSCRIPT. The most widely used *PDL*

power supply or **power supply unit.** A mains transformer that drops mains voltages down to the levels required by a computer

PPM or **ppm.** Pages per minute

presentation graphics. *Business graphics* specifically intended for presentation purposes, and therefore usually a good deal more fancy. *More information: Chapter 21*

Prestel. British Telecom's pioneering *viewdata* service

preventative maintenance. An equipment check with the aim of preventing faults before they happen — rather like a regular car service. *More information: Chapter 45*

print buffer. A *buffer* designed to match the performance of a printer more closely to that of a computer

printed circuit board. A board containing etched or printed connections between electronic components

print element. The component in printers that utilize fully formed characters that

actually strikes the ribbon against the paper — a *daisywheel*, for example

print engine (or sometimes just **engine**). The essential component of a laser printer that controls the physical part of printing — the image-producing optics, the photoreceptive transfer of image to paper via toner ink and the paper feed. There are relatively few manufacturers of this part of the laser printer; most of the apparently different products on the market use only a handful of 'engines', but they add their own electronics to decode the signals arriving from the computer and actually form the image to be printed

printer driver. A software component, usually part of the operating system or an application package, which controls the operation of a printer — usually, a very specific printer. There may be a choice of many printer drivers in a particular system to provide for different printers

printhead. That part of a printer which actually puts a character or shape on to paper

print needle. As *needle*

printout. Material produced on paper by a printer

print server. A LAN controller that handles one or more printers on the network. The server will accept material to be printed, decide which printer will be used if there's any option, add the output to a 'print queue' and possibly advise the sending workstation when the printing is complete. *More information: Chapter 15*

printwheel. Same as *daisywheel*

print wire. As *needle*

private viewdata or **private videotex.** Viewdata system for an individual organization

processor. As *CPU*

program generator. A package that enables the user to design a program on a computer. The user indicates the input, files required and what output should be produced. The program generator will automatically produce a program that should fit the job specified. *More information: Chapter 29*

program. A collection of instructions that a computer can act upon

project planning. As *project management*

Project Evaluation and Review Technique. See *PERT*

Prolog. The most popular language used for creating *expert systems* and for writing programs that exhibit some degree of *artificial intelligence*

prompt. A symbol or message inviting the user to take some action

proof. A printer's term for a specimen of a printed page, usually produced for checking before the final version is printed

proofread. To check through text for mistakes. Some *spelling checkers* are optimistically described as 'proofreaders', but that just highlights one of their major deficiencies — as well as correct spelling, proofreading is concerned with syntax, grammar and text formatting

proportional spacing. Varying the spacing between characters of printed or (rarely) displayed text

protocol. A formalized set of rules for the transfer of information

PS/2. IBM's current family of desktop computers, launched in 1987 and technically a considerable advance on the earlier PC and AT lines

PSS. Packet Switched Service — British Telecom's public-access data-only network. *More information: Chapter 30*

PSTN. Public Switched Telephone Network — the normal general-purpose voice-oriented public phone system. *More information: Chapter 30*

public domain software. Software available at no charge

Public Switched Telephone Network. See *PSTN*

pull-down menu. A *menu* that when called up by the user overlays anything already on the screen — without affecting that existing display. Such menus usually appear from the top of the display

quadrax. A type of cable with extra sheathing to shield against external interference. *More information: Chapter 15*

QWERTY keyboard. A keyboard with alphabetic keys laid out English-fashion, with QWERTYUIOP along the top line

ragged. Printer's term for lines of unequal length (i.e. not justified). The printer's instruction 'ragged left' is usually equivalent to 'ranged right'

RAM. Random-access memory (an anachronism), meaning a type of memory chip that initially has no fixed contents. It comprises the bulk of memory provided in the computer; it is available for programs and data to be loaded in, and successive loads will overwrite the previous contents. RAM loses all its contents when power is switched off. *More information: Chapter 8*

RAMdisk. An area of *RAM* that can be reserved for file storage. RAMdisks are treated by the computer as an extra disk drive; in practice, they provide much faster access to data — but of course they do lose their contents when power is switched off

ranged. Printer's term for lines which align at one end or the other (but not both — that would be 'justified'). 'Ranged left' means lines start in the same position but are 'ragged' at the right-hand end

raster image processor. Control device which interprets control commands accompanying text to construct a page for printing. In practice this usually means decoding the limited resolution of POSTSCRIPT-type commands into the much better resolution possible with a phototypesetter. *More information: Chapter 25*

read. Retrieve data for use (usually from disk or memory)

read-only memory. See *ROM*

read-only storage. See *ROS*

read/write head. That part of a *disk drive* which actually transfers data to and from the disk's surface

read-write memory. See *RAM*

reboot. Restart a computer system, wiping the current contents of memory and aborting the operation currently in progress. Usually required after a *crash*

recalculation. Required when new information has been entered into a *spreadsheet*

record. A number of related items of data that can be considered as a single unit

record locking. A facility that prevents more than one user in a multi-user or LAN system from attempting to alter the contents of a particular record within a file at the same time

Red Book. A standard set jointly by Philips and Sony for the physical aspects of *CD-Audio*, and in practice the *only* such standard currently available. *More information: Chapter 16*

Reduced Instruction Set Computer. See *RISC*

refresh rate. A measure of the frequency with which a *CRT* display is re-energized to maintain the glow from its phosphor coating (and therefore the contents of the display). *More information: Chapter 10*

reset. Usually synonymous with *reboot*

resolution. An indication of the capability of a display or printer, usually expressed in terms of the number of dots that can be produced in a square inch (*pixels* for screen displays, *dpi* for printing)

resource levelling. A project planning technique for resolving conflicts in the use of resources by proposing alternative strategies

Return. A key that may appear in place of one labelled Enter and has the same effect — in text it may start a new line or paragraph, in command mode it indicates that input has finished and the computer can try acting on the input. The name reflects a throwback to times before display screens, when computer terminals were typewriter-like hardcopy-only devices — the Return key caused a carriage return, with the typewriter carriage physically moving so that the printhead was repositioned at the first printing position on the line. *More information: Chapter 11*

reverse calculation. Synonym for *goal-seeking*

reverse indent. Printed text that starts to the left of the normal left-hand margin position

reverse video. A display *attribute* where text is shown in the background colour and the rest of the character matrix is filled with the colour normally used for character display

RF. Radio frequency — normally used with reference to one source of external interference that can corrupt data transmission

ring network. A LAN topology where devices are connected on a loop of cable

RIP. Abbreviation for *raster image processor*

RISC. Reduced Instruction Set Computer — a novel form of computer design permitting fast execution for certain types of operation. This is achieved by compressing and reducing the number of instructions that the computer has to execute

risk analysis. A facility in a few *spreadsheet* packages and most financial modellers that measures changes in results from different combinations of variations in the input data to highlight crucial factors. *More information: Chapter 22*

ROM. Read-only memory. A type of memory chip that can be filled with programs at the factory — but once the programs are in there they cannot normally be altered or erased by a user. ROM does not lose its contents when the power is turned off. Computer manufacturers tend to use ROM for *bootstrap* programs, *diagnostics* and some key elements of the *operating system* (especially all or part of the *BIOS*)

ROS. Read-only storage — rarely encountered alternative to *ROM*

RS-232C. The most commonly used standard for *serial* connection of devices. Identical to the *CCITT* V24 specification

ruler. Setting for tabs and line length in a word-processed document

run. Execute a program

save. Store information on memory or disk

scanner. Normally *page scanner*, usually synonymous with *digitizer* — a device for converting images or text on paper into digital form for subsequent use by the computer (typically for incorporation into WP or DTP documents). *More information: Chapter 25*

search-and-replace. Facility for locating every occurrence in text of a specified string of characters to be replaced automatically with another. *More information: Chapter 24*

SECAM. TV transmission standard used in France and some other countries

sensitivity analysis. As *risk analysis*

serial. A transmission technique whereby the bits that make up data are sent one after another (rather than in *parallel*). This is the norm for attachment of devices other than printers, and it is also the way comms transmissions work

server. A LAN controller that handles one or more devices or external facilities on the network. *More information: Chapter 15*

shareware. Public domain software where the user is invited to mail a payment after trying the package

sheet feeder. A device that feeds one page at a time into a printer

short-code dialling. See *abbreviated dialling*

SIG. Special interest group — originally a subsection of a users' group or some other body, often used more generally as a synonym for *closed user group*

slotted ring. A type of *ring network*

smart card. A card roughly the size of a credit card that includes an embedded microprocessor and memory. *More information: Chapter 16*

SoftStrip. A trademarked extension of *barcode* technology to hold data

software. Generic term for *programs*

solid-state. Descriptive of semiconductor-based electronic components

Source, The. A US-based public-access information and electronic-mail service — the main competitor to Compuserve. The Source charges a subscription and connect-time fees

Special Interest Group. See *SIG*

spelling checker. A program or in-built facility that checks text against a lexicon and highlights words it does not recognize. These might be mistakes for correction; or they may simply be alternative spellings or words not in the dictionary, in which case most spelling checkers will give the option of automatically adding them to the word-list

spreadsheet. A grid into which formulas, text and values can be entered for calculation. By extension, a package which provides such facilities. *More information: Chapter 20*

stacked bar graph. Histogram-type graphic display with different entities shown in due proportion on the same bar

standard paragraph. A facility for pre-storing frequently used pieces of text for subsequent insertion automatically into a document. *More information: Chapter 24*

star network. A LAN *topology* with devices connected individually to a central controller. *More information: Chapter 15*

store-and-forward. A facility in comms systems where messages are stored in a central location for subsequent access by the intended recipient

streamer or **streamer tape.** See *tape streamer*

style sheet. As *document template* — a predefined layout and formatting considerations that can be applied to a particular document at printing

subscript. A character placed slightly below the normal line of text, typically for scientific or technical expressions and formulas

substrate. The base material of a *disk* — normally a plastic in the case of a floppy disk, aluminium for most hard disks

SuperCalc. Spreadsheet package, probably second only to Lotus 1-2-3 in popularity

supercomputer. High-performance *mainframe* for fast number-crunching work like weather forecasting

supermicro or **supermicrocomputer.** A microcomputer version of a minicomputer — a substantial microcomputer intended for multi-user operation

supermini. A high-powered *minicomputer*, often used in technical applications where raw processing power is required

superscript. A character placed slightly above the normal line of text, typically for scientific or technical expressions and formulas

Supertwist LCD. A method of producing an *LCD* screen that greatly improves its legibility in normal lighting conditions

surge protector. A device that evens out fluctuations in the mains power supply

synchronous. A form of data transmission in which the start and end of a character transmitted do not have to be denoted by special start and stop characters (as in *asynchronous* transmission). Instead the start and finish of transmission is synchronized at both ends of the link such that time intervals between characters are of equal length

SYSOP. The SYStem OPerator who runs a *BBS*

system board. The main *PCB* in a computer

systems house. As *VAR*

system memory. An area of memory reserved for the operating system

System Network Architecture. See *SNA*

tape streamer. A tape cartridge device used for taking backup copies of disk files

teleco. Occasionally used abbreviation for 'telecommunications company', referring normally to providers of telecomms networks such as the *common carriers*

Telecom Gold. The major electronic mail service (and its supplier) in the UK

telecommunications. Transfer of information by the transmission of signals

telecommuting. Using telecommunications facilities to work at home or in local offices while remaining in contact with the organization's main office

teleconferencing. As *conferencing*

telesoftware. Programs (usually for home computers) that can be loaded from *teletext* or *viewdata* services

Teletex. An embryonic alternative to Telex that provide faster transmission and more flexible text editing

teletext. A method of broadcasting information that utilizes the 'spare' lines on a TV signal. A modified domestic TV set can thus receive and display the information

Telex. International communications network separate from the *PSTN* and providing subscribers with the ability to send and receive alphanumeric text (upper case only) at relatively low speeds but with acknowledgement of delivery. *More information: Chapter 36*

Telex modem. A *modem* specifically designed for use with the Telex network

template. As *document template* (predefined layout and formatting considerations that can be applied to a particular document at printing). Or a ready-to-use *spreadsheet* containing formulas and headings but no data

terminal. A device at one end of a comms link which is capable of sending and receiving data

terminate-and-stay-resident. As *memory-resident program* — describes the operation of such programs, which remain in memory and available for reactivation

text. Information comprising only alphanumeric characters, punctuation marks, and arithmetic and other symbols

text attribute. See *attribute*

TextDirect. On-line Telex bureau service in Britain

thermal printer. A type of non-impact printer which works by melting ink on to paper or by actually scorching the surface of the paper

thought organizer. As *outline processor*

timed send. A facility for dispatching previously prepared messages at specific times on specific dates

time management. Facilities provided in software packages for appointments diaries, reminder files, calendars, alarms, etc.

token ring. A type of *ring network*

toner. The dry ink particles used in photocopiers and *electrostatic* printers

TOP. Technical Office Protocol, a *protocol* developed by Boeing to link hardware from different vendors in a *LAN* installed in an office environment

topology. The arrangement of cabling and device connections in a *LAN*

tractor feed. Mechanism that moves *continuous stationery* through a printer by engaging toothed sprockets into the holes down the side of the paper and dragging it through

transaction. Literally, a change in a data item

transceiver. A device capable of transmitting and receiving

transfer rate. As *line speed*

transportable or **transportable computer.** As *luggable computer*

triax. A type of cable with extra sheathing to shield against external interference. *More information: Chapter 15*

TSR. Abbreviation for *terminate-and-stay-resident*

Turbo Pascal. Popular microcomputer version of *Pascal*

twinax. A type of cable with extra sheathing to shield against external interference. *More information: Chapter 15*

twisted-pair. A type of cable familiar from internal telephone wiring — the cheap, simple and popular option for *LAN* connections, but it has minimal shielding against external interference. *More information: Chapter 15*

type element. As *print element*

typeface. All the characters and symbols for a particular style of a particular *font*

typescript. Material produced by a typewriter

typesetter. A machine that produces high-quality text (usually in the form of *galleys*) for use in printing. Encountered most frequently these days as *phototypesetter*

underscore. Underline

uninterruptible power supply. Emergency battery pack to maintain power during blackouts

Unix. Multi-user *operating system* that is likely to become the *de facto* standard

upload. Transfer a file to a remote computer

upper case. Capital letters

UPS. Abbreviation for *uninterruptible power supply*

user memory. An area of memory available for user programs. Cf. *system memory*

user-supported software. *Public domain* software

utility. A program or facility that provides additional functions, typically for commonly required tasks not necessarily catered for by the operating system or individual packages

VADS. Value Added Data Services — data-oriented services offered on a network run by someone else. *EDI*, *BACS* and *electronic mail* services would be examples

value-added reseller. See *VAR*

VAN or VANS. Value Added Network (Services) — effectively synonymous with *VADS*

VAR. Value-added reseller, sometimes termed a *system house* — a supplier who specializes in one style of product and often one type of customer; in principle, the VAR adds something extra to a manufacturer's basic machine, usually by offering a complete service with software and support. *More information: Chapter 44*

variable leading. Varying the space between lines on a page for printing such that text fits neatly in a given area

VDU. Visual display unit — sometimes synonymous with *monitor* or *display*, but more correctly reserved for a *terminal* comprising screen and keyboard but no capability for running local applications

vertical justification. As *vertical leading*

VGA. Virtual Graphics Array, IBM's colour graphics controller for the PS/2 line of desktop computers. *More information: Chapter 15*

video conferencing. Enables many participants in a video-based link-up as a substitute for in-person meetings. *More information: Chapter 18*

videotext. A term used to cover both *viewdata* and *teletext* — any form of transmitting and displaying textual information, in fact

viewdata. Generic term for an information-dispensing service that utilizes telephone lines, one or more central computers holding the databases of information and low-cost receivers based on the simple technology of TV sets. Though originally an information retrieval service, viewdata can make use of the two-way capability of the phone lines to permit a number of interactive applications

Virtual Graphics Array. See *VGA*

VisiCalc. The pioneering *spreadsheet* package

visual display unit. See *VDU*

VM. Abbreviation for *voice messaging* or *voice mail*

voice annotation. A facility for adding spoken comments to digitized text

voice conferencing. As *audio conferencing*. *More information: Chapter 40*

voice mail. As *voice messaging*

voice messaging. A spoken version of *electronic mail* — verbal messages can be entered by users, stored in the system and passed on to the recipients. *More information: Chapter 39*

wait state. A pause for one or more clock cycles each time the processor references memory to synchronize memory access. *More information: Chapter 6*

wide-area network. A private network (or a private facility within a public network) connecting geographically dispersed users

wideband. A comms link with a very wide *bandwidth* (over 3kHz) that is therefore capable of carrying multiple independent transmissions

widow. One word or a short line left at the top of a column or a page. Cf. *orphan*

WIMPs. Portmanteau compression of windows, icons, menus (or mice) and pointers — describes the kind of *applications environments* and other front-ends that feature these

windows. Small displays that might appear superimposed on the screen's current contents — generally holding a *menu*, information or help, or another file for reference or *cut-and-paste* operation. *More information: Chapter 19*

word processing. Using a computer to create, store, revise and print text. The key point is that text preparation is separated from the output. *More information: Chapter 24*

worksheet. A *spreadsheet* grid

workstation. Broadly, any working microcomputer system — especially one that is part of a local area network. More rigorously, the term should be reserved for extra-powerful special-purpose microcomputers for applications like computer-aided design that place a premium on raw processing power

WORM disk. A *CD-ROM* disk that provides 'Write-Once, Read-Many times' storage — in other words, a CD-ROM disk that the user can write to once only. The principal application is in archival storage and in creating in-house reference material. Synonymous with *DRAW*, for 'digital read after write'. *More information: Chapter 16*

WP. Word processing

write. Store information on disk

write-protect. Prevent the contents of a floppy disk from being altered by use of a sticker or movable tab

WYSIWYG. What You See (on the screen) Is What You Get (from the printer)

Xenix. Multi-user *operating system* derived from *Unix*

X/OPEN. A group (mostly European) of computer-industry companies seeking to establish common formats for the *Unix* operating system

Yellow Book. A standard set jointly by Philips and Sony for the physical aspects of *CD-ROM*, and in practice the *only* such standard currently available

zero-slot LAN. A type of local network with no controller cards required in the workstations, typically a simplified system connecting a small number of users to a shared hard disk via RS-232 cables. *More information: Chapter 15*

zero wait states. Implies fast performance — indicates that the processor does not pause for one or more clock cycles each time it accesses memory to synchronize memory access. *More information: Chapter 6*

Books

There are, of course, numerous titles of particular relevance — especially on individual aspects of the information systems technology (LANs, electronic mail, desktop publishing, specific packages). These are books that I have found to be of wider relevance:

> *Management Guide to Office Automation*
> by Joseph St John Bate
> published Collins 1987; paperback
> ISBN 0-00-383353-4

Somewhat wordy, and the figures seem like OHP foils designed to reinforce points in a verbal presentation rather than a purposeful set of illustrations, but a generally sound and legible approach to designing and (especially) implementing information systems for top management

> *Winning the Information Systems Game*
> by Nelson T. Dinerstein
> published Kogan Page 1987; paperback
> ISBN 1-85091-322-6

Claims to 'teach you how to use the computer to get ahead' — somewhat breathless and very American, but can be an easy, stimulating read

> *Networking Personal Computers in Organizations*
> by James R. Weidlein and Thomas B. Cross
> published Kogan Page 1987; paperback
> ISBN 1-85091-321-8

Sane, quite readable, largely non-technical introduction to local networks for managers

> *Tomorrow's Office Today*
> by David Birchall and Valerie Hammond
> published Hutchinson Business Books 1981; hardback
> ISBN 1-85091-322-6

Ignore the hype in the main title; the subtitle is more relevant — 'Managing Technological Change'. Despite its age, this is one of the best practical guides to the introduction of *any* new technology system into existing office structures. Majors (quite sensibly) on work design and basic organizational psychology

> *Datatheft*
> by Hugo Cornwall
> published Heinemann 1987; hardback
> ISBN 0-434-90265-9

Rambles a bit, but overall an excellent antidote to the front-page stories about esoteric computer-based crime — written for a non-technical audience by the (pseudonymous) director of a computer security specialist, rams home the point that most computer-related malfeasance consists of using a desktop computer to copy the contents of one floppy disk on to another

> *The Electronic Office and You*
> by Lyn Heigl
> published Gower 1985; hardback
> ISBN 1-85091-322-6

An excellent guide to information technology for secretaries and office staff — but some good pointers to management of IT as well

Newspapers

Most of the quality nationals have at least one staff member with a watching brief on information technology, but in practice only Jack Schofield's *Guardian* page is worth reading regularly.

> Computer Guardian
> *The Guardian*
> Thursdays

At the time of writing (Winter 1987) this is the only national newspaper with decent regular coverage of information systems in general and computers in particular

Computer Horizons
The Times
Tuesdays

The only other option — very variable in the depth and insights it offers

Financial Times
Thursdays

The *FT* has occasional management-level coverage of information systems and a regular 'technology page' that includes primarily new-product information

Computer magazines

There are several dozen computer-related publications (over a hundred, in fact) — quite apart from those published outside the UK. Those listed here are excellent for product reviews and practical tips on specific packages, and most are quite good at insights into the computer industry *per se* **(especially on the relevance of product announcements). But they do depend on advertising, which means their editorial coverage is often highly specific; applications and more general management-oriented articles are not their staple diet.**

Some of these magazines are free on application to qualified readers; these are indicated as 'controlled circulation' in the references.

I should stress that the comments are *personal*.

Which Computer
monthly, subscription and newsstand
Priory Court, 30-32 Farringdon Lane,
London EC1R 3AU

Solid coverage of (mostly IBM-compatible) desktop computers, primarily reviews — *Which Computer* established the UK tradition of writing about computers for *users* and potential purchasers, at a time (late seventies) when most of its competitors were preaching to those who worked in the computer business

Practical Computing
monthly, subscription and newsstand
Quadrant House, The Quadrant, Sutton,
Surrey SM2 5AS

Has probably the most consistently good product reviews of the magazines listed here

PC User
monthly, subscription and newsstand
Priory Court, 30-32 Farringdon Lane,
London EC1R 3AU

To my mind, the best of the magazines devoted to IBM-compatible desktop computers, especially for its product reviews

Personal Computer
monthly, subscription and newsstand
VNU House, 32-34 Broadwick Street,
London W1E 6EZ

Successor to *PC*. A direct competitor to among monthlies for IBM-compatible computers; looks good, reads well, but I still prefer *PC User* for reviews

Personal Computer World
monthly, subscription and newsstand
VNU House, 32-34 Broadwick Street,
London W1E 6EZ

The best all-round coverage of desktop computers; knowledgeable, opinionated staff makes for entertaining reading, and the volume of ads provides interesting insights into what is available and why. Articles (especially reviews) can be long and boring, however, and the catch-all coverage means that much editorial will not be of interest

Lotus
bimonthly, subscription
331 Goswell Road, London EC1B 1LA

Very glossy but very full magazine dedicated to Lotus products

Multi-User Computing
monthly, controlled circulation
42 Colebrooke Row, London N1 8AF

Occasionally very technical, but in my view the best of what is currently a poor bunch of Unix-specific magazines

Business Computing and Communications
monthly, controlled circulation
30 Calderwood Street, London SE18 6QH

Good general coverage of its field at a management (rather than a technical) level

Micro Decision
monthly, subscription and newsstand
VNU House, 32-34 Broadwick Street,
London W1E 6EZ

For small-computer users in a smallish organization. Often oversimplifies, and contains much business-specific information, but provides a gentle introduction to microcomputing

Network
monthly, controlled circulation
VNU House, 32-34 Broadwick Street,
London W1E 6EZ

Aimed at the corporate user — and reads as if it is particularly aimed at information centre management

ICL Today
monthly, controlled circulation
331 Goswell Road, London EC1B 1LA

Glossy but variable ICL-specific coverage, not too technical

PC Business World
weekly, controlled circulation
331 Goswell Road, London EC1B 1LA

Usually called *PCBW* — a glossy weekly tabloid biased towards IBM-compatible computers. Interesting, readable, good at finding scoops; but sometimes too news-oriented for its own good.

DEC User
monthly, controlled circulation
Priory Court, 30-32 Farringdon Lane,
London EC1R 3AU

The only serious candidate for coverage of DEC computers at the time of writing, which is the only reason it rates a mention here

Comms File
monthly, subscription only
TP Group, PO Box 509, London N1 1YL

One of my company's subscription-oriented newsletters; explanation, news, reviews, no ads — aimed at the practicalities of being a comms user, but not for professional telecomms management

One of the problems with office information systems is that there is too much information of the wrong kind. In terms of products, it is all too easy to become submerged under a blizzard of brochures and buzzwords; finding practical, pragmatic advice and information about applications is much more difficult.

User groups

A user group is, in principle, exactly what the term implies — an association of computer users with similar requirements. There are user groups for just about all makes of computer and for most of the common software packages. The best user groups are independent, active, publish a regular newsletter and (probably) offer a dial-up on-line information service and bulletin board; they provide:

- A relevant but independent source of information on new products and manufacturer-specific developments
- A mechanism for members to exchange views and request assistance, through meetings and publications
- Discounts on products and consumables for members
- A library of public-domain utilities and other programs
- A conduit for the kind of feedback from users which manufacturers often lack

The last point is very important. The best user organizations will have a fairly close relationship with the manufacturer, and can affect product development and policies on sales and support. In practice, the relationship is often *too* close: the user group may be funded or even run by the manufacturer, in which case it will significantly be resourced from the vendor's *Marketing* department ... *Caveat emptor*, but I would argue that membership of any kind of user group is better than nothing.

The range of styles in user groups is very wide, from small non-profit organizations run as a sideline by one or two keen and/or concerned individuals to highly professional limited companies with a permanent staff. The former tend to get bogged down in their own enthusiasms, hampered by a lack of perspective, and evidently strained in terms of resources; the latter can be too glossy and too sophisticated to cater for the queries and the requirements of the individual user.

But the annual membership fee is modest. Any and all user groups of relevance are worth joining — for the discounts, for the query-answering, and perhaps even for the sense that one is not alone. Contact the manufacturer in the first place to ascertain whether a user group in fact exists, or scan the list of groups published regularly in *Personal Computer World* magazine.

Exhibitions

The calendar is full of computer-related exhibitions, and they are packed with exhibitors. As a means of obtaining a snapshot of the current state in product offerings, shows are unrivalled. They also permit more hands-on demonstrations and more product presentations than you could ever cram into an ordinary day.

This of course means that computer shows can be an easy way to acquire so much information that it becomes unusable, or to become so prejudiced by the quality of a *presentation* that you lose sight of the quality of the *product*.

The best way to approach shows involves two tactics:

- *Preparation*. Go to a show with a limited number of objectives, and preferably with a limited number of stands that you intend to visit. Stroll around rubbernecking by all means, but concentrate on a few demos. If possible make two visits — one quick tour to pick up the show catalogue, one more considered appearance when you have decided which stands to visit.

- *Awkwardness*. Don't accept jargon — the people who man the stands should be able to use language you understand, so do not let them get away with *anything*. Be aggressive if you feel that the product is not particularly easy to use, or if direct competitors have extra features. Try to 'crash' the product on view — see how it responds to the kind of inadvertently wrong keystrokes that someone will inevitably make sooner or later.

Computer shows are advertised widely in the business and computer press; entrance is usually free to qualified people, which in general means just about any adult. My own preferences are the *Personal Computer World Show* (London, summer) and the *Which Computer Show* (NEC Birmingham, just after the New Year); both are large and offer a good all-round coverage, particularly for desktop computing.

The press

I have indicated some preferences in Chapter 48. In general, while accumulating information from the press you should always be aware that (a) most publications depend on advertising for their revenue and (b) the competence, knowledge and maturity of journalists varies widely. With those pinches of salt, the press can be a genuinely useful medium for gathering information.

National Computing Centre

The NCC is a somewhat anomalous body originally set up as a QUANGO but now a profit-making organization that still retains a yen to be seen as Britain's public overseer on computers. In truth, the quality of information and support it can provide is generally high; it has an active publications list of (sometimes overpriced) books covering a range of computer topics, it organizes conferences and seminars, and it operates a number of public-benefactor organizations such as the National Computer Users' Forum (which has representatives from most of the large-computer user groups and seeks to influence government and industry policy).

Membership of the NCC is available to organizations, but in practice would only be relevant to those with a traditional DP bias that can take advantage of the members' discounts and events in training, seminars and publications.

Individuals can utilize the NCC's services and products on a straight commercial basis, and it may be worth requesting further information:

National Computing Centre
Oxford Road
Manchester
M1 7ED

Tel: 061-228 6333

Microsystems Centres

One of the NCC's activities has been the establishment of a number of these advisory centres around the country. They have demonstration rooms with a number of desktop computers and software packages (contributed by manufacturers, usually); consultants are on hand at reasonable rates for basic advice; and they may be able to point you towards sources of more specific help or information. Try the *Yellow Pages*, or start with the London office:

Microsystems Centre
11 New Fetter Lane
London EC4A 1PO

Tel: 01-353 0013

Standards are important for both users and suppliers.

For *suppliers*, standardization offers a simplified design framework (it may not be regarded as the best possible option in technical terms, but it saves the cost and effort of producing the in-house alternative) and a guaranteed market. (User pressure to follow standards ensures the marketability of the supplier's products. Common standards may also increase competition, but the positive attitude is that the supplier should be able to win over other vendors' customers.)

For *users* they provide:

- An assurance of compatibility: disparate elements of the system will work together.
- Greater independence from individual suppliers.
- Simplified operation because there are fewer radically different approaches to understand.
- Improved support for end-users — the information centre has to keep tabs on a smaller range of options and so can accumulate more detailed knowledge of practical problems.
- Expandability for new services and additional components — adding them will be less traumatic if they meet current standards.
- Longevity for the system's structure — the components may alter, but the problems of change will be minimized if new facilities match current standards.

Types of standards

In practice, two kinds of standards apply in information technology:

- *Formal* standards are those specified by recognized institutions, and are often identified by the institution's initials followed by a reference number.

The standards-setting bodies include:

ISO. *International Standards Organization*, to which most national standards bodies belong. An ISO standard is likely to apply worldwide; there is no guarantee that national standards apply outside the country of origin.

ANSI. *American National Standards Institute* — the US member of ISO, notably responsible for the ASCII character set.

BSI. *British Standards Institution* — the UK member of ISO.

CCITT. *Comité Consultatif International Téléphonique et Télégraphie*, the committee of the International Telecommunications Union that recommends data transmission standards.

CODASYL. *Conference on Data Systems Languages* — a body composed largely of US manufacturers which has specifications for the COBOL programming language and some DBMS standards.

ECMA. *European Computer Manufacturers' Association*, a grouping occasionally active in proposing standards (or modifications to other standards).

IEEE. *Institute of Electrical and Electronics Engineers*, a US body responsible for some key interfacing and LAN standards.

ITU. *International Telecommunications Union*, a body with members drawn from most of the world's suppliers of telecomms networks. Its committees, notably CCITT, are active in recommending standards.

□ *De facto* standards usually originated with individual manufacturers but have subsequently achieved widespread use (sometimes by default, often because the manufacturer got it right). Many *de facto* standards have made the transition to formal status — in local networking, for instance, IEEE has formalized the EtherNet approach as IEEE 802.3 and Token Ring as IEEE 802.5.

Key standards

Terminal operation

The simplest data comms will be 'Teletype-compatible' or turn the computer into a 'glass Teletype'. The original Teletype 33 was a hardcopy terminal comprising keyboard, printer and a connection to a computer. Teletype-compatible implies the use of a low data rate and straight ASCII text characters (with no graphics).

The VT52 and VT100 were more advanced VDU terminals from DEC. VT100-compatibility implies the ability to transfer data using a variety of asynchronous protocols and some special control codes.

The IBM 3270 was an IBM terminal with a good deal of local intelligence and the ability to communicate using IBM's synchronous protocols. 3270-compatibility has become the norm for interactive access to IBM mainframes, and it is offered by several other manufacturers too.

Character sets

The ASCII character set defines bit-pattern codes for virtually all the characters that can be produced by a standard keyboard plus some extra comms-oriented control characters. Despite competition from an alternative set of character codes from IBM, EBCDIC, it has become the norm for all comms and computer usage — though in some cases it has been extended to provide for additional characters (notably by IBM, which added some graphics characters for use with its PC line; 'IBM Extended ASCII' is something of a *de facto* standard in its own right now).

Computers in general

The notable *de facto* standard is of course IBM-compatibility — use of IBM-type device controllers and character generators, IBM-like expansion slots, IBM-style keyboard, an operating system and BIOS that follows IBM's design, and disk drives of the same format and capacities. The net result should be that a compatible computer can use any software, any add-in boards and any add-on devices that will work on the equivalent IBM model.

The three styles of compatibility are with IBM's PC (implies 360KB disks, original keyboard, 8088 or 8086 processor), the AT (1.2MB disks, ATE keyboard, 808286 processor) and PS/2 (720KB or 1.44MB 3½in disks, 80826 or 80386 processor, OS/2 operating system).

Printer attachment

The printer manufacturer Centronics was one of the early leaders in its market, and the connections it used for attaching its printers to computers have become a *de facto* standard for parallel interfaces (in parallel data transfers, the linking cable includes enough wires for all the bits that make up a character move in parallel at the same time).

Parallel transfer is how a computer moves data internally, and it is fast; there are, however, problems with connecting certain types of devices in this way, and the maximum length of cable is limited to a few feet. The Centronics parallel interface is the usual method of connecting printers (and just about nothing else) to computers.

On-line operation

The market dominance of the Dialcom electronic mail system, which is licensed internationally, means that many e-mail services have the same procedures and similar commands.

Prestel has had a similar effect in standardizing many aspects of viewdata operation — page-based display, access to information through numeric references, block graphics.

Use of packages

The presentation and style of commands in Lotus 1-2-3 is widespread, as is the use of WIMPs — a generic 'environment' of windows, icons, mice (or pop-up menus) and pointers.

Data interchange formats

Files produced by particular packages often have a purpose-designed format indicated by a specific suffix on the file name. In several cases, other packages have the ability to use (and sometimes produce) files with that format — particularly when the originator has a strong market position.

This particularly applies to the Lotus 1-2-3 WKS and WK1 formats for spreadsheets and PIC format for graphics. Pre-Lotus, VisiCalc popularized a DIF format for file transfer; this is similar to and largely compatible with SuperCalc's CSV format. Another popular format produced by spreadsheets is the SYLK format originated by Microsoft for Multiplan.

For text files, there is much compatibility with IBM's DCA format as produced by the DisplayWrite word processor. Microsoft is trying to establish its RTF format as a *de facto* standard for windows-based word processor files.

Interconnection in general

The seven-layer OSI model is being adopted universally by manufacturers. In theory, it should provide for easy interconnection of devices over internal or external links. In practice, there is a good deal of leeway. However, not all the specifications have been laid down yet; some manufacturers are offering products that claim OSI-compatibility in advance of the formal specification. Nor have all the elements of OSI been stable — the earliest OSI-compatible systems met the specifications of the time but are having to be revised to meet updated standards.

IBM's System Network Architecture represents an alternative (and earlier) approach to system interconnection for IBM devices. SNA-compatibility is still required to communicate with many IBM mainframe applications, but IBM is moving SNA towards compatibility with OSI.

The CCITT's X25 standard for packet-switched data transfers over public networks (aimed at suppliers of public networks) and the X400 standard for interchange of electronic mail and other text documents (aimed at providers of actual services on the networks) fit parts of the OSI model.

Local networks

IBM's token ring and (to a lesser extent) the Cambridge ring are the standard for local network ring topologies; EtherNet's use of CSMA, baseband operation and single-bus cabling is the other widely followed approach.

Applications-oriented systems that appear to be achieving some measure of success are General Motors' MAP and Boeing's TOP for manufacturing and office environments respectively. TOP, the Technical Office Protocol, can be implemented cheaply using baseband cabling. MAP, the Manufacturing Automation Protocol, is more expensive — it utilizes broadband cable to cater for larger data transfers and provide better resistance to the kind of external interference that might be encountered on the shop floor.

Both are practical implementations of the OSI seven-layer model, intended to provide manufacturer-independent solutions; at the time of writing, however, both are still in the development stage and it is widely felt that simpler solutions like EtherNet will meet all current requirements until MAP and TOP are a lot more mature.

Other interface standards

These define the cable connections between two devices — the meanings of the signals that are passed and the use of the connectors in the plug and socket link. The interface most frequently encountered is RS-232, also known (more accurately) as RS-232-C; it is virtually identical to the CCITT V24 recommendation.

RS-232 covers serial connections between two devices. It was originally intended very specifically to connect a VDU terminal and a modem, however, and its subsequent adoption for other devices has caused some problems in deciding exactly what control signals are to be passed over the interface. As a result, RS-232 is not a very standard standard.

It is usable, though, and it is used very widely — most computers and other devices have a socket for RS-232 connections. RS-232 is good for relatively short connections (typically no more than 50ft) at relatively low data rates (up to 9600 bps). Characteristic uses are in connecting a computer and:

- A modem
- Another computer (for file transfer)
- A plotter
- A printer
- A slide-producing camera
- A shared hard disk (in a zero-slot LAN)

Modem standards

These define the connections between modems and computers, and the operating procedures for modems. The CCITT's V series recommendations mostly apply to data transmission over telephone networks where digital-to-analogue conversion is required; they are followed by modem manufacturers and telecomms service suppliers in Europe and most of the rest of the world outside the Americas. The key recommendations are:

- V21 covers full-duplex asynchronous transmission at speeds up to 300 bps over public switched telephone networks. The lowest-common-denominator approach — the simplest kind of transmission, the cheapest modems. V21 is totally incompatible with the equivalent US standard for 300 bps transmission, Bell standard 103/113.

- V22 covers full-duplex asynchronous transmission at speeds up to 1200 bps over public switched telephone networks. This represents a decent speed for file transfers and general

comms work; some dial-up services do not support 1200 bps communications, however. V22 is largely but not totally compatible with the equivalent US standard for 1200 bps transmission, Bell standard 212A.

- V22 *bis* covers full-duplex synchronous transmission at speeds up to 2400 bps over public switched telephone networks (which is the fastest speed possible on normal PSTN lines without special 'conditioning' to reduce the chances of data corruption). Most dial-up services do not support communications at anything above 1200 bps, and the price of V22 *bis* modems reflects the extra speed and capability. There is no direct Bell-standard equivalent.

- V23 covers half-duplex asynchronous transmission at split speeds — sending at 75 bps, receiving at 1200 bps — over public switched telephone networks. This is sometimes called '1275' operation; intended originally for viewdata services, it has found wide application for other dial-up information retrieval applications where the user will be doing more receiving than sending. Most dial-up services support 1200/75 bps operation. There is no Bell-standard equivalent for split-speed working.

- V26 covers full-duplex synchronous or asynchronous transmission at speeds up to 2400 bps over private leased lines for bulk transfer of data. V26 modems are generally pricey.

- V26 *ter* covers full-duplex synchronous or asynchronous transmission at speeds up to 2400 bps over public switched telephone networks.

- V26 *bis* covers half-duplex synchronous or asynchronous transmission at speeds up to 2400 bps over public switched telephone networks. It is largely compatible with the equivalent US standard for 2400 bps transmission, Bell 201C.

- V27 covers full-duplex synchronous or asynchronous transmission at speeds up to 4800 bps over private leased lines.

- V27 *ter* covers half-duplex synchronous or asynchronous transmission at split speeds — sending at 75 bps or 150 bps, receiving at 4800 bps — over public switched telephone networks. There is no Bell-standard equivalent.

- V29 covers full-duplex synchronous or asynchronous transmission at speeds up to 9600 bps over private leased lines.

- V32 covers full-duplex synchronous or asynchronous transmission at speeds up to 9600 bps over public switched telephone networks (9600 bps is the fastest speed feasible on PSTN lines, and even then it may not be available). V32 is likely to supersede V29 because of the full-duplex capability.

- V25 covers autoanswering by modems.

- V25 *bis* covers autodialling by modems.

For direct connection to a US comms service over public (non-digital) telephone networks, a European modem will have to offer the option of compatibility with one of the Bell standards. Some indeed do this.

- Bell 103/113 covers full-duplex asynchronous transmission at speeds up to 300 bps. It is not compatible with CCITT V21.

- Bell 201C covers half-duplex asynchronous transmission at speeds up to 2400 bps. It is largely compatible with CCITT V26 *bis*.

- Bell 202C covers full-duplex asynchronous transmission at speeds up to 1200 bps. It is not compatible with CCITT V23.

- Bell 212A covers full-duplex synchronous transmission at speeds up to 1200 bps. It is largely compatible with CCITT V22.

- Bell 208A covers half-duplex synchronous or asynchronous transmission at speeds up to 4800 bps. It is not compatible with CCITT V27 *ter*.